Speech and Language Processing

Speech and Language Processing

C. Wheddon

Head of the Speech and Language Processing Division
British Telecom Research Laboratories

and

R. Linggard

Head of group working on Speech Analysis and
Machine Intelligence, British Telecom

CHAPMAN AND HALL

LONDON • NEW YORK • TOKYO • MELBOURNE • MADRAS

UK	Chapman and Hall, 11 New Fetter Lane, London EC4P 4EE
USA	Van Nostrand Reinhold, 115 5th Avenue, New York NY10003
Japan	Chapman and Hall Japan, Thomson Publishing Japan, Hirakawacho Nemoto Building, 7F, 1-7-11 Hirakawa-cho, Chiyoda-ku, Tokyo 102
Australia	Chapman and Hall Australia, Thomas Nelson Australia, 480 La Trobe Street, PO Box 4725, Melbourne 3000
India	Chapman and Hall India, R. Sheshadri, 32 Second Main Road, CIT East, Madras, 600 035

First edition 1990

© 1990 Chapman and Hall

Printed in Great Britain by St Edmundsbury Press Ltd
Bury St Edmunds, Suffolk

ISBN 0 412 37800 0
   0 442 31207 5 (USA)

British Library Cataloguing in Publication Data

Speech and language processing
   1. Speech. Synthesis. Application of computer systems
   I. Wheddon, C. II. Linggard, R. (Robert), *1939–*
   006.54
   ISBN 0–412–37800–0

Library of Congress Cataloging-in-Publication Data

Available

CONTENTS

FOREWORD

This book is a collection of papers which describe the work of the Speech and Language Processing Division at British Telecom's Research Laboratories (BTRL) in Suffolk, England. This division is one of thirty which are dedicated to developing technology appropriate to BT's Telecommunications Networks and peripheral businesses. The Speech and Language Processing Division employs over 100 Scientists, Engineers and Technicians on a variety of projects ranging from short-term development of Speech-Interactive products to long-term studies of human/machine interaction via natural language. The papers collected together in this book are a fair representation of the work in progress in 1988/89. Naturally, the opinions expressed in these papers are those of the authors and do not necessarily represent official BT policy.

In selecting papers for this volume, we were mainly concerned to provide a representative sample of the work of the division. In this we have succeeded with only one exception: the work on commercially sensitive applications has been omitted for reasons of confidentiality. However, this work will be published eventually, and in an increasingly competitive world, we are grateful to the Group Technology and Development Director at BTRL for permission to publish the papers contained herein.

We are also grateful to the Services Division at BTRL, for the fine job they did in typesetting this book. In particular, we thank David Clough for his painstaking editorial work, and the Illustration Studio for the diagrams and photographs. But our last and largest thanks go to the authors of the papers, who worked hard, mainly in their own time, to prepare the original manuscripts.

C Wheddon and R Linggard
British Telecom Research Laboratories
Martlesham Heath
Suffolk
England

SPEECH COMMUNICATION

C Wheddon

ABSTRACT

The principal means of human communication is speech. It has evolved over many centuries to become the rich and elaborate language structure of today. Speech is more than just a string of words. It reflects the moods, the ideas and the personality of the speaker. The processing of speech and language therefore encompasses many disciplines — physiology, psychology and technology. Aspects of these are discussed in this paper, which surveys speech from its human origins through to machines that involve the use of artificial intelligence to provide improved man-machine communication.

"Speech is civilisation itself. The word, even the most contradictious word, preserves contact — it is silence which isolates." — Thomas Mann, The Magic Mountain, 1924.

1. Introduction

The universal acceptance of telecommunications based on digital networks offers a wide range of advanced services. Digital services involving the transmission of data, facsimile, vision and videotex are beginning to proliferate on a global basis; carried by a variety of optical cables, satellite and radio systems.

These also carry the basic telephony service — speech. Speech still dominates the world's communications and the telephone system is the most extensive structure of all time; over 800 billion telephone calls were made in 1986 from an estimated 625 million telephones [1]. There is a familiarity with the telephone terminal and there exists in most countries a large number of trained users. This established telephone culture is now converging with the growing tendency to store more and more information in computer databases. Computer databases are increasingly being used to store the latest information on timetables and for financial, commercial and medical purposes, in fact anything which can be converted into binary data for fast archiving and retrieval.

Telephony access to databases is often obtained by communicating with a telephone operator trained to use a computer terminal. This method of indirect access is limited by the number of operators available to answer calls and deal with inquiries, which imposes limits on the information transaction times. The ubiquity of the telephone system therefore presents an opportunity for direct access to computer databases by speech, providing the problems of interactive speech systems can be overcome. Speech technology has already been applied to some systems where the use of a telephone keypad to access the computer databases and receive relevant information from stored or synthetic speech are becoming established [2].

While this approach is suitable for many applications, the telephone keypad and the 'menu' type of dialogue associated with it sets a limit on the range of applications which may be addressed. Interactive speech systems using automatic speech recognition and speech response promise a much more flexible solution.

To date the processing of speech signals has concentrated on replicating certain aspects of the human production and perception processes. This modelling approach has been aided and supplemented by modern digital signal processing technology. However, the processing technology has now revealed limitations in modelling only the physiological aspects of speech. New areas of research point towards the replication of neural processes to achieve the necessary improvements in speech recognition and understanding.

To fully exploit the potential of speech recognition interaction with machines, the additional component of Artificial Intelligence is required. Artificial Intelligence, speech recognition (input) and speech synthesis (output) are the key or core technologies for interactive speech systems of the future and are being pursued on a worldwide scale.

With so much attention directed at the future, a pause to reflect where human speech processing began would be beneficial. Also it will allow the value and the achievement of past pioneers to be placed in perspective.

2. Origins of speech and language

If speech is the foundation of civilisation then the ability to converse is the most essential feature in the social development of human beings. We, as humans living on planet Earth, are able to converse in an estimated 4000-5000 languages which have developed from our forefathers over many years and have been influenced from many sources. The ability to speak is believed to have been dependent upon the physiological changes in the development of the larynx and the increase in cranial capacity. This might have occured around 45 000 BC [3,4]. There is no argument that the primary organ in the evolution of speech is the brain and in particular the cerebral cortex. However, anthropologists differ in their estimation of when humans developed the complete biological apparatus to utter speech-like sounds. Many suggest that the adoption of an upright posture (bipedalism) led to brain growth [4,5] and the freeing of the hands or forelimbs led to changes to the upper part of the respiratory tract.

This evolutionary change might have enabled the species Australopithecines to control the larynx to produce vowels and consonant noises; and this would place the origins of speech some 4 million years ago. Figure 1 illustrates the estimated development of the human species.

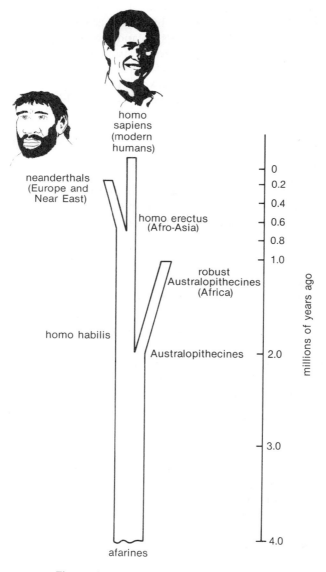

Fig 1   Human evolutionary development

Exact dating of human speech is hampered by the lack of fossil evidence. In an attempt to investigate the origin of speech on positively dated fossils a reconstruction of the

3

vocal tract of the skeletal remains of a Neanderthal man dated 35 to 45 thousand years ago was analysed by computer simulation [6].

This analysis showed that Neanderthal man was not capable of producing three of the human formant frequencies corresponding to the human vowel sounds i, a and u (formants or resonances are produced by a speaker naturally changing the length and shape of the vocal tract). Nevertheless, Neanderthals had a more extensive ability than other living creatures at that time. An additional factor is that the brain of the Neanderthals was as large as modern man, thus it is fairly certain that Homo Sapiens had both the neural and the supralaryngeal vocal tract development for speech, which places the ability for humans to communicate by speech-like sounds at least 50 000 years ago.

Language, in general terms, is a system that enables a speaker to make more effective use of words. Most is learnt during childhood. And although linguistics has become one of the most sophisticated disciplines in the life sciences, there is no full agreement on the definition of language. The ability to represent language in symbolic form may have also been coincident with the ability to utter repeatable and recognisable sounds which provided a distinction between self and others. The earliest evidence of written language originated in China somewhere between 5000-4000 BC and the gap between this fact and the estimate of spoken language is some 45 000 years — an interesting mystery. The ability to represent concepts and sounds in an orthographic form has evolved under the influence of changes in climatic conditions in cultural organisation and social integration, with no clear beginning.

The vocal accompaniments of language—patterns of stress, the tone, the timing of hesitation imposed on the spoken word—provide the rich source expression that enables the human species to communicate and socialise by conversation. This now natural process of conversation is provided by the unconscious mastery of what seem to be extremely complex and impenetrable cognitive processes. These processes are brought to bear on the planning and generation of spontaneous conversational speech and are aided by non-verbal gestures, such as facial expressions, posture, eye and hand movements.

The processing of speech signals within the existing constraints of natural language has interested and excited scientists for many years. The goal is now to produce machines that can not only produce and recognise fluent speech but also to act on the received information to produce a response required or expected by the user.

3. Human speech production

Speech seems to be almost a by-product of evolution since no organ concerned in generating speech is uniquely dedicated to that task. The lungs, larynx, tongue, nose, lips, teeth all have a primary purpose in supporting life by breathing, tasting and eating.

To produce speech sounds the air from the lungs is forced through the vocal chords or folds which are located in the larynx. As the air flow builds up complex pressure differences are produced by the nature of the glottis causing the vocal folds to vibrate in manner similar to the reed in a wind instrument [7]. This process is known as phonation and sounds produced in this way are termed 'voiced' sounds, the vowel sounds frequencies being determined by the tension in the vocal folds. The range of pitch (vibration) for adults is typically two octaves with the range for females being about an octave higher than for males. Another source of sound generation is produced by breath noise, sounds produced in this manner are termed 'un-voiced' sounds such as 's' and 'ch'.

As these sounds produced by the vibration of the vocal chords or breath noise pass along the vocal tract and out through the mouth, the characteristics of speech are impressed upon them by two types of modulating processes which produce forms of resonances known as formants. One source of resonance can be described as a shaping of the energy-frequency distribution and is achieved by the passage of the sound through the multiple resonance chamber formed by the mouth and tongue; further shaping may be affected by the lips and teeth. The other modulation process is achieved by closing off the vocal tract by the tongue, lips or teeth and then releasing the sound energy. The sounds produced are termed plosives or stops; 'p' and 't' are examples of these.

The human vocal tract is capable of making an infinite number of distinct sounds. At the linguistic level the basic unit of speech is the phoneme which is considered as a working definition of the perceptual unit of language and the manifestation of each phoneme depends on the word being spoken and the position of the phoneme within the word. The vocal tract may be reproduced electronically by emulating the various functions of the human voice production process as illustrated in Fig 2. The English language contains about 40 phonemes. The world record for the number of phonemic descriptions is the language Ubykh from Caucasus [8] which has 82 distinct units, but which by now may be extinct as there were only 20 speakers in 1962.

4. Human speech perception

Unlike the vocal tract, the ear seems to be custom built for the purpose of detecting and analysing sounds. With the exception of the organ for balance and posture, and the eustachian tube, the remainder of the ear is dedicated to converting sound pressure waves into impulses that stimulate the auditory nerve fibres that connect into the brain.

The auditory system consists of three sections — the outer, middle and inner ear, as shown in Fig 3. The outer ear has two roles: it aids sound localisation by altering the spectrum of the sound, depending on the direction of the source and it transmits sounds to the tympanic membrane. The tympanic membrane or eardrum vibrates under the influence of sound pressure waves, much like a diaphragm in a microphone.

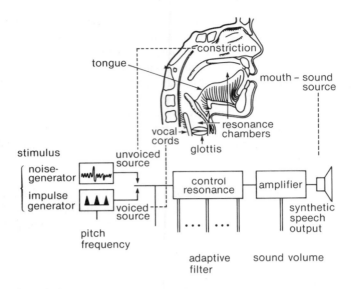

Fig 2   Simplified electronic representation of the human speech production system.

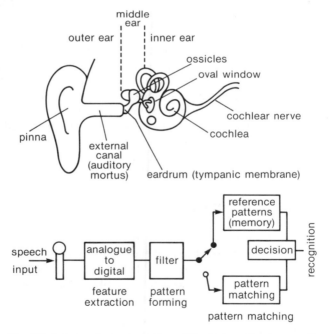

Fig 3   Simplified electronic representation of the human speech perception system.

The middle ear contains three small bones, the malleus, incus and stapes, known as the ossicles which transfer vibrational energy to the inner ear. It is the stapes which vibrates against the oval window and as the oval window is smaller, an increase in the sound pressure is transferred to the inner ear.

The inner ear is a system of fluid filled cavities and the oscillations of the stapes sets up a pressure wave within which causes the fluid in the inner ear to vibrate, particularly in the cochlea. The cochlea not only converts mechanical vibration into nerve signals, but also selects the frequencies of the incoming sounds — a direct physiological example of a set of filters. Contained with the cochlea is the basilar membrane, this is graded in width and stiffness along its length, being narrow and stiff at the basal end, becoming wider and more flexible towards the apex. The auditory transducer which turns sound energy into nerve stimuli is the organ of Corti which is attached to the basilar membrane. It contains a large number of specialised and complex hair cells which perform the transduction process [9]. Mechanical vibrations in the basilar membrane are converted into impulses by the inner hair cells to the auditory nerve fibres which contact into the brain.

The ear and its electronic counterpart can be modelled in part by the use of digital filters [10,11]; acoustic patterns and a pattern matching device are necessary to form simple speech recognition as illustrated in Fig 3. It is the brain, however, which plays the key role in human speech recognition and perception.

5. The pursuit of artificial speech synthesis and recognition

5.1   Early speech synthesis

In 1779 a prize was offered by the Imperial Acadamy of St Petersburg for a scientific explanation of the physiological differences between five vowel sounds and demonstrating apparatus for producing the sounds. By 1780 Professor Christian Kratzentein had designed a 'Vox humana' capable of producing the vowel sounds from a set of different shaped tubes. Some unusual shapes were created in the attempt to produce the same resonances as the human vocal tract.

In 1791 Wolfgang Ritter Von Kempelen [12] constructed a talking machine which he began designing in 1769; it consisted of a bellows, a mouth shape, nostrils and whistles. The machine included a compressable leather tube and an air chamber equipped with a reed leading to a soft leather resonator which could be manually shaped for the formation of the vowel sounds. Consonants were created by holes which the 'player' closed by movement of the fingers. The Von Kempelen machine could produce about twenty different sounds!

Some time later Charles Wheatstone produced a modified version of the Von Kempelen machine and a replica of this model is shown in the photograph in Fig 4.

Fig 4   Replica of Charles Wheatstone's mechanical synthesiser.

5.2   Electronic speech synthesis

Complete synthesis of speech can be achieved from information describing the time variance of natural speech which includes:

- the shape of the spectrum,
- the type of energy,
- the pitch of the voice.

The articulators define the shape of the spectrum and the remaining variants contribute to the naturalness and emotion which provide assistance in the communication process.

The earliest electronic synthesis of speech was achieved by Dudley in 1936 and he was able to demonstrate a complete system for the analysis and synthesis of speech. In 1939 he demonstrated a manually controlled speech synthesiser at the New York World's Fair which he called the VODER (Voice Operated Demonstrator). The complete system of analysis and re-synthesis with further refinements was termed the VOCODER (Voice Coder) [13] and was demonstrated in 1939.

Soon after the Second World War development began in the Post Office of techniques to analyse and re-synthesise natural speech. The motivation for this area of research was the recognition of the potential for sending telephony over very long distances [14]. The techniques were fundamentally the same as modern electronic synthesis of speech in that the analyser was required to model two anatomical systems. One was the source of acoustic energy emitted during a 'voiced' sound, e.g. a vowel, and the other was the position of the articulators, the tongue, lips and velum which specify the particular sound. A bandwidth compression ratio of 10:1 were the aim of these early pioneers who required to do their processing with the analogue technology of the day. A photograph of the analyser synthesiser is shown in Fig 5, the height of the rack is approximately 2 metres. The modern day digital equivalent is shown in Fig 8.

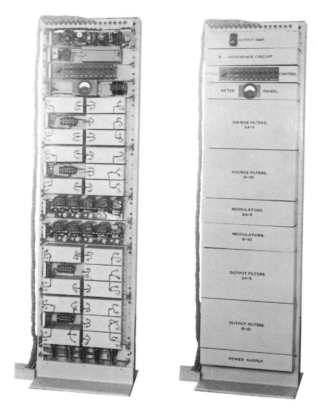

Fig 5   An early voice synthesiser.

It was also thought that vocoder could be used to generate artificial speech sounds, since the synthesiser processed signals that specified the acoustic signal. This was achieved by specifying the complete set of electronic control signals (parameters) from models of the sound sources which when modified by a set of controllable filters and stimulated by an artifical energy source produced synthesised speech (see Fig 2). In this way the early pioneers laid the foundations which are still used in today's systems.

5.3   Early speech recognition

Von Kempelen's mechanical speaking machine was all the more successful when one considers that he started in 1769 without the benefit of hindsight or prior inspiration from contemporaries or published material.

The earliest attempt at voice recognition was the voice-operated phonographic alphabet writing machine built by J Flowers [15]. The machine combined electrical, mechanical and optical systems to convert speech into symbols which could be subsequently interpreted as text.

The method of operation of Flowers' machine, illustrated in Fig 6, was to convert speech into electrical signal via the telephone transmitter. The resonator circuits were

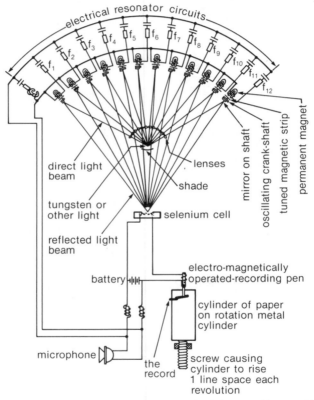

Fig 6   Flower's voice-operated phonographic alphabet writing machine.

tuned to specific frequencies, similar to a bank of band pass filters, which performed a crude spectral analysis on the uttered word. The resonator tuned to the main frequency component of the utterance would respond the most, which in turn caused a mechanical movement in a mirror positioned to reflect received light into a selenium cell. In the normal position of rest the mirror reflects the light beam into a blank space at the middle of the selenium cell. When the light is reflected to both sides of the cell under the influence of the resonator circuit the resistance of the selenium cell will vary allowing the electromagnetic recording pen to trace a wavy line on a paper sheet. The wavy lines were interpreted from a phonographic alphabet formed by another combined optical, electrical and mechanical device which produced pattern forms of the spoken alphabet.

The literature does not cite the accuracy of this machine but the ingenuity deserves to be recognised as the first attempt at speech recognition.

5.4   Electronic speech recognition

The earliest attempts at electronic speech recognition took place in the 1950s [16] and in the main concentrated on the recognition of spoken digits. An accuracy of around 95% was claimed from these early systems [17] by a user speaking each word in isolation. The user was required to give at least one previous example of each word in the vocabulary.

These earlier devices used analogue circuits to perform the spectral analysis by filtering and decision logic to make the pattern match between the uttered word and the reference word.

6. Interactive speech — the components

Speech is a fascinating human attribute that can be analysed, synthesised and recognised; it can also be compressed, stored and enhanced by digital signal processing techniques. However, processing of speech on its own is not sufficient to build interactive speech systems that operate over telephone networks. Other important aspects need to be understood and well integrated before successful user acceptance. It is the mix of speech processing hardware, software, human factors engineering and a knowledge of the operational constraints of the telephone network that are the main ingredients of interactive speech systems. The main speech components associated with interactive systems rely on the following technologies:

- recognition,
- synthesis,
- analysis and coding,

and the complementary support of natural language processing and artificial intelligence. Figure 7 illustrates the varied interdisciplinary research areas linked to a number of interactive speech systems currently under development at the British Telecom Research Laboratories (BTRL).

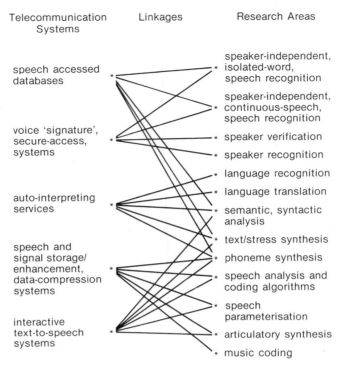

Fig 7   Interactive speech systems and their strategic research areas.

Similar areas of research are being pursued elsewhere in the world [18,19,20] where local regulatory, cultural and linguistic differences add interesting and challenging technical problems which must be taken into consideration.

6.1   Speech input

Speech recognition seems so natural and simple for humans that it has been assumed that it could be easily achieved by machines. However it has proved to be an extremely complex and difficult task to get machines to respond to even simple spoken commands. Computer speech recognition is hampered by variations in pronounciation, even single words are rarely pronounced in the same way twice. This intra-word variability in level and duration is not just a random perturbation — a spoken word contains more acoustic information than its written equivalent. The age, sex, mood and accent of the speaker may be deduced even from a single utterance and therefore the speaker's psychological and physiological state influence the speed and consistency of delivery.

Speech recognition is complicated further by consonants adopting aspects of neighbouring consonants and vowels in fluent speech. This co-articulation problem does not really exist for humans because we apply context, semantics and common sense to resolve any ambiguities. Machines, however, do not have this world knowledge and can only rely on acoustic clues to distinguish words and phrases such as 'abominable' from 'a bomb in a ball' [21]

Although it is a rather artificial distinction, most speech recognition systems consist of a feature extractor and a pattern matching process (classification) and are either:

- speaker dependent — where the user must train the recogniser with each word required for the application, or
- speaker independent — where the vocabulary is prescribed and cannot be changed.

Both arrangements rely on classical pattern matching techniques where features are extracted from the acoustic signal and then passed to a classifier which determines which of the words in the recogniser's vocabulary was spoken.

Features are typically derived using transform or digital filtering techniques to reduce the amount of data. The matching processes generally attempt to optimally align the resulting patterns by dynamic programming techniques [22] (also called dynamic time warp — DTW) which brings the test pattern into time registration with reference patterns. Statistical models are also used; currently the most popular for speech recognition is based on hidden Markov models [23]. Here a sequence of features is reconciled with a set of probablistically defined word models.

In practice the application will usually determine the particular techniques, with speaker independent recognisers requiring extensive pre-training and testing on a prescribed vocabulary. Additionally they usually carry a higher computational overhead than speaker-dependent recognisers.

Many systems using speech recognition operate on single utterances and in use require the user to speak isolated words. These systems are dependent on the user giving at least one example of each word to 'train' the system prior to use.

The feature extraction and pattern matching techniques outlined may also be extended to cope with connected words [24] which is a more complicated task as the number of words to be recognised is unknown and the boundaries between words cannot be easily determined in real time. As a result of the added complication the matching process requires an increase in computation [25] and a concomittant increase in hardware complexity.

6.2   Speech output

Speech output from computer-based equipment has been commonly achieved by storing whole messages in digitised form. These messages require the recording by a speaker and although a natural sounding voice output is achieved, significant amounts of data storage are required. An additional constraint on system design and extension arises when the messages need to be changed or updated if the original speaker is not available.

Message flexibility can be achieved by storing each individual word separately and re-combining them into sentences to form the desired output [26]. It is difficult to achieve word or sentence recombination or concatenation without introducing noticeable discontinuities which must be ameliorated by extensive editing and hand crafting of the message phrase.

Electronic speech synthesis relies on a parameterised model of the human vocal tract being driven by a stimulus to produce an output of synthesised speech. Various models exist [27] which emulate the naturally occuring resonances or formants in the vocal tract by adaptive digital filters. These filters are adapted by parameters which are derived from natural speech by computer analysis [28].

Figure 8 illustrates a parallel formant synthesiser implemented in modern digital signal processing (DSP) hardware.

Fig 8   Parallel formant synthesiser.

An alternative to the derivation of parameters by computer analysis of natural speech is to convert textual input directly into synthesiser parameters. This conversion process is called text-to-speech synthesis (TTS) [29,30] and is based on the linguistic knowledge of how orthographic text may be converted into speech. The text to sound rules must be able to cope with the arbitrary combinations of letters and punctuation which are found in all languages. The English orthographic system has not undergone any substantial reform since the inception of what can be reasonably called English in circa 500 AD. Thus the gap between graphemic and phonemic representation of words is large and an English text-to-speech system requires an exceptions dictionary to convert some words into their correct phonetic spelling. A photograph of a complete text-to-speech system incorporating the linguistic rules, exceptions dictionary and formant based synthesiser is shown in Fig 9.

Fig 9   Text-to-speech — hardware implementation.

6.3   Speech coding

The most common form of speech coding is pulse code modulation (PCM) which is used in the conversion of telephone bandwidth speech into a digital rate for transmission through telecommunication networks.

The transmission of speech is primarily concerned with a conversational interaction between humans and accordingly the requirement for acceptable quality and robustness imposes limits on the sampling, quantizing and companding techniques which has set the transmission rate of 64 kbit/s for telecommunication systems.

This transmission rate is the basis of the design and planning of digital networks on a world scale. However, the theoretical limit of representing speech can be roughly calculated as the average number of phonemes produced in 1 second of speech multiplied by the number of bits to give adequate representation. As the dynamics of the vocal tract limits the production of phonemic events to around 15 a second and with each event represented to a precision of 5 bit/s, the fundamental limit is theoretically 75 bit/s.

However, whilst speech is a highly redundant signal, a transmission rate approaching the fundamental level would require prior knowledge of the words (strings of phonemes) to be articulated.

The art of speech coding is to deceive the ear by taking advantage of its tolerance to quantizing flaws and secondly by employing algorithms adapted to the specific properties of speech. A range of coding techniques is currently used for digital transmission and coding techniques which can be categorised into three broad categories [31,32,33] as shown in Fig 10 against the relative quality of 64 kbit/s PCM. Digital speech coding algorithms may be broadly divided into three categories:

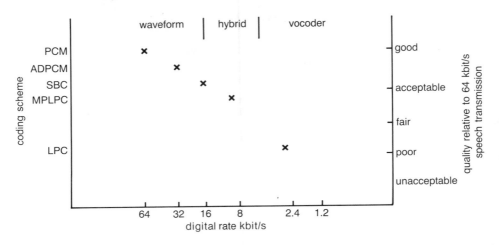

PCM = pulse code modulation
ADPCM = adaptive differential pulse code modulation
SBC = sub-band coding
MPLPC = multi-pulse linear predictive coding
LPC = linear predictive coding

Fig 10   Relative quality of speech coding schemes.

- waveform, where the speech signals are digitised directly from samples,

- parametric, where only certain parts of the signal are extracted and processed,

- hybrid, using algorithms employing features of waveform and parametric coding techniques.

Applications for low bit rate speech coding systems usually find favour in digital cellular radio and satellite systems where developments have been driven by the shortages in radio frequency spectrum. These applications impose constraints on the design, such as robustness to errors, delay and transparency to signalling tones.

Efficient digital speech coding is also used in interactive speech systems where the storage of digitised speech for retrieval purposes is a requirement.

An important aspect of a speech system is the way users adapt themselves to interfacing to the machine. Indeed user's motivation in using the technology can often be the key to success or failure. In this respect the dialogue control, response time, the quality and intelligibility of the voice and the accuracy of the speech recognition are some of the factors that need to be engineered to produce acceptable man-machine communication systems.

6.5   Network interface

In considering the design of a telephony interface for an interactive speech system, due consideration must be made for the mix of signals incident on the circuits which separate the send and receive paths, that is the telephone hybrids. The telephone interface may be required to detect and decode dual-tone multi-frequency (DTMF) signalling tones generated from telephone keypads and in this case the equipment is required to adapt to the prevailing line conditions. In the design of some voice systems based on keypad control, occasions have arisen where the user's voice has mimicked DTMF tones. The resultant confusion is not only annoying for the user, it is usually difficult to diagnose.

A significant problem with all methods of information entry, signalling tones or speech input (recognition), is that these signals are difficult to detect in the presence of outgoing speech, and in some cases the outgoing speech can give rise to false signals.

7. Interactive speech systems

7.1   Telephone retrieval of database information — CAESAR

Caesar is a programmable voice response unit that links into a database containing network records called NERO. It is designed to provide on-line information to engineers who install telecommunication equipment in customers' premises. The equipment is accessible from remote locations by DTMF signalling from the telephone keypad over the telephone network. An illustration of the CAESAR architecture is shown in Fig 11.

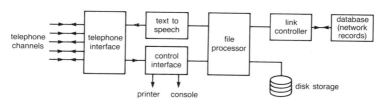

Fig 11   Caesar base unit.

The line engineer requiring information from the computer database follows a simple and secure log-in procedure to gain access to the system. Once access is gained, a logical data entry based on the telephone keypad is followed to obtain information relevant to the network route, such as line plant installation, customer's telephone number and address. This information is converted from text stored in the database, to speech by a text-to-speech synthesiser and delivered to the engineer under control of the telephone keypad. The engineer can request additional information or repeat information by simply pressing the appropriate key. Although the repertoire of responses is limited, it is possible to elicit most of the information normally provided by the human operator, who is in fact available if the appropriate request for help is keyed in. The system has been trialled in the North West of England and some interesting user reactions have been revealed.

The trial of the CAESAR system was conducted with the assistance of engineers who used the system as part of their normal jobs. Of the 73 engineers who participated in the 6-week trial, most reported that the quality of voice output from the text-to-speech synthesiser was acceptable and the feature to speak and spell unusual words was helpful. Most were able to use the facilities offered by the system without any prior training. Just under half of the trialists made use of the equipment after the first three weeks, reporting that response times from the system seemed longer than from the operator and that the number of keystrokes required was an imposition (extra keystrokes were incorporated to improve security). The results of this trial are being used in the design of an improved system for use in British Telecom's network which is due for operational implementation in April 1988.

The general arrangement of the CAESAR architecture makes it easy to adapt to other applications such as credit card verification and remote job dispatch.

7.2   Voice control of mobile telephones

The use of speech to control the dialling functions within a vehicle whilst in motion, requires a recognition and dialogue strategy matched to ease of use and safety. From the safety point of view it is necessary to operate the mobile telephone in an eyes and hands-free mode. Thus the user requires the recogniser to operate from a microphone remotely situated from the speaker's mouth; and a voice guidance response dialogue that is tailored to operate within the constraints of a vehicle in motion [35], i.e. wiper and heater fan noise, road surface and wind noise.

One of the first hands-free speech recognition car phones to be designed for commercial use is the TOPAZ mobile car telephone which is shown in Fig 12. The position of the handset (for use when the car is stationary) is placed within easy reach of the driver, the microphone for hands-free use is located in the sun visor and a display is mounted on the dashboard in line with the instrument panel. A single operation on/off control button is also located on the dashboard. The voice control module (VCM) which controls the recognition and the voice feedback is a separate unit capable of integration with the radio transceiver. The voice feedback guides the user through the sequence of voice commands necessary to dial the required number. The VCM is shown in Fig 12.

Fig 12   Voice control module for the Topaz car phone.

To improve the recognition response the VCM measures the noise spectrum just prior to the start of the utterance and using this measurement the noise spectral component is subtracted from the speech utterance. The dialogue flow for the operation of the VCM is shown in Fig 13.

7.3   Secure voice systems

The human ability to distinguish individuals by their speech, particularly if they are known, is commonplace even over a telephone. Speaker verification refers to the machine realisation of this function and is an aspect of speech recognition research and development outlined earlier. Confirming a user's authenticity by direct assessment of their speech waveforms has many advantages over other forms of identification, such as passwords or using physical entry tokens such as keys which may either be copied, stolen, or lost. Convenience is another benefit which occurs to a biometric system, since biometric attributes cannot be forgotten [36]. Where the information provider is remote from the user, a secure voice system that operates over the public telephone network should appeal to all providers of computer services who are concerned with security.

dialogue control for VCM

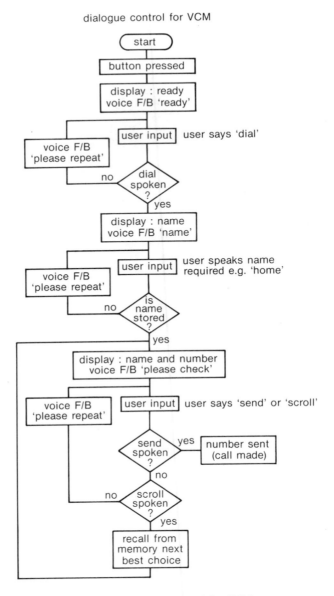

Fig 13   Dialogue control for VCM.

The telephone-based bank enquiry system under development at British Telecom Research Laboratories [37] employs a number of important features that enables the system to confirm the identity of the user by the voiceprint techniques and then recognise the command words spoken by the user to obtain the relevant information.If required, a personal identification number may also be entered by use of the telephone's keypad.

The system allows authenticated callers to make balance enquiries, order cheque-books or statements and transfer money between accounts using spoken commands.

The system uses speaker recognition to discover the claimed identity of the caller and speaker verification to ensure that only valid users are allowed access to financial information. The spoken output is in the form of concatenated examples of natural utterances, this gives a slightly disjointed delivery but of high clarity. This speech output method is preferred because the message repertoire is small. An outline of the automated telephone banking system is shown in Fig 14.

To use the Telebanking system, a user would first need to register examples of their voice for analysis to determine the characteristic voice features. The parameters relating to these features are stored in the system's memory for future use on validating the enquirer.

If mimicking of eavesdropped transactions are perceived as significant risks (although this would be unusual for users operating from their own premises) it is possible to devise a system of multiple passwords with random selection prompted by the system.

An important additional requirement of any large user application such as telephone banking is that the word recognition during the main dialogue should be essentially speaker independent. This is necessary so as to economise on storage and user training. To achieve a high degree of accuracy in speaker recognition, a strategy of collecting a large speech database for training and testing has been undertaken [38]. To test the initial performance, informal trials have been carried out on the telephone banking system involving a number of subjects from a wide mix of UK regional origins who first recorded their chosen passwords for registration and verification on the system. No other training or registration was involved other than a brief description of the services offered by the demonstration system. Throughout the trial, a total of 1528 words were spoken over the telephone and a total of 280 transaction tasks were attempted, some of these tasks requiring multiple commands.

The results of this trial indicate that the dialogue control for the system enabled a success rate of approximately 98%, albeit some users were required to repeat certain requests.

7.4   Voice operated database inquiry system

The potential for intelligent voice dialogue was recognised by the Alvey Directorate in 1985 as one of the exemplar projects for the UK national collaborative research programme in information technology. The project called VODIS (voice operated database inquiry system) [39] involves British Telecom, Logica and Cambridge

University Engineering Department and is aimed at producing a voice-based man-machine interface to databases over the telephone network. The voice operated database inquiry system main components are shown in Fig 15.

The demonstration system is intended to operate in near real-time to provide a voice operated inquiry about train times between London and Aberdeen. In operation the knowledge-base starts by asking the user a question and predicting the likely responses to it. The knowledge base builds a 'frame' representing the users enquiry; frames are an established artificial intelligence (AI) technique and consist of a package of information about a particular piece of knowledge. Frames are constructed with a number of slots — each slot having a name and value denoting an aspect of the frame's knowledge. In the domain of train timetables, slots might contain information on times and places which are required for the interaction. The syntax generator within the linguistic processor uses grammar rules to prime the recogniser. These rules are converted into a finite state network with loop backs and wildcards suitable to control the speech recogniser. The recognised reply is analysed by the parser to give one or more syntactic structures using semantic template grammar for a 'where to' slot denoting the destination and 'when' slot denoting either arrival or departure.

An unacceptable match or failure results in an error recovery dialogue being initiated. The database accessed by a software interface and is able to provide up-to-date timetable information.

The ways in which humans frequently engage in dialogues in which one party tries to retrieve information from another has been studied and extensively analysed for this project. The results have been used to construct dialogue interactions of optimal speed and accuracy to improve the performance of man-machine communication by speech for a goal-orientated information retrieval system over the telephone network. Some 60 hours of audio recordings of calls made to a public travel information service were examined to pinpoint the following aspects of the caller's behaviour [40] in the given context:

- phrases frequently used,
- the order in which words were used within the phrases,
- the number and order of phrases which constituted a complete inquiry.

Based on the generated analysis, it was possible to predict which class of words and phrases could be expected at a given dialogue point. This knowledge enhances the performance of the speech recogniser by reducing the number of speech templates active at a given point (node) in the dialogue.

Another important aspect of the human factors input is to determine users' reactions to the speech synthesiser used in the VODIS project. A number of assessment methods have been developed to test the quality, intelligibility and naturalness of the text-to-speech synthesiser used for this project. The philosophy of testing has been to base the listening trials on naive users, that is subjects who have not been exposed to synthetic or computer generated speech before.

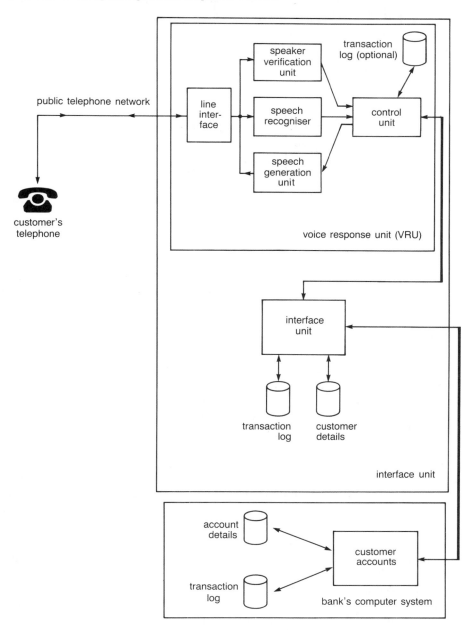

Fig 14   Automated telephone banking system.

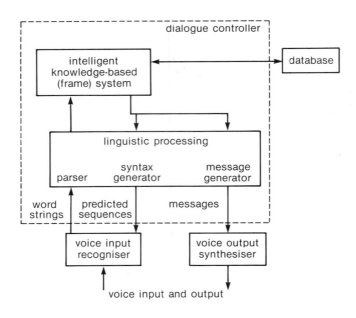

Fig 15   Voice operated database inquiry system.

7.5   Man-machine communication by speech — future research directions and applications

One of the speech systems of the future in which automatic speech recognition would provide the necessary breakthroughs is the speech typewriter. The thought of machine assisted speech transcription to enable direct textual output from spoken dictation has attracted a great deal of interest on a world scale. Such a system for use in this country would have to be able to recognise at least the average active vocabulary of an adult, around 6000 words and for useful office applications, a vocabulary of 20 000 words would be necessary [41]

Another long-held dream has been the thought of machines facilitating the simultaneous translation of speech from one language to another. Although far short of a practical system, the system outlined by Stentiford and Steer [42] points towards the future and gives the spur to designers of automatic speech recognition systems capable of accepting fluent speech for any speaker with good accuracy.

Speech and language processing has progressed to a stage beyond which significant advances can only be made by the use of artificial intelligence (AI). An aspect of AI which has seen a substantial revival and has much to offer is the use of neural-network models, or connectionism. These connectionist systems based on brain modelling are applicable to a number of cognitive science problems which include natural-language processing (NLP), speech processing and vision.

The computational flexibility of the human brain comes from its large number of neurons intertwined in a filigree of axons and dendrites. The communication between neurons is via the synapse and afferent fibres. There are many billions, probably trillions, of neural connections in the human brain. At a simple level it can be considered that nerve impulses are comparable to the phonemes of speech or to letters in that they do not themselves convey meaning but indicate different intensities [5] which are interpreted as meaningful units by the 'language of the brain'.

Models of neural networks use a particular topology and a learning rule for the interactions and interelations of the connections of the 'neural units'. Neural networks process information in a number of different ways and are able to exhibit useful properties — such as association, generalisation, differentiation, optimization which are forms of self organisation that cannot be easily achieved by conventional digital computers. In the area of speech processing [43] a number of techniques are emerging that indicate that forms of neurocomputing, such as multi-layer perceptrons [44] and topologically self ordering neural networks [45] are showing exceptional promise to the previous intractable problem of automatic speech recognition.

The mechanisms in speech and language processing for automatic speech recognition and synthesis systems are illustrated in a simplified manner in Fig 16. Without some

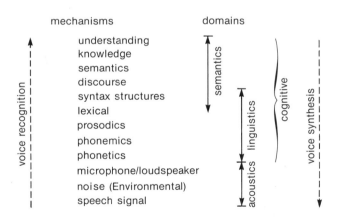

Fig 16   Mechanisms in speech and language processing.

understanding of human cognitive processing involved in speech production and perception, the aim for machines to exhibit a greater degree of intelligence is likely to fall short of the expectations that are being generated by the interactive speech systems that are emerging from research laboratories around the world.

8. Conclusions

This paper has briefly surveyed the historical development of speech and language processing from the earliest times to the emerging interactive speech systems being developed for present day use. The history of speech processing for communication purposes shows a regular cycle between the twin barriers of fundamental knowledge and technology implementation; that is, as the processing technology becomes more cost effective, gaps are revealed in the fundamental knowledge of how humans generate, perceive and understand speech. Although some man-machine communication systems operate with the current computer speech recognition and synthesis components aided by the application of dialogue and error recovery control strategies, they are nevertheless limited in their scope. Thus the promise and expectation of high-performance interactive speech processing systems can only be achieved by design and research methodologies appropriate to more complex cognitive systems than currently replicated by electronics.

Investigations into neural networks and the realisation of circuits based on the function of the brain will in time give a measure of natural conversation with a machine.

If speech is civilisation, the future aim of designers must be to produce human computer interfaces that enable a more natural and useful dialogue flow in the form of a conversation.

Acknowledgements

The author would like to acknowledge the help and contribution of his many colleagues in the Speech and Language Processing Division and in particular to R D Johnston for his helpful suggestions. Thanks are also due to Dr C Stringer of the Natural History Museum for pointing out some of the early references.

References

1   ZEITSCHRIFT fur Information Stechnik und TeleKommunikation: NTZ (November 1986)

2   Wheddon C: 'Interactive speech systems — man-machine communication by speech', 5th World Telecommunication Forum, Geneva (1987).

3   Spuhler J N: Biology, Speech and Language, Annual Review of Anthropology, 6 (1977).

4   Liberman P: The Biology and Evolution of Language, Harvard University Press (1984).

5   Young J Z: 'Programs of the brain', Oxford University Press (1975).

6   Crenlin E S, Klatt D H and Lieberman P: 'Phonetic ability and related anatomy of the newborn and adult human, Neanderthal Man, and the Chimpanzee', American Anthropology, 74 (1972).

7   Linggard R: 'Electronic synthesis of speech', Cambridge University Press (1985).

8   Catford J C: 'Mountain of tongues: the language of the Caucasus', Annual Review of Anthropology, 6 (1977).

9   Pickles J O: 'An introduction to the physiology of hearing', Academic Press (1982).

10 Linggard R & Ambibairajah E: 'A computational model of the basilar membrane', Speech Science and Technology Conference, Canberra (1986).

11 Ainsworth W A: 'Mechanisms of speech recognition', Pergamon Press (1976).

12 Dudley H and Tarnocey T H: 'The speaking machine of Wolfgang von Kempelen', Journal of the Acoustical Society of America, 22 , No.2 (1950).

13 Dudley H: 'The Vocoder', Bell Labs Record, 18 (1939).

14 Swaffield J: 'The potentialities of the Vocoder for telephony over very long distances', The Post Office Electrical Engineers Journal, 41 , Part 1 (1948).

15 Flowers J B: 'The true nature of speech', Journal of the Acoustical Society of America (1916).

16 Davies K H, Budulph R and Balashek S: 'Automatic recognition of spoken digits', Journal of the Acoustical Society of America, 24 , pp 637 (1952).

17 Denes P B: 'Automatic speech recognition, old & new ideas', Speech Recognition Ed. D Raj Reddy, Academic Press (1975).

18 Mariani J J: 'Speech technology in Europe', 1st European Conf on Speech Tech, Edinburgh (1987).

19 Baker J M: 'State-of-the-art speech recognition US research and business update', 1st European Conf on Speech Tech, Edinburgh (1987).

20 Fujisaki H: 'Overview of the Japanese national project on advanced man-machine interface through spoken language', 1st European Conf on Speech Tech, Edinburgh (1987).

21 Michie D and Johnston R: 'The creative computer', Viking Press (1984).

22 Sakoe H and Chibass: 'Dynamic programming algorithm optimisation for spoken word recognition', IEEE Trans Accoust Speech and Signal Proc, 26 (1978).

23 Cox S J: 'Hidden Markov models for automatic speech recognition: theory and applications', Br Telecom Technol J, 6 , No.2, (1988).

24 Bridle J S, Brown M D and Chamberlain R M: 'An algorithm for connected word recognition', Automatic Speech Analysis and Recognition, Reidal Publishing Company (1984).

25 Atal B S and Rabiner L R: 'Speech research directions', AT&T Technical Journal 65 , Issue 5 (1986).

26 Frame P B and Cheeseman D S: 'Customer controlled supplementary services using voice guidance system', Proc Int Switching Symposium, Paris (1979).

27 Holmes J N: 'Formant synthesisers: cascade or parallel?', Speech Communication, 2 (1983).

28 Hughes P M: 'Formant based speech synthesis', Br Telecom Technol J, 6, No.2 (1988).

29 Stephens A P and Holmes J N: 'Use of flexible voice output techniques for man-machine communication', Behaviour and Information Technology 3, No.2 (1984).

30 Gibson D L, Gillott T J and Helliker L A: 'Textalk: the BT text-to-speech system', Br Telecom Technol J, 6, No.2 (1988).

31 Lind L, Attkins P M and Challener P: 'An improved implementation of adaptive quantizer for speech waveform encoding schemes', Br Telecom Technol J, 6, No.2 (1988).

32 Southcott C B, Boyd I, Coleman A E and Hammett P: 'Low bit rate speech coding for practical applications', Br Telecom Technol J 6, No.2 (1988).

33 Schroder M R: 'Linear predictive coding of speech review and current directions', IEEE Communications Mag 23, No.8 (1985).

34 Waterworth J A: 'Human processing of machine speech', Br Telecom Technol J, 4, No.4, (1986).

35 Forse N J A: 'Speech recognition for telephony applications', Proc of the Inst of Acoustics, 9 (1987).

36 Doddington G R: 'Speaker recognition — identifying people by their voices', Proc IEEE 73, No.11 (1985).

37 Cameron I R and Millar P C: 'Speaker recognition for security', Proc Inst of Acoustics, 9 (1987).

38 Millar P C, Cameron I R, Greaves A J and McPeake C M: 'Phone-in competitions: a development and evaluation tool for voice-interactive systems', BTTJ, 6, No.2 (1988).

39 Bruce I P C: 'Engineering an intelligent voice dialogue controller', Computer-Aided Engineering Journal (1987).

40 Talbot M: 'What can human factors offer the speech-based human-computer interface', Proc Int Speech Tech Conf London (1987).

41 Alvey programme: Annual Report, Poster Supplement (1987).

42 Stentiford F W S and Steer M G: 'Machine translation of speech', Br Telecom Technol J, 6, No.2 (1988).

43 Bridle J S: 'Adaptive networks and speech pattern processing', Pattern Recognition Theory and Applications, Ed. by P A Devijner and J Kittler, NATO ASI Series, F30, Springer-Veelay Berlin, Heidelberg (1987).

44 McCulloch N, Ainsworth W and Linggard R: 'Multi-layer perceptrons applied to speech technology', Br Telecom Technol J, 6, No.2 (1988).

45 Tattersall G D, Linford P W and Linggard R: 'Neural arrays for speech recognition', Br Telecom Technol J, 6, No.2 (1988).

LOW BIT RATE SPEECH CODING FOR PRACTICAL APPLICATIONS

C B Southcott, I Boyd, A E Coleman and P G Hammett

ABSTRACT

The speech quality achieved by low bit rate speech codecs has improved greatly in the last few years. When these codecs are used in practical applications, however, many other requirements must be satisfied besides adequate speech quality. This paper examines these requirements and reviews current speech coding methods in the light of their ability to meet the requirements of telecommunications applications. The selection of speech codecs for particular applications and some network planning aspects of their use are then discussed.

1. Introduction

There are good grounds for claiming that the speech codec is the most important part of many speech systems. In digital transmission or speech storage systems it is normally the speech codec which defines the basic speech quality for the whole system; no amount of sophistication elsewhere in the system can compensate for degradation introduced in the codec. The user's perception of the system is strongly influenced by the quality of this one component.

A few years ago the prospect of low bit rate speech coders being used for public telecommunications services seemed remote; there was little demand for them and the available speech quality was too poor. Since then the growth of competition and the introduction of new services has led to a large number of important applications. Advances in speech coding techniques have been rapid too, leading to greatly improved speech quality at low bit rates.

Unfortunately the demands on speech codecs are not limited to providing good speech quality under favourable operating conditions. In a telecommunications environment a codec must be able to work under a wide range of adverse conditions whilst giving good speech quality, low transmission delay and a low bit rate. In addition they should be cheap to manufacture and consume little power.

If speech production and perception were perfectly understood then it might be possible to achieve these objectives at bit rates less than 1 kbit/s; unfortunately they are not. Since good models of speech production and perception are not yet available it is necessary to resort to computationally intensive (number crunching) techniques rather than elegant analytical solutions to get good results. With these techniques the lowest rate at which most of these objectives can currently be met is about 8 kbit/s.

This paper reviews low bit rate (less than 16 kbit/s) speech coding techniques and their suitability for telecommunications environments. Designs and techniques are discussed together with the subjective testing methods used for selecting suitable codecs for real operating environments.

1.1   Applications of low bit rate speech codecs

Low bit rate speech codecs are used for two basic reasons: to increase revenue and/or to provide a service which could not otherwise be provided.

Saving money is an important factor in the use of low bit rate codecs to multiplex several conversations onto a channel which would normally carry a single conversation (e.g. to replace one 64 kbit/s PCM channel with 8 speech channels carrying speech coded at 8 kbit/s). This is quite common on private communication circuits and on expensive international links in public networks (such as submarine cable links.) It is rare on the normal inland circuits of public networks, though, because the availability of low cost optical fibre circuits reduces the possible cost benefits.

Cost reduction is also important in the use of low rate coding for speech storage. The amount of random access memory (RAM) or disc memory needed can be greatly reduced in voice mailbox or telephone answering machines, for example.

The most important use of low bit rate speech codecs, however, is likely to be in making efficient use of the radio spectrum. Such codecs are already in use on satellite circuits.

The whole area of personal cordless and mobile communications is becoming increasingly important as users expect to have continuous access to communications services (and to be instantly contactable) without being tied to a particular location. The CEPT has recently standardised a 13 kbit/s codec for use in the forthcoming pan-European digital cellular mobile telephone service and has decided to introduce codecs at half this bit rate when suitable ones become available. Inmarsat is currently selecting a 9.6 kbit/s codec for use in a digital aeronautical telephone service. Sales of cordless telephones are increasing rapidly and the next generation of these in the UK will use 32 kbit/s speech codecs. In all of these mobile services the number of customers who can be served (and hence the revenue available to service providers) is crucially dependent on the bit rate at which the speech codecs can achieve the required performance. Lower bit rate codecs will be used as soon as possible. This emphasises the importance of developments in speech coding.

Services using digital radio links are inevitably subject to transmission errors. Low bit rate speech codecs are used for these services not only to save bandwidth but also because they can be made very robust to digital errors. The capacity of digital cellular telephone systems, for example, is limited by radio interference between cells using the same frequencies (which causes errors in the received digital signal). The ability of the speech codecs to give good speech quality which is very little affected by these errors allows the radio frequencies to be re-used much more intensively than in analogue systems; this is just as important in increasing the system capacity as the reduction in bandwidth.

Another service which cannot easily be provided without low bit rate codecs is highly secure telephony over analogue connections. Analogue encryption is not very efficient but low bit rate codecs may be used with digital encryption devices and modems to give the same level of security as is available on digital connections.

Apart from working at a single fixed bit rate, speech codecs may be designed to work at bit rates which vary continuously according to the content of the speech being coded or to be switchable between several fixed bit rates. Such codecs can be very useful in providing the flexibility to mix speech and data services over the same connection.

1.2   Performance required of low bit rate speech codecs

This section discusses the requirements imposed on speech codecs by their applications.

Speech quality

The objective for speech codecs for public telecommunications systems is usually to achieve the same speech quality as in a long distance telephone call on the analogue PSTN (often referred to as 'toll quality'). Since such calls are very variable in quality, toll quality is a rather nebulous concept and some of the claims made for codecs are difficult to justify.

A more precise target is to meet the transmission performance standards agreed by the CCITT for PSTNs. The CCITT distortion limits are discussd in sections 3.2 and 4.

There are also services where it would be uneconomic to meet these quality criteria with currently available technology and where lower speech quality is deemed acceptable. Current analogue cellular radio telephone services, for example, whilst much better than older mobile services, give a quality below that of the fixed PSTN. The codec for the CEPT cellular radio standard was chosen to give quality which, on average, is better than the analogue cellular systems. Similarly, lower speech quality is accepted for maritime radio telephones and for aeronautical telephones. However, for cordless telephones it is considered necessary to meet the appropriate CCITT distortion standards.

Robustness to digital transmission errors

For speech storage applications virtually no digital errors at all can be expected between the speech coder and the decoder. Transmission systems using radio links, on the other hand, may have very high error rates with the errors probably occuring in bursts. Error correcting coding will usually be applied to the radio link (possibly with interleaving to break up error bursts) but this will still leave a residual bit error rate at the speech decoder typically averaging between 1 in 50 and 1 in 1000.

Robustness to acoustic inputs

To be useful in a public service, speech codecs usually need to be able to work well with a wide range of speakers (from adult males to young children), with a wide range of speech levels (a dynamic range of at least 25 dB is usually required), with distorted speech, with background acoustic noise (which in some applications can be very high), and with more than one person talking at a time. Each of these conditions is very difficult for certain types of codec to handle and they are all likely to arise with speech derived from the analogue PSTN.

Delay

For applications where the codecs are used purely for speech storage the delays introduced by speech codecs are likely to be unimportant. For transmission applications, though, delay is important for two reasons: firstly because excessive delay (more than about 400 ms) causes conversational difficulties and secondly because if there are any sources of echo (either electrical or acoustic echo) in the transmission path then propagation delay can cause the resulting echoes to become objectionable.

Both of these considerations can impose limits on the codec delay; the limit in any particular application will depend on the other delays in the connections involved. For example, if a codec is to be connected to the UK PSTN then its delay must be limited to 5 ms unless echo control devices are also provided.

Tandem connections

When certain types of codec are connected in tandem with other codecs (of similar or of different types) it is possible for a small amount of distortion introduced by the first codec to cause a large increase in the distortion introduced by the second codec. The selection of the codec design should therefore reflect the distortion requirements of the total end-to-end connections.

Non-speech signals

Speech codecs are sometimes required to pass modem data signals, multi-frequency signalling tones and information tones (such as telephone ringing tones and engaged tones) without introducing significant distortion.

2. Review of speech coding techniques

This section commences with a short introduction to speech production and perception and illustrates how researchers are using some of the knowledge gained about speech production and perception in the design of speech codecs. Linear predictive coding (LPC) analysis is the most important speech analysis technique currently used so a large part of this section is dedicated to LPC analysis and quantization. The remainder of the section discusses different coding algorithms and the advantages and disadvantages of each. Emphasis is placed on speech coding algorithms which use analysis-by-synthesis coding techniques for low bit-rate encoding (4—16 kbit/s) as these algorithms are the most successful at coping with practical operating conditions.

2.1   Speech production and perception

Speech can be broadly classified as either voiced or unvoiced. Voiced speech (e.g. the vowel sound /a/) is produced when air from the lungs is forced through the vocal cords causing them to vibrate (Fig 1). The vocal cords are two flaps of soft tissue which are held under tension for the production of voiced speech. The frequency of vibration of the vocal cords is dependent on the air pressure in the trachea and the degree of tension. The frequency of vibration is known as the fundamental frequency and the perceived frequency is known as pitch. The pulses of air emitted from the vocal cords excite the vocal tract (Fig 1) giving rise to resonant frequencies in the radiated signal. The mobile articulators, namely the lower jaw, tongue, lips and uvula (a flap which opens or closes the nasal cavity) are constantly in motion during speech production. These movements change the size and shape of the vocal tract, thus changing the resonant frequencies, and give rise to the distinct speech sounds which we perceive.

For unvoiced speech the vocal cords are loose and air from the lungs passes unaffected into the vocal tract. In this case excitation occurs by placing a constriction at some point along the vocal tract. For example, the fricative /f/ is produced when a constriction is formed by raising the lower lip to touch the upper teeth.

A model of this speech production process which has received wide acceptance is illustrated in Fig 2. Voiced excitation is modelled by a train of unipolar, unit amplitude impulses at the desired pitch frequency. Unvoiced excitation is modelled as the output from a psuedo-random noise generator; the voiced/unvoiced switch selects the appropriate excitation.

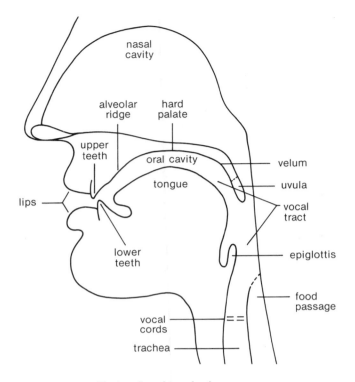

Fig 1   Speech production organs.

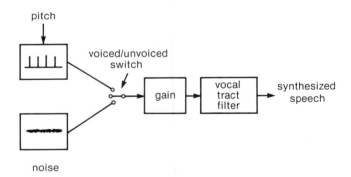

Fig 2   Speech production model.

Just as the human speech production process is used as a model in the design of speech coders, so features of speech perception are also exploited. Some of these features are so fundamental that they are taken for granted. For example the current analogue telephone network, with a bandwidth extending from 300 Hz to 3.4 kHz, takes advantage of the following two features.

- The pitch of a speaker can be perceived from a high-pass filtered speech signal even though the fundamental frequency is not present (for adult male speakers, the fundamental frequency is almost always below 300 Hz);

- The ear is more sensitive to low frequency sounds than to high frequencies so most of the important information in the speech signal is carried by the lower frequencies. Therefore, although many speech sounds have significant energy in the frequency band extending to 10 kHz, speech is still intelligible if it is band limited to 3.4 kHz.

The variable frequency sensitivity of the ear outlined above is exploited even further by frequency domain coders which split the input signal into several frequency bands and quantize the lower bands more accurately than the higher bands. The distortion introduced by the more crudely quantized upper frequency regions is not as readily detected by the ear as distortions in low frequency bands.

The phenomenon of masking, where one sound 'drowns out' another sound, is also exploited by many coders. It is well known that a tone of sufficient energy will mask noise close in frequency to the tone and conversely, if the noise energy is sufficient. This masking principle is employed by many speech coders which use the speech signal itself to mask quantization noise. More information on the speech production and perception processes can be found in Ainsworth [1].

2.2 *LPC analysis and quantization*

Models of the speech production process usually treat the vocal tract and the air entering the vocal tract (the 'excitation') separately. The LPC model is the most widely used model of the vocal tract. In combination with various models of the excitation it forms the basis of many different types of speech codec.

In LPC analysis [2] the vocal tract section of the speech production model (Fig 2) is represented by a time-varying linear digital filter. This filter must represent the effects of lip radiation, glottal pulse shape, and nasal cavity coupling where required. The aim of LPC analysis is to extract a set of parameters from the speech signal to specify the filter transfer function which gives the best match to the speech to be coded. An all-pole filter of order p (usually in the range 10 to 20) is used to model the vocal tract. This is a good model for reasons relating to both the way in which speech is produced and perceived. For example, the spectral envelope of the short-term speech signal contains a number of peaks at frequencies closely related to the formant frequencies, i.e. the resonant frequencies of the vocal tract. With regard to speech perception, it is the spectral peaks and not the spectral troughs which are the most significant. An all-pole filter model reproduces the spectral peaks much better than the troughs.

Consider the LPC all-pole model of the vocal tract. The transfer function $H(z)$ of the LPC filter may be written as:

$$H(z) = \cfrac{G}{1 - \sum_{k=1}^{p} a_k z^{-k}} = \frac{G}{A(z)}$$

where: G is the gain parameter;
a_k are the filter coefficients;
p is the order of the filter;
$A(z)$ is the 'inverse filter'.

Having made the assumption that an all-pole filter of order p will model the vocal tract, the LPC analysis must extract sets of coefficients (a_k values) periodically from the speech signal. The vocal tract shape generally changes relatively slowly and it is thus sufficient to update the parameters once every 10 to 20 ms.

The residual signal is the signal that would be obtained if the speech signal were filtered by the inverse filter $A(z)$. The optimum set of a_k coefficients for a given block of speech will be those which minimise the residual signal power over the block [2]. It can be shown that in the frequency domain these same coefficients give a $H(z)$ whose frequency response best matches the speech spectrum for the block. With the filter order p in the range 10 to 20, the frequency response of $H(z)$ will match only the spectral envelope of the speech signal and not the fine spectral detail. If the spectrum of the excitation is assumed to be flat, which is the case both for white noise and an impulse train excitation, then the spectral envelope will correspond to the frequency response of the vocal tract. The optimum set of a_k coefficients is thus the set which minimises the residual energy signal power, E, in equation (1).

$$E = \sum_{n=1}^{N} (s(n) - \sum_{k=1}^{p} a_k \, s(n-k))^2 \qquad \qquad \dots\dots(1)$$

where: $s(n)$ is the nth speech sample;
N is the number of speech samples in the analysis frame.

The optimum set of a_k coefficients is readily obtained from equation (1).

From the speech coding point of view, the most important features of the LPC model are that it uses a linear filter of low order to represent the vocal tract and that the coefficients of this linear filter are updated every 10 to 20 ms. Some limitations of LPC modelling are:

● a low order linear filter gives only an approximate representation of the spectral envelope of the speech signal;

- the relatively slow updating of the coefficients means that occasional sudden changes in the spectral envelope of the input speech are not well followed.

Scalar quantization of LPC parameters

For codec implementations the LPC parameters must be quantized as efficiently as possible. Direct quantization of the a_k values requires an excessive number of bits to yield accurate and stable quantized filters. An alternative set of parameters which may be used to specify the filter are the reflection coefficients. These may be obtained directly from the a_k coefficients by a transformation [3]. The reflection coefficients have the useful property that provided the modulus of each coefficient is less than 1, the all-pole LPC filter is guaranteed to be stable. The reflection coefficients may be efficiently quantized if they are individually transformed by an inverse sine or an inverse hyperbolic tangent and then uniformly quantized. For a 10th order LPC filter approximately 40 bits are required per filter: these bits are non-uniformly allocated among the coefficients [15] as the coefficients are not equally important.

Vector quantization of LPC vocal tract filters

Vector quantization is a pattern matching or block quantization technique, also known as codebook coding [4]. In vector quantization a copy of a codebook containing a set of quantized vectors is stored at both the encoder and decoder. The quantization process involves mapping an input vector onto a codeword such that the difference between the input vector and the quantized vector is minimised according to some chosen criterion. The index number of the selected codeword is transmitted to the decoder where it is used to summon the appropriate quantized vector from the decoder's copy of the codebook. Vector quantization reduces the bit-rate because fewer bits are needed to transmit the index number than to transmit the vector itself.

Vector quantization can be very effectively used to quantize the LPC filter parameters. Each filter, which is specified by a set of coefficients, is regarded as a vector. The codebook comprises a set of stored vectors or filters which have been chosen from the set of possible vocal tract filters. For scalar quantization, LPC analysis and coefficient quantization form two separate stages. However, with vector quantization the analysis stage, (which aims to identify the filter which minimises the residual signal energy) may be bypassed by using the residual energy as the distortion measure for selecting the optimum filter from the codebook [5]. Figure 3 illustrates an LPC based codec employing vector quantization.

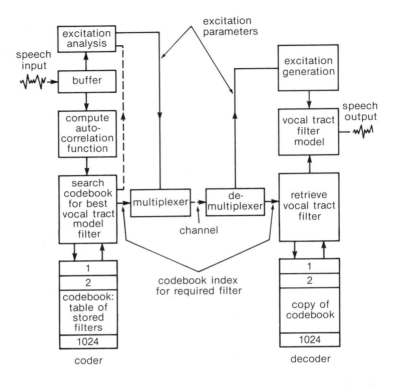

Fig 3   Vector quantization — application to vocal tract model in speech coders.

It is important to select an appropriate set of filters for the codebook entries. These entries are generated using a clustering algorithm by analysis of a large training sequence of speech [5,6].

Vector quantization of the LPC filters can be very useful in speech coding for reducing the bit-rate. However, the restriction of the filters which can be used to only those stored in the codebook (usually only 512 or 1024) can result in a noticeable reduction in speech quality.

Tree structured codebooks

A full search of a codebook is computationally expensive since a distortion computation must be carried out for every filter in the codebook. If the codebook is arranged as a tree structure (an operation which must be carried out at the design stage [4]) then the search efficiency can be dramatically improved. A binary tree is illustrated in Fig 4. There are two filters at the first level, four at the second and 1024 at the tenth level. The vector to be quantized is first compared with the two filters at the first level and the branch corresponding to the best matching filter selected. The vector is then compared with the two filters at the second level. This is repeated at each level until the final level where the filter selected is the filter used. Only 20 distortion computations and comparisons are needed compared with 1024 for the full searched codebook. The disadvantages of binary tree structured codebooks are that more storage is required for the encoder codebook and the quantization performance is inferior. An alternative design, which offers improved quantization performance and reduced storage in comparison to the binary tree, is the graded tree illustrated in Fig 5 . This design requires 30 distortion calculations and comparisons to search the codebook and gives a performance very close to a full search [7].

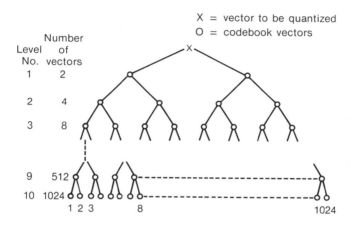

Fig 4   Binary tree structured codebook.

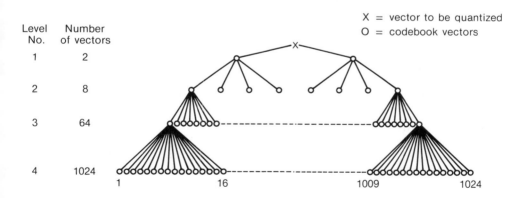

Fig 5   Graded tree structured codebook.

The fundamental performance advantages of vector quantization, as explained by the rate distortion theory [8], will need to be exploited much more in the future as better quality low bit rate encoding is pursued. Recent speech coding papers [9,10], which have proposed the use of very efficient and complex vector predictive coding schemes, illustrate the increasing use of vector quantization by researchers.

2.3 Classification of algorithms

Speech coding algorithms can be classified into the following three types:

- waveform coding,
- vocoding,
- hybrid coding.

Generally speaking, waveform coding requires a high bit rate (> 16 kbit/s), but can give speech quality suitable for use on the PSTN; vocoding requires a very low bit rate (< 4.8 kbit/s) but gives only synthetic quality speech and hybrid coding requires a low bit rate (4.8-16 kbit/s) and gives speech quality that is not quite as good as that of waveform coders.

2.4 Waveform coding

The most basic waveform coders do not attempt to exploit any knowledge of the speech production process in the encoding of the input signal. The aim of waveform coding, as the name implies, is to reproduce the original waveform as accurately as possible. As such they are not speech specific and handle many non-speech signals, background noise and multiple speakers without difficulty. The penalty of a relatively high bit rate, however, must be paid for this 'acoustic robustness'.

The simplest and best known waveform encoding technique is pulse code modulation (PCM). When PCM employs non-uniform quantization (A-law or μ-law) with 8 kHz sampling, very good quality speech is obtained at 64 kbit/s.

By quantizing the difference between successive samples, rather than the samples themselves, differential coding schemes exploit the correlation between adjacent samples. Examples are differential pulse code modulation (DPCM) [11] and delta modulation (DM) [12]. By adapting the quantizer step-size according to the short-term speech power adaptive differential pulse code modulation (ADPCM) [13] and adaptive delta modulation (ADM) are obtained. A continuous variable slope delta (CVSD) modulator is an example of an ADM coder [14]. ADPCM is superior to CVSD and gives good speech quality at bit rates in the range 24-48 kbit/s.

Differential encoding can be extended by using adaptive prediction. In this case the next speech sample is predicted from the previous (4-20) samples (short-term prediction) and the difference (prediction error) between the actual speech sample and the predicted value is quantized. When the prediction process also includes long-term prediction and noise shaping, the encoding process is known as adaptive predictive coding (APC) [15]. (APC is a generic term which also covers codecs using LPC for the prediction — see section 2.6). The long-term prediction exploits longer term correlations in the speech signal and the noise shaping filter redistributes the noise, i.e. the error between the input and quantized speech signals, such that it is 'perceptually reduced' [15].

The time-domain coding algorithms outlined above have their counterparts in the frequency domain; for example sub-band coding (SBC) [17,18,29] and adaptive transform coding (ATC) [19] are two very widely used techniques. In sub-band coding the input signal is split into several frequency bands (usually 2 to 16) using an analysis filter bank. Separate waveform coders are used to quantize each sub-band signal for subsequent multiplexing and transmission. The waveform coders used in each frequency band may have a fixed number of bits assigned to them or the bit assignment may be varied on a frame to frame basis to maximise speech quality according to some suitable criterion. Sub-band coders give good speech quality at bit rates in the range 16 to 24 kbit/s. In adaptive transform coding the input signal is split into many more bands than in sub-band coding. A block transformation, such as the discrete cosine transform, is employed for the band splitting operation. Adaptive transform coders give good speech quality at 16 kbit/s and some complex adaptive transform coders operate at bit rates down to 4.8 kbit/s [30]. Additional information on the speech coding algorithms outlined above and other waveform codecs is available elsewhere [20—28].

2.5 Vocoding

Unlike waveform coders, the operation of vocoders is very closely based on the speech production model of Fig 2. The vocal tract section of the model can be described in several ways — for example, it may be described by the short-term amplitude spectrum of the speech signal evaluated at specific frequencies (channel vocoder) [21], the major spectral peaks (formant vocoder) [21], or linear predictive coding (LPC) coefficients (LPC vocoder) [31].

The excitation is usually modelled in vocoders as shown in Fig 2. This model is poor for several reasons including the following:

- speech does not fall neatly into the two categories of voiced and unvoiced;

- in voiced speech the pitch is not constant but subject to 'micro-variations' — the constant pitch of the excitation over several voiced excitation periods contributes to the synthetic sound of vocoders.

As vocoders are so strongly based on the simple speech production model of Fig 2 they perform very poorly with high levels of background noise, multiple speakers and non-speech signals.

LPC vocoding is the most widely used vocoding technique today. LPC vocoders usually operate at around 2.4 kbit/s and give synthetic quality speech which is unacceptable for PSTN applications. It is, however, acceptable for military applications as a means of providing secure low bit rate communications. A US standard algorithm [31] known as LPC-10 is widely used. (The '10' indicates that a 10th order LPC analysis is employed.)

2.6   Hybrid coding and analysis-by-synthesis techniques

Hybrid coders combine features from vocoding and waveform coding and generally operate at a bit rate between the two. Several hybrid coders employ an analysis-by-synthesis process to derive some of the codec parameters. This, as the name implies, is the use of synthesis as an integral part of the analysis process. A block diagram of an analysis-by-synthesis system is illustrated in Fig 6. The aim of analysis-by-synthesis speech coding is to derive at least some of the codec parameters so that the difference between the input and synthesized signals is minimised according to some suitable criterion. A local decoder is employed alongside the encoder to synthesize the encoded signal. Codecs based on the analysis-by-synthesis principle are robust to background noise and non-speech signals in the same way as waveform coders. A number of important hybrid and analysis-by-synthesis speech coding algorithms are presented below.

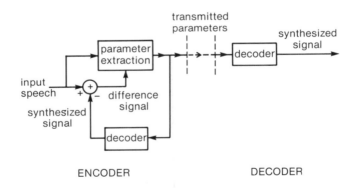

Fig 6   An analysis-by-synthesis process.

2.6.1   Hybrid coding

The inverse LPC filter $A(z)$, introduced earlier in this section, removes the short-term correlations from the speech signal and leaves a noise-like waveform, known as the LPC residual signal. If the speech is voiced the residual waveform will contain aperiodic spikes at the pitch frequency (Fig 7). If the LPC residual is then passed unquantized through the unquantized all-pole filter the original speech signal is reproduced. Even if the filter is quantized, provided the quantization is relatively accurate, the reproduced speech is almost indistinguishable from the original. With this in mind, if only the residual signal could be quantized accurately and efficiently a high quality practical speech codec could be obtained.

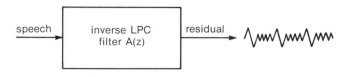

Fig 7   Inverse LPC filtering.

Adaptive predictive coding

The most obvious solution is to treat the residual as a waveform and quantize it directly. This technique is another form of adaptive predictive coding (APC). However, as the residual is noise-like there is almost no correlation between adjacent samples so none of the differential encoding schemes can be effectively employed and a relatively high bit rate is required. Thus APC gives very good speech quality at bit rates > 16 kbit/s. (With some very clever manipulation of the residual and entropy encoding, good speech quality can, however, be obtained at bit-rates down to 10 kbit/s [15].)

RELP Coding

A variant on APC is known as residual excited linear predictive coding (RELP) [16]. For a RELP coder the prediction error is low-pass filtered (to band-limit the residual to around 1 kHz) and down-sampled. As the prediction error has been down-sampled there are fewer samples to be transmitted and hence fewer bits are required to quantize this band-limited residual signal. A full-band signal is obtained at the decoder by non-linear distortion techniques [16].

As the bit rate of both APC and RELP codecs is reduced towards 8 kbit/s the number of bits available to represent the residual becomes insufficient and the speech quality deteriorates rapidly. In recent years, however, some very promising coding techniques have been introduced which perform well at bit rates less than 10 kbit/s. These are referred to as 'residual substitution' algorithms.

2.6.2   Analysis-by-synthesis coding techniques

The residual substitution algorithms lend themselves well to the analysis-by-synthesis technique mentioned above.

Multipulse excited LPC

As the quantized residual itself is not suitable for low bit rate coding, a substitute excitation waveform is required. This substitute excitation should:

- produce an output from the LPC synthesis filter similar to that obtained using the unquantized residual;

- be sufficiently accurately represented by much fewer bits than is required for the residual.

In 1982 Atal and Remde [32] presented one such substitute excitation which they named multipulse excitation. A multipulse LPC (MPLPC) decoder is illustrated in Fig 8. In MPLPC a series of non-uniformly spaced pulses with different amplitudes is used to excite the filter. Unlike LPC vocoding, no distinction is made between voiced and unvoiced speech: the same type of excitation waveform is used for all speech segments. For good quality speech several pulses are required per pitch period. However, as all the pulse positions and amplitudes must be transmitted a quality versus bit rate trade-off has to be made. The derivation of the appropriate pulse positions and amplitudes at the encoder is, of course, crucial to the coder performance.

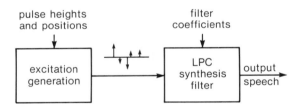

Fig 8   Multipulse decoder.

A MPLPC encoder is illustrated in Fig 9. The most important point to note about this figure is that the method of deriving the multipulse excitation involves an analysis-by-synthesis procedure, i.e. the input and synthesized speech are compared and the excitation is derived to minimise the error between the two signals. This analysis-by-synthesis technique is very advantageous when the input signal is corrupted by noise. In LPC vocoding, if the input speech is noisy, errors occur in the voiced/unvoiced decisions, the pitch periods selected and the LPC parameters. The resulting synthesized speech is, therefore, severely distorted. However, for MPLPC, due to the feedback loop, errors in the LPC analysis are compensated by the excitation selected. The coded output speech is thus a relatively accurate representation of the noisy input.

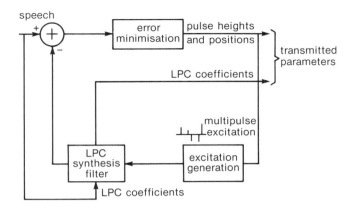

Fig 9   Basic multipulse encoder.

The excitation analysis procedure requires the partitioning of the input speech into small blocks (32—128 samples), and a search for the pulse positions and amplitudes which minimise the error, between the input and synthesized speech, over the block. A one-pass solution to finding the optimum positions and amplitudes is a highly non-linear problem and is thus extremely complex. One possible method of finding the excitation is to split the problem into two parts, and try every possible combination of pulse positions. Given the pulse positions, the pulse amplitudes which minimise the error can be found relatively easily. The pulse positions and amplitudes which yield the lowest error over the block form the optimum excitation signal. Unfortunately, even for a small block size and only a few pulses per block, the number of possible combinations is relatively high, and results in an excessive computational load. Sub-optimal methods have thus been developed which find the pulse positions and amplitudes one at a time [32, 34,40]. These sequential methods reduce the error minimisation process to that of selecting a pulse position as the location at which a maximum occurs in a cross-correlation function. Once a pulse position has been found the calculation of the corresponding pulse amplitude is straightforward. Given both the pulse position and amplitude, the cross-correlation function can be updated and the search for the next pulse can proceed. With a moderate increase in complexity, the performance of the sequential pulse search methods can be improved considerably, using a technique known as amplitude re-optimisation [35]. This entails jointly optimising the amplitudes of all the pulses in a frame once all their positions have been found. An alternative technique, which offers some advantages over amplitude re-optimisation for lower bit rate coders, is known as position re-optimisation [36].

The MPLPC coder described above can be extended [35] to include long-term prediction and perceptual weighting (Fig 10). The long-term prediction included in the encoding process takes advantage of the long-term correlations in speech which arise primarily as a result of pitch related correlations in voiced speech. With the

45

inclusion of long-term prediction fewer pulses are required per pitch period to obtain the same speech quality [35]. The long-term prediction parameters can be accurately quantized with relatively few bits.

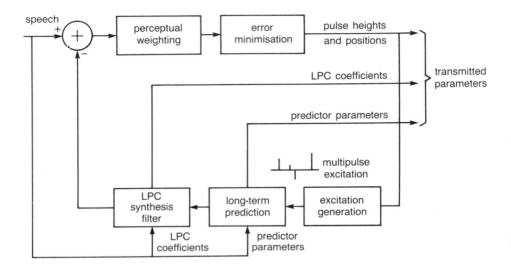

Fig 10   Multipulse encoder including perceptual weighting and long term prediction.

Perceptual weighting of the error is included at the encoder so that the pulse positions and amplitudes are chosen such that the perceived distortion is minimised rather than the mean squared error. The approximately flat noise spectrum obtained at the subtractor output (Fig 10) is shaped by trading-off increases in the noise power around spectral peaks (formants) in the speech, with decreases in the noise power between peaks (Fig 11). Due to auditory masking effects this shaping of the noise spectrum allows the speech signal to more effectively mask the noise [35]. Multipulse codecs can operate successfully over a very wide range of bit rates — codecs operating at bit rates from 8 kbit/s to 16 kbit/s have been reported with the higher bit rate codecs giving good speech quality and the lower bit rate codecs providing acceptable speech for specialist applications [37].

Regular pulse excited LPC

The regular pulse excited (RPE) LPC coder [38] is a variant of the multipulse coder. For a regular pulse excited coder the excitation signal pulses are spaced uniformly, usually every 3-5 sample positions. With pulses spaced every four positions there are four possible candidate excitation vectors (Fig 12). The encoding process involves finding the best candidate vector and the appropriate pulse amplitudes. An index defining the candidate vector and the quantized pulse amplitudes must be transmitted to the decoder. At the same bit rates the speech quality obtained with RPE and

MPLPC coders is similar but it is reported that the complexity of the RPE coder can be reduced to be much lower than a MPLPC with only a small loss in quality [38]. The 13 kbit/s codec algorithm adopted by the CEPT as the standard for the forthcoming pan-European digital cellular mobile telephone service is essentially a regular pulse excited LPC algorithm which includes long-term prediction.

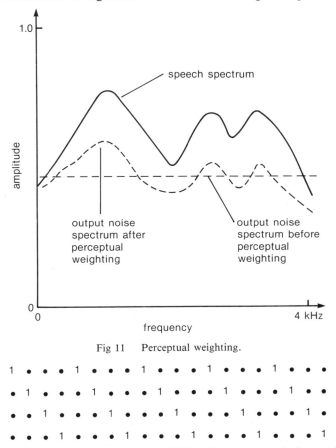

Fig 11   Perceptual weighting.

1	•	•	•	1	•	•	•	1	•	•	•	1	•	•	•	1	•	•	•
•	1	•	•	•	1	•	•	•	1	•	•	•	1	•	•	•	1	•	•
•	•	1	•	•	•	1	•	•	•	1	•	•	•	1	•	•	•	1	•
•	•	•	1	•	•	•	1	•	•	•	1	•	•	•	1	•	•	•	1

Fig 12   Four possible candidate vectors for an RPE coder — the ones indicate pulse positions.

Code excited LPC

The code excited LPC (CELP) coder, also known as the stochastic coder, is another coder based on an analysis-by-synthesis technique [33]. A block diagram of the encoder is shown in Fig 13. The LPC (vocal tract) filter, long-term predictor and perceptual weighting filter are exactly as described for the multipulse excited LPC coder. CELP coding differs from multipulse coding in the excitation function; the excitation pulses being replaced by an 'innovation sequence'. At the decoder each block of M reconstructed speech samples is produced by filtering this innovation sequence, which consists of M samples of white Gaussian noise, through the pitch filter and then the LPC vocal tract filter. At the encoder (Fig 13), there is a codebook which contains many of these white noise sequences (which are simply vectors of random numbers produced by a Gaussian random number generator). The 'optimum' innovation sequence is selected by filtering each sequence in the codebook in turn; the sequence which results in the minimum weighted mean squared error is chosen. A copy of the codebook is stored at the decoder and an index number is transmitted to identify the selected innovation sequence. Again, no distinction is made between voiced and unvoiced speech, the same method of analysis being used to determine the excitation waveform for all speech segments. The innovation sequence length M, is typically 32 samples and the LPC and long-term predictor analysis is performed typically every 16 ms (128 samples) so four sequences are selected for each set of filters. CELP codecs are usually designed to operate at bit rates between 4 and 8 kbit/s.

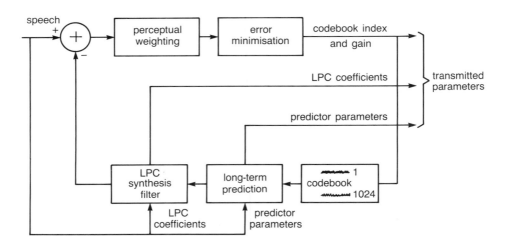

Fig 13   Code excited LPC encoder.

The main problem with the method as outlined above is the large amount of computation which is needed at the encoder to select the optimum innovation sequence. Atal reported that his simulation ran 100 times slower than real time on a Cray 1 computer [33]. Fortunately it is possible to reduce the computational complexity of the encoder to a level where real-time hardware implementation is practical without compromising to a great extent the performance of the coder. Vector quantization may be used to quantize the vocal tract filter very efficiently as described in section 2.2. If this is used in the CELP coder then the 'denominator storage method' may be used to dramatically reduce the computation needed in selecting the optimum innovation vector [39]. This method exploits the fact that when vector quantization is used there are a relatively small number of possible vocal tract filters. Part of the error function for selecting the optimum innovation vector is pre-computed for all possible filter/innovation vector combinations and stored in ROM. Approximately

1000 multiply/add operations per sample are needed when this 'denominator storage' method is used which is approximately 48 times less than for the original CELP algorithm. Using this method, the complexity of the CELP coder is comparable to that of the multipulse coder but the CELP coder requires a large capacity ROM (approximately 1 Mbyte).

CELP has, however, been found to be very sensitive to the accuracy of the quantization of the LPC filter; the subjective performance degrades rapidly as the quantization error increases. This means that particular care must be taken if vector quantization of the LPC filter is used.

When more accurate quantization of the filter is employed, using either scalar or vector predictive quantization, an alternative technique known as 'Rotational CELP' [41] may be used to reduce the complexity of the codec implementation. This technique makes use of knowledge from multipulse LPC as an aid to reducing the complexity of a sparse vector CELP coder [42] by an order of magnitude.

Backward excitation recovery and self-excited vocoders

Other codecs which also use analysis-by-synthesis methods in the derivation of some of their parameters are the so called backward excitation recovery (BER) codecs [43] and the self-excited vocoder (SEV) [44]. Both the BER codecs and SEV use some past signal available at both the encoder and decoder as the excitation. The excitation signal itself therefore need not be transmitted; instead the excitation is derived at the decoder, from past information, using the same strategy as that used by the encoder. Some of the BER schemes offer low bit rate (4.8 kbit/s) combined with low codec delay (of the order of only a few milliseconds). Low bit rate together with low delay is not feasible in the SEV case. The BER schemes and the SEV, however, are equally susceptible to transmission errors. These types of backward adaptive codecs require periodic resetting of encoder and decoder to mitigate the effects of transmission errors. BER codecs and the SEV are both aimed at bit rate in the range 4—8 kbit/s. The speech quality obtained from both types of codec is comparable with CELP codecs at the same bit rate.

3. Subjective assessment

The assessment of low bit rate speech codecs poses problems quite different from the assessment of the waveform codecs (such as A-law PCM) used at higher bit rates. The first reason for this is that the distortions produced by low bit rate codecs are so diverse in character; they may be correlated with the speech signal or random and they range from spurious tones to weird squawks and gargling sounds. Different types of low bit rate codec can produce totally different types of distortion. Moreover, different people's assessments of these diverse degradations can vary significantly; some people find background noise or other non-speech sounds generated in the codecs more disturbing than distortion of the speech whilst others are prepared to accept noise if the speech is clear, for example.

Another difficulty is that the performance of low bit rate codecs can be strongly dependent on their inputs (for example, some codecs perform much better on certain voices than others). To make matters worse, there can be interactions between the effects of the different impairments introduced by low bit rate speech codecs and other network devices. (For example, it has been found that the disturbing effect of echoes is increased if the echo has been distorted by passing through a low bit rate speech codec.) Experiments must be carefully designed to evaluate these interactions.

The most straightforward way of assessing speech codecs is to make objective measurements (such as those specified in CCITT Recommendation G.712 for PCM systems). Unfortunately no objective tests have yet been devised which will reliably give the same results over a range of different coding methods as subjective assessment by potential users.

Subjective testing may be used to check that speech codecs meet the requirements of their intended applications or to establish data (which may be incorporated in CCITT Recommendations, for example) that can be used by network planners to ensure that adequate transmission performance is achieved over all possible connections. To be suitable for these tasks, the measurements have to be reliable, carried out in a way that takes account of the major interactions between the codec and the other parts of the transmission system, and calibrated in some way so that results from different laboratories can be compared. The 'informal' listening tests sometimes carried out on speech codecs can be unreliable and many of the claims for codec performance based upon them turn out to be incorrect or to relate only to a very restricted set of operating conditions.

Many of the degradations introduced by low bit rate speech codecs have not been tested before and their effects on other systems in the network are unknown. Therefore the only reliable method of evaluation is the conversation test where the effects of delay, echo etc. and their interactions can be taken into account.

Listening tests can play an important preliminary role in codec assessment, and can supply useful information serving to narrow the range of combinations needing complete conversation tests. They can also give a good indication of the speech quality of the codec and allow reasonable comparisons to be made.

Full information on conducting both conversation and listening tests can be found in the CCITT Red Book [45,46].

3.1   Subjective test conditions

A speech codec should be tested to evaluate the effect of all the factors which are expected to affect its performance. The purpose of this section is to draw attention to parameters that should be considered in testing low bit rate speech codecs for telecommunications applications.

Range of input levels

Speech input level is a very important variable which must be taken into account in testing any non-linear system. Some systems may perform quite well in a narrow range of input levels centred on an ideal level, but deteriorate rapidly when input levels depart from this range.

Different speakers use different vocal levels, even in the same conditions (standard deviation about 3 dB), and when one makes allowance for other causes of variation (handset movements, different telephone sending sensitivities which also include wide fluctuations of sensitivity in carbon microphones, deliberate raising or lowering of the voice, influence of sidetone, and influence of quality and level of received speech), it becomes evident that one must allow for an input range of 25 dB for the mean active speech level [47] catering for loud to quiet speakers. If the coder input is to be the output of a switched transmission system then the codec dynamic range must be increased to take account of variations in the transmission loss. For the analogue PSTN these variations can be considerable (up to 16 dB between terminal exchanges within the UK). The dynamic range over which the codec is tested must be chosen accordingly.

Figure 14 demonstrates typical effects of changes in speech input level.

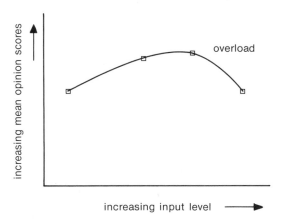

Fig 14   Mean opinion scores for speech input level.

Range of listening levels

It is commonly asserted that comparisons of systems need only be carried out at one listening level (a 'natural' or 'optimum' level). There are several objections to this.

- There is no universal optimum listening level.

  Estimates of optimum listening level for speech heard via handsets vary with uncertainties related to the measurement method and the criterion for 'optimum'. The best level for ease of understanding is known to be generally higher than the level that sounds most pleasant [47], and both depend on bandwidth and room noise and other related factors.

- A variety of listening levels will occur in practice.

  The variation caused by the range in input level will be reflected in the listening level. In addition, there are further variations affecting the receiving path only: network losses, mismatches, movements of the handset as applied to the ear, and different telephone receiving sensitivities which can include volume controls. All these are sources in the real situation: one must cover a still wider range of listening levels in an experiment, independently of the input level, in order to estimate the two effects separately and locate the optimum for both. With new systems, the gain of the output stage may not have been finally decided, and allowance must also be made for a range of values of this in an experiment.

- Interactions may occur.

  It is likely that optimum listening level will not be the same for all systems. It can be expected to be higher where the bandwidth is narrower, the noise level is higher, or certain other degrading influences are present. On the other hand, for some systems with severe non-linear distortion a lower listening level is better because the distortion products are then less prominent. It would be unfair to test different systems at a level that might be optimum for some systems and not others. By testing a range of levels, one avoids having to determine the optimum level for each system in advance; moreover, even if this could be determined, the possibility would remain that some systems would be preferred to others simply because the listening level was more pleasant.

Changes in listening level are a very potent variable in subjective performance: in other words, performance tends to change rapidly as a function of listening level. It is quite likely that the slopes of these functions are different for different systems, so that the subjective differences between them depend heavily on the listening levels at which the comparisons are done. At one level

A may be superior to B, at another level B may be superior to A. This is what is known as interaction in statistical terms. The only way of detecting it and making allowance for it is to do all the assessments at several listening levels.

Figure 15 demonstrates typical effects of changes in listening level.

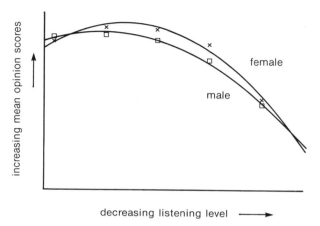

Fig 15   Mean opinion scores for listening level.

Different speakers

Sophisticated processes often affect male and female voices differently and therefore the codec should be tested for voice dependency.

Moreover, to reduce the danger that the results may depend heavily on peculiarities of the voices chosen, it is essential for more than one male and more than one female voice to be used.

Figure 15 also demonstrates typical effects of the difference between male and female voices.

Transmission errors

The codec must, of course, be robust to errors. The expected error distribution will depend on the application. If the errors are generated by line systems within the PSTN then they are likely to be randomly distributed, but for radio applications the errors are likely to occur in bursts. Codecs must be tested with the appropriate error conditions and with speech samples long enough for the effects of the errors to be realistically evaluated.

Figure 16 demonstrates the effect change in bit error rates.

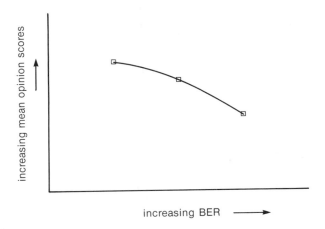

increasing mean opinion scores

increasing BER

Fig 16   Mean opinion scores for difference bit error rate.

Transcodings

It is important to establish the effects of tandeming systems that utilise encoding at different bit rates. It is essential that the most probable combinations are considered.

Table 1 illustrates possible applications in the future.

Table 1   Possible future transcoding applications.

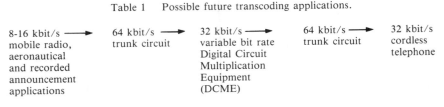

| 8-16 kbit/s → mobile radio, aeronautical and recorded announcement applications | 64 kbit/s → trunk circuit | 32 kbit/s → variable bit rate Digital Circuit Multiplication Equipment (DCME) | 64 kbit/s → trunk circuit | 32 kbit/s cordless telephone |

Environmental noise (sending)

The effect of environmental noise is important for the following reasons.

- Noise added to the input signal can have a more adverse effect on certain low bit rate speech codecs than on conventional waveform coding systems.

- Low bit rate speech codecs may well be used in noisy environments such as moving vehicles (mobile radio) or aircraft.

Multiple speakers

It is important to know the robustness of the codec to multiple-voice input signals, and to find out whether any adverse effects occur, such as 'break-up' of transmission, spurious signals, etc. If only handset use is to be considered then the mixing of two different speakers with input speech levels 20 dB apart is possibly sufficient.

However, if the codec is to be used in a conference (i.e. hands-free) mode, where more than one speaker can speak at the same time, then one must ensure that the encoding algorithm can deal with multiple speakers where the difference in speech levels could be zero.

3.2   Use of subjective test results for network planning

One of the responsibilities of the planners of transmission networks is to ensure that acceptable transmission quality is achieved on all connections within the network. The transmission performance of any communication link is a function of all its component parts which may include switching, multiplexing and coding equipment as well as the transmission system and the terminal equipment. Transmission planners use a set of rules (usually enshrined in CCITT Recommendations) which define the maximum acceptable distortion on a certain type of connection, the maximum distortion to be contributed by each part of the connection and the way in which these distortions should be added to estimate the total distortion of the link.

CCITT Recommendations currently include 64 kbit/s PCM and 32 kbit/s ADPCM coding but not coding at lower bit rates. The rules are defined in terms of quantization distortion units, 1 qdu being defined as the distortion arising from one commercial A-law or μ-law PCM codec. It has been found that simply adding the quantization distortion of waveform codecs connected in tandem gives a good representation of the performance of these connections.

To extend the planning rules to cover codecs at lower bit rates it is necessary to be able both to measure and to add the distortions introduced in a meaningful way.

Because of the complex behaviour of low bit rate speech codecs already described, considerable research will be needed to achieve this. In the meantime, to give some measure of performance, the test methods devised for PCM codecs have been applied. As recommended by the CCITT, this involves subjective tests in which the speech passed through the codec is compared with speech to which distortion has been added by a 'modulated-noise reference unit' (MNRU). Use of the MNRU allows results from different experiments in different laboratories to be compared [48,49].

The MNRU is calibrated in terms of signal to correlated-noise ratio (Q). The following formula relating the qdu value of a codec and the Q setting of the MNRU which gives subjectively equivalent distortion has been found to give reliable results for the 64 kbit/s PCM and 32 kbit/s ADPCM [50].

$$qdu = 10^{(37-Q)/15}$$

This formula has been used to prepare Table 2.

Table 2   Impairment unit assignments for codecs with different bit rates.

Bit rate Kbit/s	Q,dB	qdu
64 kbit/s, A-law PCM (G.711)	37	1
32 kbit/s, ADPCM (G.721)	29	3.5
13 kbit/s	23—25	7—8*
9.6 kbit/s (male voices)	17	22**
9.6 kbit/s (female voices)	19	16**

*   from limited information available this would appear to be the best achievable at present.

**   for these codecs it is important to separately quote ratings for male and female voices because their effect on codec performance is a significant factor.

Note: the Q values shown in Table 2, derived from several subjective listening tests, are only valid at one particular listening level.

It must be emphasised that the MNRU gives distortion subjectively similar to that produced by logarithmically companded PCM systems, so that the qdu ratings are not truly representative of the performance of codecs introducing other types of distortion. In addition, there is not sufficient evidence available to show that qdu ratings of low bit rate codecs can be simply added together to give the overall performance. However, it can still be seen that the distortion increases significantly as the bit rate is decreased.

4. Use of low bit rate speech codecs in telecommunications environments

As described in previous sections, low bit rate speech codecs generally incorporate a model of the speech production process and transmit the parameters of that model which best match the speech to be coded. A good model and an effective method of determining parameter values allow speech to be transmitted at a low data rate by removing redundant information. A model which was very efficient in this sense would model very specifically the speech of the speaker currently being coded; to work in most real applications, therefore, it would have to adapt itself rapidly to each speaker. It would also need to be able to adapt to cope with acoustic inputs which do not conform to the model of a single speaker, such as extraneous noise and several people talking at once.

Efficient adaptive models like this are not yet available. The most useful current approach to removing redundancy whilst retaining the flexibility required in real services is the analysis-by-synthesis method described in section 2.6 (as employed in the multipulse and CELP codecs, for example). Here, the incorporation of a decoder within the speech encoder allows the selection of the set of parameters which minimises in some sense the error between the speech input and the speech synthesized at the decoder. This gives these codecs the redundancy removal of a parametric codec with the robustness to acoustic inputs of a waveform codec.

Current embodiments of the analysis-by-synthesis principle are still far from perfect, however. The optimisation process only modifies the excitation parameters and can only choose from a restricted number of subsets of these parameters. It is also far from clear what the criteria should be for choosing the best set of parameters. As mentioned in section 1, there is still no objective measurement which will adequately represent the subjective performance of speech codecs; likewise there is no test that can be applied within an optimisation loop to choose parameters which will always give the best **subjective** match to the input speech. In addition, the vocal tract models used (such as the LPC model described in section 2.2) are simple and the analysis methods used for deriving their parameters do not take account of acoustic noise or multiple speakers. This means that the excitation optimisation process has to compensate for errors in the vocal tract model which are often large. The result of all these imperfections is higher bit rates and lower quality.

Robustness to digital transmission errors is one of the strengths (perhaps surprisingly) of low bit rate speech codecs. Codecs may be designed to be inherently robust, giving negligible degradation of the speech at error rates of 1 in 1000 (at which 64 kbit/s PCM is virtually unusable). Moreover, these codecs can be protected against worse error conditions more easily than waveform codecs. This is because the encoder outputs are a mixture of different types of parameter and these different parameters are not equally susceptible to errors. By determining the subjective effect of errors in each transmitted parameter and applying error correction to each parameter accordingly, it is possible to make low bit rate speech codecs robust to very severe error conditions at a minimal cost in extra transmission capacity.

Delay, on the other hand, is a weakness of most current low bit rate speech codecs. In order to achieve a low bit rate, most codecs make use of the fact that speech is quasi-stationary and only update some of their parameters every 10 to 20 ms. The input speech is therefore stored and analysed in blocks 10 to 20 ms in duration. The analysis requires a great deal of computation and this takes further time. The parameters then have to be assembled in the correct order for transmission, often over a serial connection, adding further to the delay. All this means that the delay of currently available low bit rate speech codecs is generally within the range from 25 to 60 ms.

For some applications (particularly for speech storage) this delay is unimportant. For transmission applications where echo control is already provided it may not matter but for other transmission applications it means that echo control sometimes has to be provided where it would not otherwise be needed. Even digital connections often need acoustic echo control; this can introduce its own degradations, especially in noisy environments.

Long delays are not essential to low bit rate speech codecs, however. Some methods have inherent delays (excluding processing time) of just a few milliseconds and increasingly powerful integrated circuits will continue to reduce processing times so that low-delay implementations of low bit rate speech codecs will become available.

The speech coding issue most often discussed is, of course, speech quality. Whilst the quality currently achievable is considered adequate for certain services (e.g. 13 kbit/s for mobile radio-telephones and 9.6 kbit/s for aeronautical telephones) the quality must satisfy the normal planning rules before codecs can be generally used in switched public telephone networks.

Section 3.2 defines the quantization distortion unit (qdu) and gives the qdu rating for currently available codecs at various bit rates. The CCITT planning rule for an international connection is that a maximum distortion of 5 qdu is allowed for each national part of the connection and 4 qdu for the international part, giving a total of 14 qdu. This means that unless it can be guaranteed that a codec cannot be used in an international connection then the maximum distortion allowed for that codec is 5 qdu.

As can be seen from Table 2 this condition is not currently satisfied by codecs at 13 kbit/s or less. There are doubts about the appropriateness of the CCITT limit (which is to be reconsidered and may be revised upwards) and of the validity of using the qdu to characterize low bit rate codecs. It is clear, however, that both improvements in quality and studies of the performance of the codecs in real network situations will be required before low bit rate codecs can have general usage on public switched networks.

5. Conclusions

A number of different types of low bit rate speech codec are now available. Progress has been rapid and performance has improved dramatically over the last few years but no codec can yet satisfy all the requirements of all potential applications. Different types of codec have different strengths and weaknesses and the choice of codecs for particular applications must be made with care. In order to be sure that a codec is suitable, carefully designed subjective tests which exercise the codec over the expected range of operating conditions must be carried out.

Although low bit rate speech codecs are already good enough for application in many services, most of these services would benefit from the availability of the same (or better) performance at lower bit rates and many other services require higher quality.

Speech coding is still a relatively immature science and developments are occuring rapidly. These developments are being matched by developments in integrated circuits which will continue to make possible the economic implementation of more and more complex algorithms, enabling higher quality to be achieved at lower bit rates.

Development of speech codecs must not concentrate simply on improving speech quality, though. Developing an algorithm which gives excellent speech quality but which works well only under favourable laboratory conditions with unquantized parameters may be an interesting academic exercise and increase our knowledge of speech coding but if a codec is to be useful in practical applications then all the demands of the application must be satisfied. Lower delays and better robustness to both acoustic and transmission environments should be sought. Since these features cannot easily be added to an algorithm after development the demands of the real world must be considered from the outset.

References

1. Ainsworth W A: 'Mechanisms of speech recognition', Pergamon Press (1976).

2 Makhoul J: 'Linear prediction: a tutorial review', Proc of the IEEE, 63 , No 4, pp 561—580 (April 1975).

3 Rabiner L R and Schafer R W: 'Digital processing of speech signals', Prentice-Hall, p 443 (1978).

4 Gray R M: 'Vector quantization', IEEE Acoustics Speech and Signal Processing Magazine, pp 4—28 (April 1984).

5 Buzo A, Gray A H, Gray R M and Markel J D: 'Speech coding based upon vector quantization', IEEE Trans on Acoustics Speech and Signal Processing', ASSP-28 , No 5, pp 562—574 (October 1980).

6 Linde Y, Buzo A and Gray R M: 'An algorithm for vector quantizer design', IEEE Trans on Commun, COM—28 , No 1, pp 84—95 (January 1980).

7 Hammett P G: 'Tree-structured codebooks for vector quantization of vocal tract filters in low bit-rate speech coders; internal memorandum (1986).

8 Berger T: 'Rate distortion theory, a mathematical basis for data compression', Prentice Hall, New Jersey (1971).

9 Davidson G, Yong M and Gersho A: 'Real-time excitation coding of speech coding at 4800 BPS', Proc Int Conf on Acoustics Speech and Signal Processing, pp 2189—2192 (1987).

10 Shoham Y: 'Vector predictive quantization of the spectral parameters for low rate speech coding', Proc Int Conf on Acoustics Speech and Signal Processing, pp 2181—2184 (1987).

11 Jayant N S: 'Digital coding of speech waveforms: PCM, DPCM and DM quantizers', Proc of the IEEE, 62 , pp 611—632 (May 1974).

12 Steele R: 'Delta modulation systems', Pentech Press, London (1975).

13 Benvenuto N, Bertocci G and Daumer W R: 'The 32 kbit/s ADPCM coding standard', AT&T Techn J, 65 , No 5, pp 12—21 (September 1986).

14 Dhadesugoor V R, Ziegler C and Shilling D L: 'Delta modulator packet voice networks', IEEE Trans on Commun, COM—28 , No 1, pp 33—51 (January 1980).

15 Atal B S: 'Predictive coding of speech at low bit rates', IEEE Trans on Commun, COM—30 , No 4, pp 600—614 (April 1982).

16 Dankberg M D and Wong D Y: 'Development of a 4.8—9.6 kbit/s RELP vocoder', Proc IEEE Int Conf on Acoustics Speech and Signal Processing, pp 554—557 (1979).

17 Crochiere R E, Webber S A and Flanagan J L: 'Digital coding of speech in sub-bands', Bell Syst Techn J, 55 , pp 1069—1085 (October 1976).

18 Hanes R B, Westall F A and Goody C: 'A 16 kbit/s speech coder using a single DSP device', Proc Int Conf on Acoustics, Speech and Signal Processing, San Diego, pp 27.12.1—27.12.4 (March 1984).

19 Zelinski R and Noll P: 'Adaptive transform coding of speech signals', IEEE Trans Acoustics, Speech and Signal Processing, ASSP—25 , No 4, pp 299—309 (August 1977).

20 Jayant N S: 'Coding speech at low bit rates', IEEE Spectrum, pp 58—63 (August 1986).

21 Flanagan J L, Schroeder M R, Atal B S, Crochiere R E, Jayant N S and Tribolet J M: 'Speech coding', IEEE Trans Comm, COM—27 , No 4, pp 710—737 (April 1979).

22 Cox R V: 'Recent trends in digital speech coding', IEEE Conf Proc Globecom 83, pp 23.1.1—23.1.5 (1983).

23 Gold B: 'Digital speech networks', Proc of the IEEE, 65 , No 12, pp 1636—1658 (December 1977).

24 Crochiere R E, Cox R V and Johnston J D: 'Real-time speech coding', IEEE Trans on Commun, COM—30 , No 4, pp 521— 634 (April 1982).

25 Hanes R B: 'The application of speech coding to telecommunications networks', British Telecom Technol J, 4 , No 2, pp 57—67 (October 1983).

26 Crochiere R E and Flanagan J L: 'Current perspectives in digital speech', IEEE Communications Magazine, pp 32—40 (January 1983).

27 Bylanski P and Chong T W: 'New developments in speech coding for communications', Telephony, pp 54—69 (October 1984).

28 Seidl R A: 'A tutorial paper on medium bit rate speech coding techniques', ATR, 17 , No 1, pp 61—72 1983).

29 Lind L F, Attkins P M and Challener P: 'An improved implementation of adaptive quantisers for speech waveform encoding schemes,', Br Telecom Technol J, 6 , No 2 (1988).

30 Moriya T and Honda M: 'Transform coding of speech with weighted vector quantization', Proc Int Conf on Acoustics Speech and Signal Processing, pp 1629—1632 (1987).

31 Tremain T E: 'The Government standard linear predictive coding algorithm: LPC—10', Speech Technology, pp 40—49 (April 1982).

32 Atal B S and Remde J R: 'A new model of LPC excitation for producting natural — sounding speech at low bit rates', Proc IEEE Int Conf on Acoustics Speech and Signal Processing', pp 614—617 (1982).

33 Schroeder M R and Atal B S: 'Code-excited linear prediction (CELP): high quality speech at very low bit rates', Proc IEEE Int Conf on Acoustics Speech and Signal Processing', pp 937—940 (1985).

34 Ozawa K, Ono S and Araseki T: 'A study on pulse search algorithms for multipulse excited speech coder realization', IEEE Journal on Selected Areas in Communications, SAC—4 , No 1, pp 133—141 January 1986).

35 Singhal S and Atal B S: 'Improving the performance of multi-pulse LPC coders at low bit-rates', Proc IEEE Int Conf on Acoustics Speech and Signal Processing, pp 1.3.1—1.3.4 (1984).

36 Boyd I: 'Position reoptimisation for a multiple excited LPC coder', European Conf on Speech Technology 2 , pp 37—40 (September 1987).

37 Ozawa K and Araseki T: 'High quality multipulse speech coder with pitch prediction', Proc IEEE Int Conf on Acoustics, Speech and Signal Processing, pp 1689—1692 (1986).

38 Deprette Ed F and Kroon P: 'Regular excitation reduction for effective and efficient LP-coding of speech', Proc IEEE Int Conf on Acoustics Speech and Signal Processing', pp 25.8.1—25.8.4 (1985).

39 Hammett P G: 'Complexity reduction in fully vector quantized stochastic coders', IEE Electronic Letters, 23 , No 6, pp 253—254 (1987)

40 Berouti M, Garten H, Kabal P and Mermelstein P: 'Efficient computation and encoding of the multipulse excitation for LPC', Proc IEEE Int Conf on Acoustics Speech and Signal Processing, pp 10.1.1—10.1.4 (1984).

41 Freeman D K and Boyd I: 'A reduced complexity CELP scheme', IEE Colloquium on Speech Processing, pp 8/1-8/3 (1988).

42 Davidson G and Gersho A: 'Complexity reduction methods for vector excitation coding', Proc Int Conf on Acoustics Speech and Signal Processing, pp 3055—3058 (1986).

43 Gouviankias N and Xydeas C S: 'Advances in analysis by synthesis LPC speech coders', J Institution of Electronic and Radio Engineers, 57 , No 6 (Supplement), pp S277—S286 (1987).

44 Rose R C and Barnwell T P: 'The self excited vocoder — an alternate approach to toll quality at 4800 bps', Proc Int Conf on Acoustics Speech and Signal Processing, pp 453—456 (1986).

45 CCITT: 'Methods used for assessing telephony performance', Supplement No 2, Red Book V (1985).

46 CCITT: 'Subjective performance assessment of digital processes using the modulated noise reference unit (MNRU)', Supplement No 14, Red Book, V (1985).

47 Richards D L: 'Telecommunication by speech: the transmission performance of telephone networks', pp 185—189, Butterworths (1973).

48 CCITT: 'Modulated noise reference unit (MNRU)', Recommendation P70, Red Book V (1985).

49 Law H B and Seymore R A: 'A reference distortion system using modulated noise', The Institute of Electrical Engineers, pp 484—485 (November 1962).

50 CCITT: 'Subjective performance assessment of digital processes using the modulated noise reference unit (MNRU)', Annex C to Supplement No 14, Red Book, V (1985).

AN IMPROVED IMPLEMENTATION OF ADAPTIVE QUANTIZERS FOR SPEECH WAVEFORM ENCODING SCHEMES

L F Lind, P M Attkins and P Challener

ABSTRACT

Adaptive quantizers are often used in speech waveform encoding schemes. This paper discusses a method for computing the large dynamic range of step sizes that can occur in the quantizer adaptation strategy. This strategy is tolerant to transmission errors occurring prior to the decoding process.

The method makes use of efficient logarithmic polynomial approximations, based on Chebyshev economisation of series. This permits a digital speech processing chip to be used to calculate the quantizer step size accurately over the entire range of interest. Some numerical results are presented which show the trade-offs between accuracy and degree of approximation. The method has been implemented in a 16 kbit/s speech coder, using a Motorola 56 000 processor chip.

1. Introduction

On British Telecom's digital networks, telephone quality speech is normally transmitted in 64 kbit/s slots and is coded using pulse code modulation (PCM). In PCM (Fig 1), speech is first band-limited to lie within the frequency range 300—150 i.e. 150—3400 Hz by means of an analogue bandpass filter prior to sampling at a rate of 8 kHz. Each sample is quantized using a 256 level quantizer whose levels are not uniformly spaced, but instead follow a logarithmic law. In this way small signals are quantized very accurately and only a small amount of quantization distortion results; larger signals are more coarsely quantized resulting in more significant quantization distortion, but this distortion is masked by the presence of the large signal itself, and is therefore not disturbing. Finally, the quantized signal levels are coded, using an 8-bit code to cover all 256 levels, and these bits are transmitted to line. The 8-bit codes, sent at an 8 kHz sampling rate, make up the total 64 kbit/s coding rate.

Although PCM is an internationally agreed, standard technique for coding speech signals, the use of 64 000 bits of either transmission or storage capacity for every second of speech can prove to be a very costly overhead on a system. The most severe transmission problems occur where limited radio spectra must be shared between a large number of users; an example of this is the new 'pan European' digital mobile radio system being planned for use all across Europe in the 1990s. The most severe storage requirements usually occur where large numbers of randomly accessible messages must be stored, such as in voice guidance or messaging systems. In these kinds of application area, system designers are willing to accept more complicated, expensive processing in the speech codecs, if they can achieve more cost effective transmission and storage. However, although technology now permits significant compression of the 64 kbit/s PCM coding rates, this is not always achieved without loss of speech quality. Hence, in any practical system, there is a complicated balance to be found where coding efficiency, codec cost and speech quality all affect the choice of solution selected for particular schemes. There are a number of low bit rate speech coding algorithms [1] in use, but the schemes most appropriate to the technique outlined in this paper operate at between 32 kbit/s and 16 kbit/s.

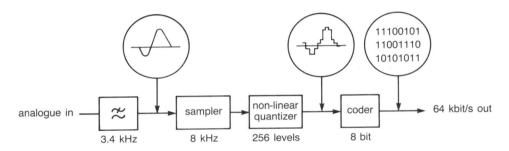

Fig 1   Pulse code modulation encoder.

At 32 kbit/s there is now an internationally agreed speech coding standard based on the technique of adaptive differential pulse code modulation (ADPCM) [2]. This scheme (Fig 2) retains many of the elements of PCM, but has two important differences — the 'A' and 'D' in ADPCM.

The 'A' indicates that the scheme does not quantize signals with a fixed level quantizer (like that used in PCM) but instead uses an *adaptive* quantizer. Adaptive quantizers normally have linearly spaced gaps between their quantization levels, but employ a scheme for expanding the gaps when coding big signals, or compressing them when coding small signals [3]. This overcomes the need for logarithmically spaced quantization levels and allows designers to obtain similar performance to a fixed quantizer with far less levels (and hence less bits per sample). The 'D' indicates that the signal being quantized is not an absolute signal waveform value, but a *differential* value, obtained by creating a difference signal between current and previous signal values. In the simplest case, this may merely comprise a single sample delay and a subtractor, but in the internationally standardised version of ADPCM, a 'predictor' circuit is also employed. Most predictors utilise linear combinations of previous signal values to provide an intelligent estimate of the next signal value. When incorporated into an ADPCM circuit, as shown in Fig 2, the prediction is subtracted from the input signal leaving only a very small residual signal. This residual signal is fed to the quantizer, which now need only cope with low variance input signals, so once again less quantization levels are required to encode the signal adequately. If the arrangement of Fig 2 is examined carefully, it can be seen that both the predictor input and the quantizer adaptation are driven from previous coder outputs and that this information is also available at the decoder input, as long as there are no transmission errors introduced on the line. Hence the scheme can adapt the quantizer and predictor independently, and in synchronism, at the encoder and the decoder without any side information accompanying the transmitted speech data; such schemes are known as backward adaptive coding schemes.

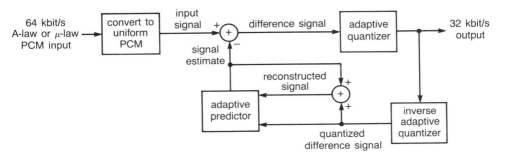

Fig 2   ADPCM encoder.

The combined effect of the adaptive quantizer and differential predictor enable telephone quality speech to be encoded satisfactorily into 32 kbit/s. This comprises 4 bits per sample, at an 8 kHz sampling rate, and offers a quality which is virtually indistinguishable from 64 kbit/s PCM.

At data rates below 32 kbit/s, additional coding complexity is required, but one scheme which works very well in the range 16—24 kbit/s is sub-band coding [4], (Fig 3). This scheme employs special bandpass filters (called mirror filters) at the encoder to split the input speech into a set of sub-bands of say 500 Hz bandwidth each. As each sub-band is band-limited, it can be downsampled to a 1 kHz sampling rate and coded independently of any other sub-band using ADPCM or adaptive PCM (APCM). At the decoder, the sub-bands are decoded, upsampled and recombined via more mirror filters to reconstitute the original speech waveform. The mirror filters are not brickwall bandpass filters, so when the down-sampling occurs, alias signals will be produced in each sub-band; however, at the recombination node in the decoder, the second set of mirror filters is designed to make the alias terms cancel, whilst permitting the wanted signals to pass without attenuation.

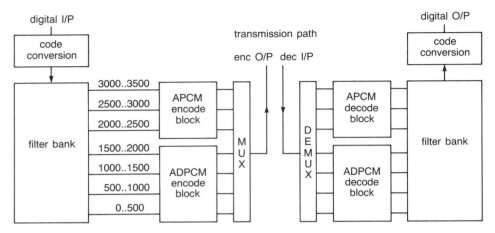

Fig 3   Sub-band codec; block diagram.

The benefits gained by splitting speech signals into a series of sub-bands are given below.

● The bands can be encoded independently, with more quantization bits allocated to important spectral regions and fewer bits to less important ones. In the case of speech, this means that more bits can be given to the low frequency bands where most of the speech energy lies and less bits given to the lower energy, high frequency bands; as the high frequency bands tend to contain signals which are inherently rather noise-like, additional quantization distortion in these bands will not be very noticeable.

● When quantization distortion occurs in a sub-band coder, it will be bandpass filtered by the decoder mirror filters prior to recombination. This means that noise generated in any band must be contained to lie within the spectral 'passband' of that band, at a frequency close to the signal frequencies in that band; it will therefore be auditorily masked.

These techniques make it possible to encode telephone quality speech at data rates of between 16 and 24 kbit/s with only slight speech impairment compared with 64 kbit/s PCM. However, the factor of 4 reduction in data rate can make this a worthwhile compromise in many applications.

2. Digital signal processing devices

In order to implement the coding schemes described above, it is necessary to build signal processing hardware, capable of performing all the filtering, adaptation and quantization functions in real time, between incoming speech samples, which arrive every 0.125 ms. Until recently, this could only be achieved by means of large boards of specialised chips such as hardware multipliers, arithmetic logic units (ALUs), cache memories, program sequencers and pipeline registers. However, in the last 10 years, advances in chip technology have seen the arrival of single chip, digital signal processors, which have revolutionised the design of this kind of equipment. These chips appear to resemble microprocessors or microcontrollers, as they contain ALUs, RAM, ROM, buses and I/O ports, but on closer examination, the differences become more obvious. Firstly, they contain a hardware multiplier, capable of multiplying two binary numbers together, possibly each 16 or 24 bits long, in a single instruction cycle. (A microprocessor performs multiplications by means of a microcoded successive shift and add routine, taking many instruction cycles to complete.) Secondly, they utilise a slightly different hardware architecture, known as Harvard architecture, to increase the throughput on repetitive signal processing tasks. This architecture (Fig 4) differs from a microprocessor Von Neumann architecture by separating the program memory and bus areas from data areas on the chip.

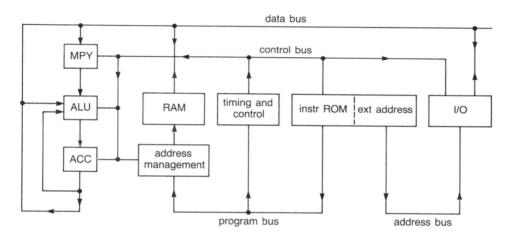

Fig 4   Harvard architecture for a DSP chip.

This allows full overlap of the instruction fetch and execute cycles with most data handling operations, offering the possibility of moving and operating on data in every instruction cycle in many circumstances. The architecture is supported by a specialised instruction set featuring very wide instruction words which permits simultaneous operation of the ALU, multiplier and buses.

Most of the current devices are fixed point processors, normally working with either 16- or 24-bit data [5,6], but there are now a few devices available with floating point architectures [7]. Currently, the floating point devices are much easier to program than fixed point devices as their instructions map more closely to high level language simulations of algorithms, and there is no need for the programmer to concern himself with such issues as numerical scaling of data. However, the floating point devices are also much more expensive than fixed point ones, and this makes them less attractive to use in low-cost products.

The schemes described in this paper are particularly applicable to implementation of coding algorithms on fixed point devices, where the most cost-effective solutions are likely to be found. However, it is also likely that they may find application in other signal processing tasks outside the area of speech coding, or even in certain microprocessor applications where fast and accurate function approximations are required.

3. The quantizer synchronisation problem

As described in section 1, backward adaptive quantizers in ADPCM systems will keep in step at the encoder and decoder, provided the information appearing at the decoder input is exactly the same as that leaving the encoder output. This will clearly not be the case on power-up of a system or when transmission errors cause any changes to the transmitted data. One way around this problem is to employ the principle of leakage to the quantizer adaptation scheme [8]. The leakage calculation includes computing the previous step size raised to the power 0.98 (or to some other power near unity), and using this to affect the current step size. After many iterations the current stepsize will be rather insensitive to old step sizes used, say 10 iterations ago. Thus the receiver will be able to recover from an error after a few iterations; how many iterations depends on the system parameters and the leakage exponent used. Figure 5 shows the adaptation scheme diagrammatically, where $I(n)$ is the input to the adaptation process, which originates from the output of the ADPCM quantizer. The output of the adaptation scheme in the nth cycle is the step size used in that cycle, $d(n)$, but the computation indicated in the adaptation diagram is for $d(n+1)$, for use in the $(n+1)$th cycle. This is computed from $d(n)$ by the formula

$$d(n+1) = m*d(n)^{(0.98)} \qquad \qquad ......(1)$$

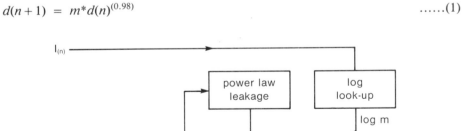
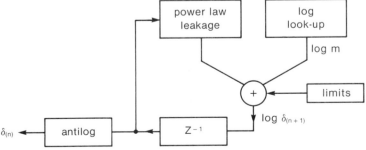

Fig 5   Step size adaptation, logarithmic computation.

where m is the adaptation coefficient [8] appropriate for the input $I(n)$. It should be noted that the range of step sizes encountered in practice is extremely large (around 72 dB in the ADPCM quantizer problem) and that this makes approximation of this function extremely difficult.

As fixed point digital signal processor chips do not include instructions for raising numbers to an arbitrary power, it is necessary to find a practical way to compute this expression. If logarithms are used, then multiplication can replace the exponentiation operation. Logarithms to an arbitrary base b give the straightforward computation.

$$\log_b(d(n+1)) = \log_b(m) + 0.98*\log_b(d(n)) \qquad \ldots\ldots(2)$$

An implementation of this equation is shown in Fig 5. The log (m) values are pre-computed and stored in a look-up table, leaving the antilog (or exponential) function to be computed (using an appropriate approximation) for each iteration. A degree of freedom, the base b, is gained with this procedure. The base should be chosen to handle the large dynamic range of the step sizes, and to be easy to implement in the fixed point arithmetic program. With this in mind, it has been found convenient to split the step size numbers into two portions, a mantissa, and an exponent, which correspond to the integer and fractional parts of logarithms, but which may be represented by a single multi-byte variable. Then the process shown in Fig 5 can be performed on these portions separately. If the base b is an integer power of four, the antilog operation then takes the form of a Chebyshev function approximation based on the contents of the mantissa field followed by a simple bit-shift operation by the number of places indicated in the exponent field. The base chosen for the quantize step size operation was 65 536. The following sections deal with the question of approximating the antilog function in Fig 5, where the input can be considered to be solely the mantissa of the step size.

4. Chebyshev polynomials

A polynomial approximation was chosen for several reasons. Firstly, it is simple to compute. The simplicity implies speed — the approximation will not require many instruction cycles of computation. Secondly, a polynomial is continuous, and has smooth derivatives of all degrees. There will therefore be no glitches or sudden jumps in the approximation curve. Thirdly, there is a well known procedure to make the error function of a polynomial approximately equiripple over the interval of interest, which is called Chebyshev economisation of series. This procedure will be used in the development below. Finally, there is a monotonic relationship between the degree of the polynomial and accuracy. The higher the degree, the more accurate the result. Thus, the trade-offs between polynomial degree (and hence speed) and accuracy can be measured.

These polynomials are equiripple on $-1 \leq x \leq +1$. By equiripple it is meant that $T_n(x)$ reaches its extreme amplitudes (of unity magnitude) $n + 1$ times in this range.

For example, $T_5(x)$ has the shape shown in Fig 6.

Outside the approximation range, $T_n(x)$ increases (or becomes negative) rapidly. It is only controlled to be equiripple in the approximation range.

A lot is known about these polynomials. For example, the nth degree Chebyshev polynomial can be found by the recursion

$$T_n(x) = 2xT_{n-1}(x) - T_{n-2}(x) \qquad \qquad ......(3)$$

with the initialising polynomials

$$T_0(x) = 1, \ T_1(x) = x \qquad \qquad ......(4)$$

This recursion is easily programmed, and will produce a complete array of Chebyshev polynomials up to degree n, n being selected by the user. Chebyshev polynomial coefficients are also tabulated in 'The Handbook of Mathematical Functions' [9].

The highest degree coefficient in an nth degree Chebyshev polynomial is also known. It is given by

$$a_n = 2^{(n-1)} \qquad \qquad ......(5)$$

For example, the 10th degree Chebyshev polynomial has the highest term

$$2^9*x^{10} = 512*x^{10}$$

4.1. *From power series to Chebyshev polynomials*

If a finite power series, say of degree 10, exists for the given function then this series can be formed by using a Taylor or Maclaurin power series expansion about some suitable point inside the approximation range. Enough terms must be used to make sure that an accurate approximation to the desired function over the range of interest is achieved, even though the degree may be high and the error might have some odd distribution. For reasons that will become evident, this polynomial can be rewritten as a sum of Chebyshev polynomials, using $T_0(x)$ up to $T_{10}(x)$. The procedure can be seen by following through a cycle of computation. Let

$$P_{10}(x) = a_0 + a_1 x + ... + a_{10}x^{10} = b_0 T_0(x) + b_1 T_1(x)$$
$$+ ... + b_{10} T_{10}(x).$$

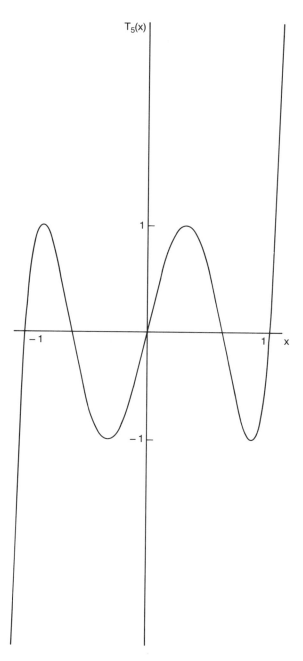

Fig 6   The fifth degree Chebyshev polynomial.

The b_{10} coefficient can be found directly, since only $T_{10}(x)$ contains an x^{10} factor. Comparing x^{10} coefficients, gives

$$a_{10} = b_{10}*2^9$$

which can be solved for b_{10}. The next stage is to form $P_{10}(x) - b_{10}*T_{10}(x)$, which will be of degree 9. Then remove $T_9(x)$, and so on, until all the b coefficients are found.

4.2   Chebyshev economisation

These b coefficients are of great interest. Hopefully, they will die away quite quickly, and the high degree ones can be ignored. Then the error will be roughly the same in magnitude as the sum of the deleted bs. The more bs that are deleted, the more efficient the approximation, but of course the greater the error. This trade-off is completely under the control of the user. Suppose that in the above example

$$b_8 = 10^{-7}, \ b_9 = 2*10^{-8}, \ b_{10} = -1.5*10^{-9}$$

If b_9 and b_{10} are disregarded, it can be seen that, over the approximation range, there can never be more error than $|b_9| + |b_{10}|$ (recall that T_9 and T_{10} have a peak magnitude of 1 over the approximation range). Since b_9 is ten times b_{10}, the error in approximating P_{10} with an eighth degree Chebyshev series will be approximately $b_9*T_9(x)$. Since $T_9(x)$ is exactly equiripple over the range, the overall error will be approximately equiripple.

This process is called Chebyshev economisation [10]. Basically, the method is redistributing the error of a lower degree power series such that this error is (almost) equiripple over the range of interest. If an exact equiripple error function is required, then optimisation procedures will be required. Such procedures are outside the scope of this paper.

Once an economised series in terms of Chebyshev polynomials has been found, the equivalent economised power series can be computed by adding the weighted Chebyshev polynomials together. Nested multiplication is used in the DSP chip to minimise the number of multiplications and additions needed to evaluate an argument.

4.3   Arbitrary approximation range

The Chebyshev polynomials above are equiripple on $-1 \le x \le +1$. They can be modified to be equiripple on an arbitrary range $x_1 \le x \le x_2$, by using the mapping $t = mx + b$, where t is the normalised Chebyshev variable $-1 \le t \le +1$. The slope m and the intercept b can be found such that

when $t = -1$, $x = x_1$
$t = +1$, $x = x_2$ ......(6)

Solving for m and b gives

$$m = 2/(x_2 - x_1), \qquad b = -(x_2 + x_1)/(x_2 - x_1)$$ ......(7)

A table of arbitrary approximation range Chebyshev polynomials can be built by using a generalisation of the recursion in equation (3):

$$T_n(x) = 2(mx + b)T_{n-1}(x) - T_{n-2}(x)$$ ......(8)

with the initial polynomials (see equation (4))

$$T_0(x) = 1, \qquad T_1(x) = mx + b$$ ......(9)

These polynomials are used to economise a power series, over a preselected range $x_1 \leq x \leq x_2$.

4.4   Power series expansion for b^x

This function can be rewritten in exponential form as follows. Let $y = b^x$. Then $ln(y) = x ln(b)$. Exponentiation gives

$$b^x = e^{Cx}, \text{ where } C = ln(b)$$

Expansion into a Maclaurin power series [9] gives

$$b^x = 1 + (Cx)^1/1! + (Cx)^2/2! + \ ...$$ ......(10)

4.5   Power series expansion for $log(x)$ (base b)

This function can be put into ln (natural logarithm) form in the following manner. Let $y = log_b(x)$. Then $b^y = x$, or $y ln(b) = ln(x)$. Solving for y,
$$log_b(x) = ln(x)/ln(b)$$ ......(11)

Expansion into a power series about $x = 1$ [9] gives the result

$$log_b(x) = [(x-1) - (x-1)^2/2 + (x-1)^3/3 - ...]/ln(b),$$
$$|x-1| \leq 1, x \neq 0$$ ......(12)

These terms are expanded, and then collected to form a power series in x. A computer program was developed to find these coefficients. First, a table of binomial coefficients was formed, the kth row of which gave the coefficients of $(1-x)^k$. Then the

73

appropriate scale factors were calculated $(-1^{(k+1)}/k)$, and the overall power series computed. Note that each additional term in equation (10) will influence all coefficients in the final power series. It is therefore important to use enough terms for accurate representation of the log function. Typically, 25 to 30 terms were used for the original power series, to hold 10 decimal places of accuracy over the approximation range. An excellent economisation was achieved with only a 6th degree polynomial.

5. Economisation results

The antilog approximation for the mantissa of the step size (base = 2) is looked at first. A 20th degree power series ($k = 2$) is used, based on equation (10), with 20 decimal digits of accuracy in the Basic program. This amount of accuracy may seem excessive, but proved to be necessary for the logarithmic approximations below. The approximation range was $-1 \leq x \leq 0$. The economised results are shown in Table 1.

Table 1 Economised results for antilog approximations.

Degree of economised series	Maximum error
2	$1.29*10^{-3}$
3	$5.53*10^{-5}$
4	$1.90*10^{-6}$
5	$5.47*10^{-8}$
6	$1.35*10^{-9}$
7	$2.92*10^{-11}$
8	$5.60*10^{-13}$
9	$9.69*10^{-15}$
10	$1.52*10^{-16}$

The specification was for 24-bit accuracy, implying a $5.96*10^{-8}$ error. Trying a sixth degree economised polynomial, gave the truncated coefficients:

a_0 = .999 999 99,
a_1 = .693 147 05,
a_2 = .240 224 35,
a_3 = .055 491 035,
a_4 = $9.580\ 058\ 4*10^{-3}$,
a_5 = $1.275\ 716\ 22*10^{-3}$,
a_6 = $1.093\ 875\ 24*10^{-4}$

An error analysis gave a peak error of $1.72*10^{-8}$ which is a 12-fold increase in the above tabular value due to coefficient quantization, but still within the desired specification.

The logarithmic approximation for the table look-up values of the mantissa (base = 2) proved more difficult to compute than the antilog one. However, in the adaptive quantizer scheme of Fig 5, it is not necessary to compute this function in real time, although this may be a request in other applications. A Basic program with 20 decimal place accuracy was used to find the logarithmic approximation. A 28th degree original power series was used in equation (12). With lower accuracy, or with a smaller power series, errors were found to enter significantly into the calculations. The logarithm function was economised to various degrees over the range $0.5 \le x \le 1.0$. The results of the economisation are shown in Table 2.

Table 2   Economised results for logarithmic approximations.

Degree of economised series	Maximum error
2	$5.58*10^{-3}$
3	$7.25*10^{-4}$
4	$1.00*10^{-4}$
5	$1.43*10^{-5}$
6	$2.12*10^{-5}$
7	$3.19*10^{-7}$
8	$4.90*10^{-8}$
9	$7.73*10^{-9}$
10	$1.35*10^{-9}$

The design goal was to produce an approximation that is accurate to 16 binary mantissa bits, that is, an error of less than $1.53*10^{-5}$. The above table shows that a fifth degree polynomial should do. The coefficients for this polynomial with about 16 binary bit accuracy are:

$a_0 = -3.794\ 15,$
$a_1 = 10.139\ 51,$
$a_2 = -14.080\ 87,$
$a_3 = 12.881\ 42,$
$a_4 = -6.551\ 61,$
$a_5 = 1.405\ 72.$

An analysis with these truncated coefficients was performed. The maximum error was found to be $2.00*10^{-5}$, which is outside specification. Therefore, a sixth degree polynomial is necessary. The coefficients for this one are:

$a_0 = -4.034\ 60,$
$a_1 = 12.179\ 79,$
$a_2 = -21.206\ 83,$
$a_3 = 25.995\ 72,$
$a_4 = -19.967\ 39,$
$a_5 = 8.641\ 19,$
$a_6 = -1.607\ 88.$

This time an error analysis gave a peak error of $4.68*10^{-6}$, which is well within specification. It can be seen that coefficient quantization error should also be borne in mind in making these polynomial approximations.

6. Conclusions

The paper has described the implementation of an improved adaptive quantizer for a speech waveform coding system. This quantizer must be able to compute a number raised to a power, or its analogue. Logarithmic and antilog polynomial approximations were used to facilitate the analogue.

These approximations are based on economisation of a series of Chebyshev polynomials. The results give nearly equiripple error performance over the desired approximation range. The ripple error could be lowered slightly by using optimisation methods to make the error exactly equiripple, but such an optimisation is unlikely to lower the degree of the final polynominals.

Various trade-offs were found. The approximation range, degree of economised polynomial, and the base b can all be varied to see their effects on approximation error. Generally, the error can be reduced by narrowing the approximation range, increasing the degree of approximation, or lowering the base b, provided this is maintained large enough to encompass the dynamic range of the approximation variables.

The approximations have been used in the design of a 16 kbit/s speech sub-band coder, for application in a new range of speech and data multiplexers. An efficient robust adaptive quantizer was implemented with a fixed arithmetic DSP chip (the Motorola 56 000), and achieved the performance indicated in Section 5. Nested multiplication has been used to minimise the evaluation times. Rounding of results within the nested routine has been found to reduce significantly the residual error of calculation.

There were two unexpected 'surprises' in carrying out this work. The first surprise was concerned with the amount of care required to find a decent logarithmic approximation. The Basic program used a 29 term power series, and 20 decimal digit accuracy. The second surprise concerned coefficient quantization. This operation lowers accuracy, and can lead to an extra term being needed in the economised power series.

References

1 Southcott C et al: 'Low bit rate speech coding for practical applications', Br Telecom Technol J, _6_, (April 1988).

2 '32 kbit/s adaptive differential pulse code modulation (ADPCM)', CCITT Recommendations G721 (1984).

3 Jayant N S: 'Adaptive quantisation with a one word memory', BSTJ, $\underline{52}$, No 7, pp 1119—1145 (September 1973).

4 Hanes R B and Attkins P M: 'The UK candidate 16 kbit/s speech codec for the GSM Pan European study on digital cellular land mobile radio', Speech Communication, No 1 (1988).

5 Texas Instruments: 'Digital signal processing applications with the TMS320 family', (1986).

6 Motorola: 'DSP56000 digital signal processor user's manual' (1986).

7 Bodie J R, Gadenz R N, Kershaw R N, Hays W P and Tow J: 'The DSP32 digital signal processor and its technical application development tools', AT&T Technical Journal, $\underline{65}$, No 5, pp 89—104 (September/October 1986).

8 Goodman D J and Wilkinson R M: 'A robust adaptive quantizer', IEEE Trans Commun, COM—23 , pp 1362—1365 (November 1975).

9 Abramowitz M and Stegun I A: 'Handbook of mathematical functions', Dover (1972).

10 Hildebrand F B: 'Introduction to numerical analysis', 2nd Ed McGraw-Hill, pp 471—475 (1974).

DEVELOPMENT OF A SPEECH CODEC FOR THE SKYPHONE SERVICE

I Boyd, C B Southcott and D P Crowe

ABSTRACT

British Telecom International (BTI) is to introduce an aeronautical telephone service to be known as the Skyphone. This service will use 9.6 kbit/s speech codecs because of the limited satellite power available. The codec to be used for the trial service has been chosen from a number of codecs developed in several different countries. This paper gives a brief description of the Skyphone and the factors which influence the speech codec design. It then describes the codec proposed by British Telecom Research Laboratories (BTRL) as a candidate for the service. Subjective test results show this codec to be better than the other candidates.

1. Introduction

With around 1000 widebodied jets in service, several million busy executives traverse the world every year. For these executives, accustomed to mobile phones and constant contact with their offices, it is unacceptable to be out of touch for the duration of long international flights. To meet this market need and to provide improved communications between airlines and their aircraft, a consortium including British Telecom, British Airways and Racal Decca has been set up to provide in-flight telephony facilities. When these facilities come into service they will enable telephone calls to be made to virtually anywhere in the world from an aircraft in flight. The service will be marketed by British Telecom International (BTI) and will be known as the Skyphone service. A trial service, with two telephony channels per aircraft, will be introduced before the end of 1988 on British Airways Boeing 747s flying trans-Atlantic routes. For this service British Telecom will provide the earth station equipment at Goonhilly, the links through to the international telephone network and the billing facilities. Racal Decca will provide the aircraft equipment required to set up calls, and the aircraft high power antenna. The system will be based on Inmarsat satellites currently used mainly for telephony between ship and shore.

The trial service, although having some limitations, will nevertheless enable passengers to make direct dialled calls, routed via the UK, to any IDD destination. With the introduction of the full commercial service an agreement between British Telecom and the telephone administrations of Norway and Singapore will come into effect.

This agreement will enable a truly worldwide aeronautical service to be offered, with telephony traffic from flights over the Pacific, Indian and Atlantic oceans.

Digital transmission is to be used between the aircraft and the BTI international exchanges. Low bit rate speech coding has to be used because of the very limited satellite power available. The codec for the trial service has been chosen from candidate codecs developed in various countries. Four candidates were considered.

The next section describes the features of the aeronautical system which affect the design of the speech codecs. The British Telecom Research Laboratories (BTRL) candidate speech coding algorithm for the Skyphone service is presented in section 3 and the implementation of the algorithm on a digital signal processing device is outlined in section 4. Section 5 presents subjective test results which compare the four 9.6 kbit/s candidate speech codecs considered for the Skyphone service. Conclusions are presented in the final section.

2. Speech codec design for the Skyphone system

The main elements of the aeronautical satellite system are illustrated in Fig 1. The operating bit rate for the speech codec was selected as 9.6 kbit/s because no lower bit rate codec examined by Inmarsat and BTI gave acceptable speech quality. Higher bit rate codecs, while yielding better speech quality, were ruled out because of the limited satellite power available.

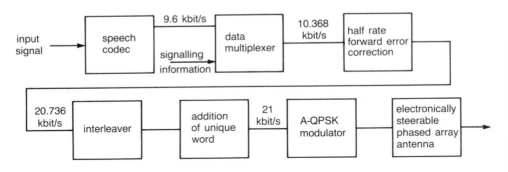

Fig 1   Simplified block diagram of aircraft transmission system.

The data multiplexer is used to multiplex the output data stream from the speech encoder and some signalling information. The 10.368 kbit/s bit rate of this combined data stream is doubled when forward error correction (FEC) is applied. The half rate FEC unit consists of a convolution encoder of constraint length seven — the corresponding decoder is an 8-level soft decision Viterbi decoder [1]. To combat the multi-path fading characteristic of the aeronautical transmission path, interleaving is applied to preserve the FEC coding gain by spreading burst errors throughout a transmission frame. A number of interleaved blocks are collected together and a 'unique word' and a few dummy bits are added to form a half second RF frame which is transmitted at 21 kbit/s (Fig 2). The RF demodulator synchronizes itself with respect to the unique word. Loss of frame synchronization is assumed to have occurred after the demodulator unique word match is below a prescribed threshold for two consecutive frames. A form of offset quadrature phase shift keying, (O—QPSK), known as aviation-QPSK (A-QPSK) [2,3], is used to modulate the 21 kbit/s signal onto the radio frequency carrier. The aircraft antenna for the trial service will be an electronically steerable high power antenna.

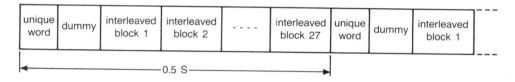

Fig 2   RF frame format.

The bit stream presented to the speech decoder after errors have been introduced on the radio path and reduced by the channel coding is expected to have an average bit error rate of about 1 in 1000. There will also be bursts of errors when the error correction cannot cope. The speech codec must be able to suppress the effects of all of these. Particular attention was paid to the different types of transmission error in the development of the BTRL codec for the Skyphone system.

The physical environment in which the airborne codecs are expected to operate requires particular care in the design of the codec hardware. The equipment will be installed in a pressurised location within the aircraft but must, nevertheless, be tested to ensure reliable operation at the temperature extremes of − 15 °C and 55 °C, at a pressure equivalent to an altitude of 15 000 feet, at 100% humidity and with severe vibration. The temperature range of this specification alone rules out the use of components with a normal commercial specification. In the hardware implementation the use of components with a military specification, good component heat dissipation, low power consumption and reliable interconnection is therefore essential.

3. The BTRL Skyphone codec

3.1   Introduction

To achieve the spectral efficiency required for the Skyphone service low bit rate speech encoding is required. A multipulse excited LPC algorithm [4] was selected by BTRL as it is robust to background noise and transmission errors.

A schematic of a multipulse-excited LPC encoder is illustrated in Fig 3. The encoding process involves splitting the incoming speech into frames of 10—20 ms duration to derive the short-term and long-term predictor parameters and an analysis-by-synthesis process to obtain the pulse positions and amplitudes. The short-term predictor models short-term correlations in the speech signal. The long-term predictor takes advantage of long-term correlations in speech, primarily arising from pitch-related correlations in voiced speech.

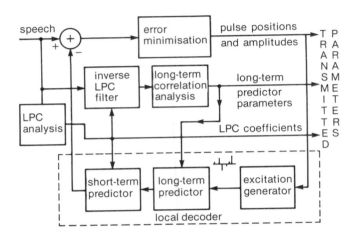

Fig 3   Multipulse excited LPC decoder.

The excitation analysis-by-synthesis procedure involves a search for the pulse positions and amplitudes which minimize the mean squared error between a block of the input speech and the speech obtained from the synthesizer in the local decoder. The derivation of the excitation may be carried out for the entire LPC block length or the LPC frame may be split into several sub-blocks and the excitation derived for each sub-block separately. To find all the pulse positions and amplitudes simultaneously for a sub-block requires the solution of non-linear equations and is thus very complex. Sub-optimal methods have therefore been developed to derive the pulse positions and amplitudes sequentially. A multipulse-excited LPC decoder corresponding to the encoder of Fig 3 is presented in Fig 4. The decoding process is very straightforward, requiring the formation of the excitation signal and the application of this excitation to the long-term and short-term predictors to give the synthesized speech output.

3.2   Short-term predictor parameter extraction

The short-term predictor parameters are obtained using standard LPC techniques. The LPC analysis problem may be outlined with reference to equation (1) below:

$$E = \sum_{n} (s(n) - \sum_{k=1}^{p} a_k.s(n-k))^2 \qquad \qquad ......(1)$$

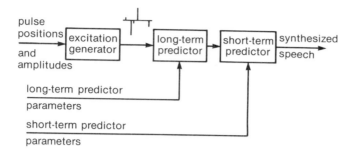

Fig 4   Multipulse excited LPC decoder.

where E is the mean squared error over a block of speech samples, $s(t)$ is a speech sample at sample point t and the a_k are a set of predictor coefficients.

The goal of LPC analysis is to derive a set of predictor coefficients such that the mean squared error E over the block is minimized. The block over which the error minimization takes place is usually between 10 and 20 ms long and the order of the LPC analysis, p, is generally between four and sixteen. The minimization of the error E is achieved by differentiating equation (1) with respect to each a_k value and solving the resulting simultaneous equations. Depending on the limits used in the summation of equation (1), the LPC analysis will either be an autocorrelation or covariance analysis. Although the covariance analysis is more accurate than an auto-correlation analysis the resulting synthesis filter is not guaranteed to be stable. An autocorrelation analysis guarantees the stability of the synthesis filter but requires the speech signal to be windowed such that the signal energy outside the block of interest is zero. A rectangular window is not generally very satisfactory and a tapered window, such as a Hamming window [5], is usually employed. For the Skyphone codec implementation an autocorrelation analysis is used and each speech frame is windowed using a Hamming window. Durbin's recursion [6] is employed as an efficient means of calculating the predictor coefficients following the autocorrelation analysis.

Direct quantization of the predictor coefficients requires an excessive number of bits to give a stable and accurate LPC synthesis filter. An alternative set of coefficients, the reflection coefficients, can be used instead of the predictor coefficients to specify the synthesis filter. These reflection coefficients are a by-product of Durbin's recursion and have the useful property that provided the modulus of each coefficient is less than one, the all-pole LPC synthesis filter is guaranteed to be stable. The predictor coefficients can be derived recursively from the quantized reflection coefficients at both the encoder and decoder. In the z-transform domain the LPC synthesis filter has a transfer function $H(z)$ of:

$$H(z) = \frac{1}{1 - \sum\limits_{k=1}^{p} a_k z^{-k}} = \frac{1}{A(z)} \qquad \qquad ......(2)$$

Thus the synthesizer output, s_o, is calculated recursively from the current input, c, and past outputs as follows:

$$s_o(n) = c(n) + \sum_{k=1}^{p} a_k \, s_o(n-k) \qquad \qquad ......(3)$$

The LPC analysis parameters adopted for the Skyphone codec implementation are given below:

- 10th order LPC autocorrelation analysis,
- 32 ms Hamming window with 37.5% overlap,
- predictor coefficient update period of 20 ms.

The reflection coefficients are quantized by first applying an inverse sine transformation to each coefficient and then uniformly quantizing the transformed coefficients [7]. The reflection coefficient quantization bits are non-uniformly allocated such that the allocation reflects the importance of each coefficient.

3.3   Long-term predictor parameter extraction

Long-term correlations in the speech signal are effectively represented by the long-term prediction filter. The long-term prediction filter has a transfer function in the z-transform domain of:

$$P(z) = B.z^{-m}$$

where B is the gain parameter of the filter and m is the delay at which the maximum correlation occurs. To find B and m the residual signal is formed first by filtering the input speech using the inverse LPC filter as illustrated in Fig 5. The delay m is taken as the sample delay which gives the following maximum autocorrelation:

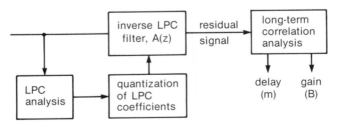

Fig 5   Long-term predictor parameter extraction.

$$AR(m) = \sum_{i=1}^{N} r(i).r(i-m) \quad \text{for all values of } m \text{ under}$$
$$\text{consideration} \qquad \qquad \qquad ......(4)$$

where $r(t)$ is the residual signal at sampling instant t and N is the block size used in the updating of the long-term correlation parameters. Once the delay m has been found from equation (4) then the gain parameter, B, can be calculated from equation 5 below:

$$B = \frac{\displaystyle\sum_{i=1}^{N} r(i).r(i-m)}{\displaystyle\sum_{i=1}^{N} r(i-m).r(i-m)} \qquad \qquad ......(5)$$

The output from the long-term predictor, P_o, is given by:

$$P_o(n) = B.P_o(n-m) \qquad \qquad ......(6)$$

For the long-term predictor in the Skyphone codec, 64 delay values are searched for the maximum correlation. The delay and gain values are updated at the same rate as the short-term predictor coefficients, i.e. every 20 ms. The gain value B is quantized using a non-linear quantizer and the delay value is encoded into 6 bits.

3.4 Determination of pulse positions and amplitudes

The goal in deriving the pulse positions and amplitudes for an excitation sub-block is to minimize the mean squared error between the input speech signal and the synthesized speech signal. The problem may be defined as follows:

$$e = \sum_{n}(s(n) - \sum_{i=1}^{r} A_i h(n-d_i))^2 \qquad \qquad ......(7)$$

where $s(n)$ is the input speech signal with the effect of the short-term and long-term filter memories removed, A_i and d_i are the r pulse amplitudes and positions respectively and $h(t)$ is the combined impulse response of the long-term and short-term prediction filters at sampling instant t. The pulse positions and amplitudes are derived to minimize the mean squared error, e, for the excitation sub-block under consideration. The optimum solution of deriving all the pulse positions and amplitudes simultaneously is not feasible because of the non-linear nature of the problem. Therefore sub-optimal solutions have been developed which find the pulses sequentially. Equation (7) can be rewritten for the case of a single pulse as:

$$e_1 = \sum_{n} (s(n) - A_1 h(n-d_1))^2 \qquad \qquad ......(8)$$

The optimum pulse amplitude is obtained by differentiating e_1 with respect to A_1, and equating to zero, thus:

$$A_1 = \frac{\sum\limits_{n} s(n) \, h(n - d_1)}{\sum\limits_{n} h^2 \, (n - d_1)} \qquad \qquad \dots\dots(9)$$

Substituting this result into equation (8) gives:

$$e_1 = \sum\limits_{n} s^2 \, (n) - \frac{(\sum\limits_{n} s(n) \, h(n - d_1))^2}{\sum\limits_{n} h^2 \, (n - d_1)} \qquad \qquad \dots\dots(10)$$

Thus to minimize e_1 is equivalent to maximizing:

$$F(d_1) = \frac{(\sum\limits_{n} s(n) \, h(n - d_1))^2}{\sum\limits_{n} h^2 \, (n - d_1)} \qquad \qquad \dots\dots(11)$$

The function $F(d_1)$ is calculated for all positions in the sub-block and the position which gives the maximum value of $F(d_1)$ is selected as the appropriate pulse position. The amplitude of the pulse can be calculated using equation (9).

To find the second pulse, equation (7) is modified to take account of the first pulse position and amplitude just found. Thus

$$e_2 = \sum\limits_{n} (s(n) - A_1 h(n - d_1) - A_2 \, h(n - d_2))^2 \qquad \qquad \dots\dots(12)$$

Let $s'(n) = s(n) - A_1 \, h(n - d_1)$

Equation (12) can then be rewritten as:

$$e_2 = \sum (s'(n) - A_2 \, h(n - d_2))^2 \qquad \qquad \dots\dots(13)$$

To find the position and amplitude of the second pulse which minimizes the error e_2, an identical process to that adopted for pulse 1 is followed. Subsequent pulses are derived by following the same procedure as that adopted for pulse 2. The operations involved in finding the pulse positions and amplitudes are summarized in the flow chart of Fig 6.

3.5   Pulse amplitude quantization

The quantization of each pulse amplitude involves two separate normalisation stages. The first normalisation process takes account of the variation in speech energy from one excitation sub-block to the next and the second process takes account of the average variation in the modulus of the pulse amplitudes within an excitation sub-block. No explicit information is transmitted to the receiver regarding either of these normalisations. After each pulse has been normalised it is quantized using a non-uniform quantizer.

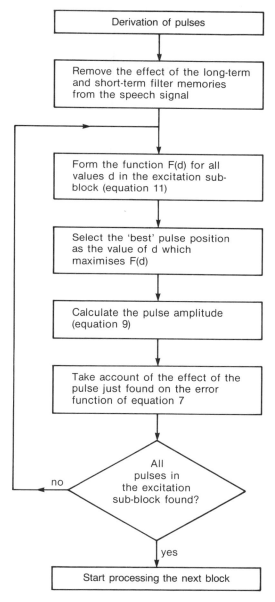

Fig 6   Operations for finding pulse positions and amplitudes.

The first normalisation stage, which accounts for variations in speech energy from one excitation sub-block to the next, is achieved by dividing each pulse amplitude by a variable gain factor. This variable gain factor is adapted in a backward fashion according to the line codes generated by the pulse amplitude quantizer. If the line code issued from the pulse amplitude quantizer corresponds to either the most positive or the most negative quantizer levels, indicating possible clipping by the quantizer, the gain factor is increased. If the line code issued, however, corresponds to either the smallest positive or negative quantizer levels, indicative of coarse quantization, the gain factor is decreased. The gain factor adaptations for all other line codes follows this same philosophy, i.e. increase the gain factor if the quantizer seems to be in danger of clipping, decrease the gain factor if the quantization seems too coarse.

During initialisation both the encoder and decoder gain factors are set to unity. Provided there are no transmission errors the decoder pulse amplitude gain factor will track the encoder pulse amplitude gain factor exactly. To minimize the effects of transmission errors a degree of leakage is included in the gain factor adjustment at both the encoder and decoder. If gf is the gain factor calculated from the adaptation rules, then the gain factor including leakage, gf_l, is given by:

$$gf_l = gf^{0.98}$$

It is this leaked gain factor, gf_l, which is used to normalise each pulse amplitude, i.e. normalised amplitude = amplitude / gf_l.

The second stage of the normalisation process is achieved by multiplying each pulse in an excitation sub-block by a set of fixed scaling factors. The fixed scaling factors were derived by finding the modulus of the long-term average of the second and third pulse amplitudes relative to the first pulse amplitude. The scaling factors adjust the pulse amplitudes within a sub-block so that **on average** they are more nearly equal. Application of these scale factors reduces the variance of the normalised amplitudes and considerably improves the performance of the pulse amplitude quantizer. The pulse amplitude information is transmitted in the order in which the pulses are found. Thus the decoder can take account of the encoder scale factors by dividing the decoded pulse amplitudes by the appropriate scale factor for that pulse. The flow chart of Fig 7 summarizes the operation of the pulse amplitude quantizer.

3.6   Error protection

The Skyphone codec was designed to cater for two different error conditions:

- the expected random bit error rate of 1 in 1000,

- burst errors caused by breaks in the radio link due either to momentary misalignment of the aircraft antenna or poor propagation conditions.

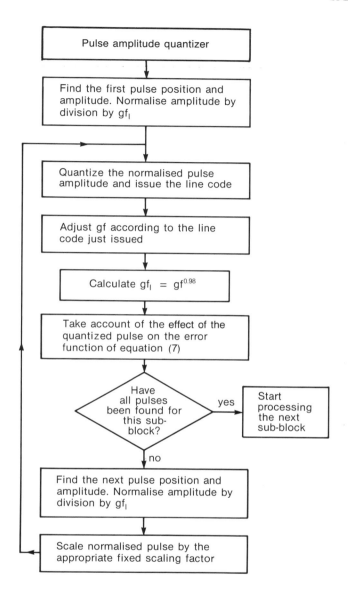

Fig 7   Pulse amplitude normalisation and quantization.

It was found that to maintain the speech quality of the error-free case for the random errors required forward error correction to be applied only to the reflection coefficient information bits. With only a few hundred bits/s of the available 9.6 kbit/s data rate used for error protection, the codec maintains the required voice quality for a random bit error rate of 1 in 1000. During the worst propagation conditions the RF demodulator cannot maintain synchronization: when this occurs the demodulator activates a codec squelch control signal. Unfortunately the squelch control signal cannot be activated until two unique word matches are below a prescribed threshold. Thus with a radio system frame size of half a second, up to one second of random data will be passed to the codec before the squelch signal operates. The codec has to detect this situation, and other severe burst error conditions, and mute the codec output signal. Some of the transmission bits in the 9.6 kbit/s data stream have therefore been reserved for burst error detection. When a burst error is detected that lasts for only one speech frame, 20 ms, it has been found that it is better, perceptually, to repeat the previous speech frame than mute the codec. If however burst errors are present for several consecutive frames then the codec output is muted until no more burst errors are detected. Figure 8 shows the burst error distribution measured at the codec input during some recent flight trials. This distribution does not take account of the times when the demodulator lost synchronization and burst errors lasting several hundred speech frames occurred.

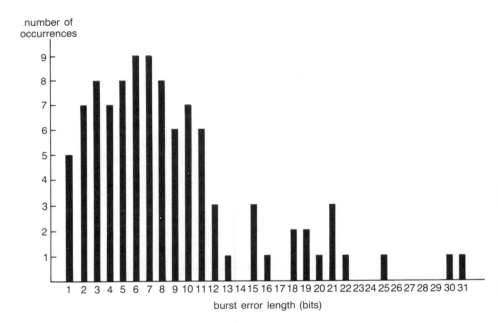

Fig 8   Burst error distribution (measured over several minutes).

4. Codec implementation

The implementation of the algorithm described in section 3 is outlined in this section. As is normal for state-of-the-art speech codecs, the algorithm is implemented on a digital signal processing microprocessor (DSP). The reasoning behind the selection of the particular DSP device for this application is presented below.

4.1   The digital signal processor

From previous experience of implementing speech codecs on fixed point devices it was clear that many man-hours are spent converting floating point high-level simulations to suitable fixed point or integer formats. This conversion process requires, among other things, appropriate scaling to maintain the accuracy of calculations. Often however, despite great care being taken in the conversion process, the speech quality obtained from the fixed point implementation is inferior to the high-level floating point simulation because of round-off and truncation errors. Fixed point DSP implementations thus have the disadvantages of firstly requiring long conversion times and secondly yielding speech quality that is inferior to the original simulation. Mainly for these reasons a floating point digital signal processing device, the WE DSP 32 [8], was chosen for the Skyphone codec implementation. This device is one of the most powerful and flexible floating point devices currently available. Some key features of this DSP are:

- 32-bit floating point arithmetic unit,

- four 40-bit accumulators,

- 2 Kbytes of ROM and 4 Kbytes of RAM on chip,

- off-chip memory expansion to 56 Kbytes,

- serial and parallel input/output ports with DMA options,

- instruction cycle time of 160 ns.

The WE DSP 32 was favoured over other floating point DSP devices because it is well supported, is one of the more straightforward devices to use and because an upward compatible CMOS device is to be introduced soon. Thus although the present version of the Skyphone codec is implemented on the NMOS part, the codec implementation will be transferred to the CMOS device when it becomes available later in 1988. The CMOS part will offer a full military specification which is an important point when the aeronautical operating conditions, as outlined in section 2, are considered. The lower power consumption of the CMOS part is also an important advantage in this application and, in fact, in any telecommunications application.

4.2   The speech codec hardware

The speech codec hardware is illustrated in Fig 9. The WE DSP32 microprocessor executes the speech coding algorithm and the remaining hardware elements provide the required analogue-to-digital/digital-to-analogue conversions and the appropriate timing signals.

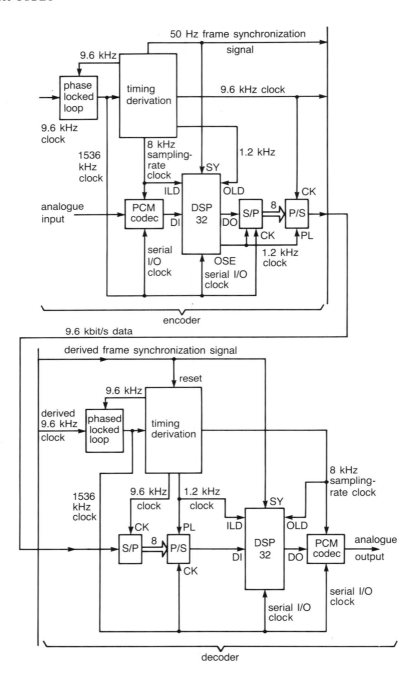

Fig 9   Speech codec hardware.

At the encoder the timing derivation blocks generates all the required clock frequencies phased locked (when required) to an externally applied 9.6 kHz clock. The clock frequencies generated are:

- an 8 kHz sampling rate clock,
- a 50 Hz frame synchronization signal,
- a 1.2 kHz clock to the DSP32 controlling the digital input/output of the coded data,
- a 1536 kHz serial input/output clock.

The 8 kHz sampling rate clock is connected to the PCM codec device which samples the incoming speech signal and generates an 8-bit *A-law* encoded PCM sample every *125* µs. The 8-bit samples are clocked out serially from the codec output to the DSP32 (serial) digital input at a clock rate of 1536 kHz. An 8 kHz clock is also connected to the input load (ILD) pin of the DSP32. Every active transition of the sampling rate clock initiates a serial input to the DSP32.

As the coded speech samples are transmitted in frames of 20 ms duration, the 50 Hz clock signal is used by the DSP32 for frame synchronization. As soon as some encoded data has been derived for the current frame the DSP32 commences to output data by loading the output serial register a byte (8 bits) at a time. The 1.2 kHz clock (one eighth of the 9.6 kHz rate) is used as the load control for this output serial register. The serial data is clocked out of the DSP32 using the 1536 kHz clock. Once 8 bits have been clocked out, the output shift register empty signal becomes active. This signal controls the 8-bit serial-to-parallel and parallel-to-serial registers at the output of the DSP32, such that the burst of eight valid data bits at 1536 kHz is converted to a continuous data stream at 9.6 kbit/s.

At the decoder a frame synchronization signal and a 9.6 kHz clock signal are provided by the radio system. The interface to the speech decoder DSP32 essentially mirrors the encoder interface.

A photograph of a complete encoder/decoder is presented in Fig 10. The PCB photographed is populated with two DSP 32 devices, program and data menory devices, a PCM codec and a logic cell array (which implements all the random logic functions). It will be possible to implement a complete encoder/decoder on a single CMOS DSP32 whenever it becomes available hence reducing the board area to half its current size.

5.1   Subjective test results

An introduction to the rationale and the procedures adopted for the subjective testing of low bit rate speech codecs is contained in the paper by C B Southcott et al [4].

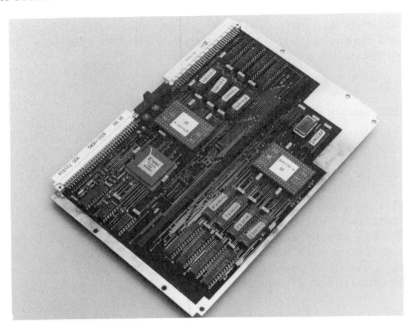

Fig 10   A complete encoder/decoder.

As part of the procedure for selecting the codec for the Skyphone service, four codecs (one from Japan, one from the USA and two from the UK) were evaluated by a series of subjective tests [9]. The four codecs were designated A, B, C and D. Only codec D, the British Telecom Research Laboratories codec, will be identified in the results. The subjective tests were designed to cover a range of input levels, listening levels and conditions representative of the operating environment of the Skyphone service. The procedure adopted for the listening tests was to assess each codec in isolation. To enable comparison to be made between different codecs it was therefore necessary to include a transfer standard in each test. The standard used was the modulated noise reference unit (MNRU) [10], which provides a range of Q values in terms of signal-to-modulated-noise ratio. Not only can one codec be comapred with another by establishing Q ratings, but each codec's contribution to total distortion can also be equated in terms of a known standard such as PCM.

The codecs were tested under the following conditions:

1.	Codec	(High Input Level)
2.	Codec	(Median Input Level)
3.	Codec	(Low Input Level)
4.	Codec + Aircraft Noise	(High Input Level)
5.	Codec + Aircraft Noise	(Median Input Level)
6.	Codec + Aircraft Noise	(Low Input Level)
7.	Codec + Errors + Aircraft Noise	(Median Input Level)
8.	Codec + Errors of 10^{-3}	(Median Input Level)

The speech material for the tests was taken from unconnected sentence recordings of male and female speakers. The aircraft noise recordings were produced and mixed at an analogue point with the speech recordings, before being input to the codecs. The noise spectrum was representative of a typical Boeing 747 aircraft cabin with the level set 12 dB below the median speech level i.e. − 30 dBv.

A block diagram of the test circuit is shown in Fig 11. A multi-path switch was used to route the various circuit conditions through the intermediate reference system (IRS) [11] to the subject. Although not shown on the diagram, the whole of the experiment was run by computer control, i.e. switching of circuits, setting of attenuators, control of tape recorders and the storage of results. Periodically throughout the test a tone of 500 Hz was used to check levels at various points in the test circuitry. The computer also performed an analysis of variance and curve fitting functions on the results.

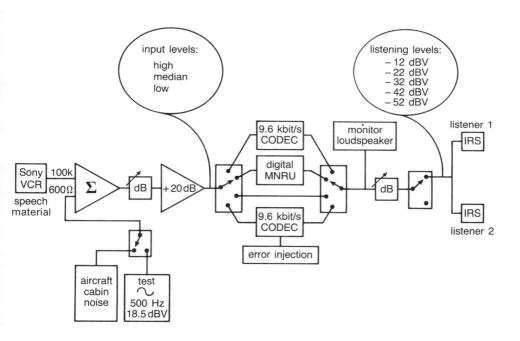

Fig 11   Diagram of test circuit for subjective test.

Separate tests were carried out with people being asked to vote on the speech quality or the listening effort required.

From the test results the mean option score for different listening levels was derived for the various test conditions. The mean opinion scores for all four codecs with a median input level and no aircraft noise or errors, (condition 2) and for a median input level with aircraft noise (condition 5) are presented in Figs 12(a)—(d). The results for male and female speakers for each condition are presented separately. From these results it is clear that codec D, the codec from British Telecom Research Laboratories, yields the highest mean opinion socres for almost the entire range of listening levels. For all the codec test conditions, 1 to 8, the BTRL codec was similarly ranked higher than the other codecs for all listening levels except the very lowest level (− 60 dBV).

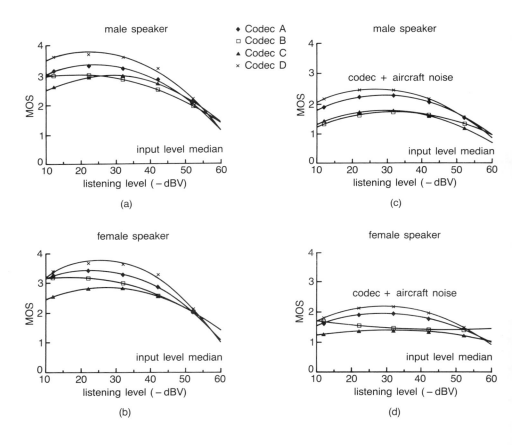

Fig 12   Subjective test results.

The Q ratings [4] for the BTRL codec (codec D) and the codec which was second best in the tests (codec A) for normal listening levels are shown in Table 1.

Table 1   Codec Q ratings (dB)

	Speech quality		Listening effort	
	Male speaker	Female	Male Speaker	Female
BTRL codec (D)	15.7	18.7	22.3	19.7
Second-best codec (A)	9.5	11.9	8.9	14.2

The subjective test report [9] gave a clear and definite recommendation that the BTRL codec was the most suitable codec for the Skyphone service in terms of speech quality.

5.2   Test results with non-speech signals

The ability of the BTRL codec to pass DTMF signalling tones has been investigated in a comprehensive set of tests [12]. The tests consisted of passing several tens of thousands of DTMF characters through a codec and analysing the received tones to ensure that the transmitted character was correctly received. The codec was tested with no bit errors, bit errors at 1 in 1000 and bit errors at 1 in 500 injected into the transmission path. The results are summarised in Table 2 below.

Table 2   DTMF test results

Error condition	% characters correctly received
No errors	100.00
1 in 1000	99.78
1 in 500	99.36

From Table 2 it is clear that the BTRL codec passes DTMF tones very reliably, even at the nominal bit error rate of 1 in 1000.

These laboratory results were confirmed during the Jetstream trials (see section 5.3 below) when numerous calls were successfully connected by DTMF dialling through the BTRL codec.

The codec has also been found to work satisfactorily with data from 300 baud modems (V21), giving a negligible increase in the error rate in the data when the error rate at the speech decoder is 1 in 1000.

5.3   Jetstream trials

During May/June 1988 the Skyphone system was tested using a Racal Avionics executive jet. During the tests many calls were made from the jet to those involved in the airlines industry (including air traffic controllers) in the UK and the USA. The unsolicted comments from those receiving the calls were that the voice quality was very good and that no appreciable difficulty was experienced in conversing over the link.

6. Conclusions

The BTRL codec implementation for the Skyphone service is a robust, 9.6 kbit/s speech codec giving good speech quality. It is also capable of transmitting DTMF signalling and low bit rate modem data. The codec is robust in terms of both background noise and transmission errors. Random transmission bit error rates of 1 in 1000 have no effect on speech quality and higher bit error rates of up to 1 in 100 have only a small effect. With a suitable error detection the effects of error bursts or breaks in transmission up to 20 ms are almost undetectable. The end-to-end codec delay is less than 40 ms with the codec requiring less than 75% of the available processing time on a WE DSP32. In a comprehensive set of subjective tests the BTRL codec was ranked significantly higher than the international competitors with which it was compared.

A public trial service of the Skyphone system is due to commence before the end of 1988. For this trial service two British Airways Boeing 747 aircraft flying trans-Atlantic routes will be equipped with BTRL speech codecs to provide two telephony channels per aircraft. As this initial trial service does not provide a separate signalling channel for DTMF dialling, the DTMF tones will be transmitted through the speech codec at call initiation. As most of the other voice codecs examined by BTI were not able to pass DTMF tones, the use of one of these codecs would have required access to international operators to set up calls during the trial service.

Other airlines are awaiting the outcome of the Airlines Electronic Engineering Committee (AEEC) standardisation activity before introducing an aeronautical telephone service on their aircraft. The AEEC have commissioned another set of subjective tests as part of this standardisation exercise and four candidate codecs are being considered. The codecs being tested are the BTRL codec, a Japanese codec, both tested in the previous set of subjective tests, and two codecs from the USA not considered previously. The results of these tests will not be known until early 1989. Until then the BTRL codec will be a very important element in the world's first transatlantic international aeronautical telephone service.

7. Acknowledgements

The authors would like to record their appreciation to the other members of the group, C D Gostling, R M Mack and D K Freeman, all of whom worked very hard on the DSP software and hardware implementation. Thanks are also due to BTI for permission to use information from Mr Crowe's report on the subjective tests.

References

1 Viterbi A J: 'Error bounds for convolutional codes and an asymptotically optimum decoding algorithm', IEEE Trans on Information Theory, IT—13 , pp 260—269 (1967).

2 Gronemeyer S A: 'MSK and O-QPSK modulation', IEEE Trans on Communications, COM—24 , pp 809—820 (1976).

3 Fang R J F: 'Quaternary transmission over satellite channels with cascaded non-linear elements and adjacent channel interference', IEEE Trans on Communications, COM—29 , No 5, pp 567—581 (1981).

4 Southcott C B et al: 'Low bit rate speech coding for practical applications', Br Telecom Technol J, 6 , No 2, pp 22—40 (April 1988).

5 Markel J D and Gray A H Jr: 'Linear prediction of speech at low bit rates', IEEE Trans on Communications', COM—30 , No 4, pp 600—614 (April 1972).

6 Makhoul J: 'Linear prediction: a tutorial review', Proc of the IEEE, 63 , No 4, pp 516—580 (April 1975).

7 Atal B S: 'Predictive coding of speech at low bit rates', IEEE Trans on Communications', COM—30 , No 4, pp 600—614 (April 1982).

8 Bodie J R, Gadenz R N, Kershaw R N, Hayes W P and Tow J: 'The DSP32 digital signal processor and its technical application development tools', AT&T Technical Journal, 65 , No 5, pp 89—104 (September/October 1986).

9 Crowe D P: 'Experimental results on 9.6 kbit/s codecs for use in the proposed aeronautical satellite service', Internal Memorandum (1988).

10 CCITT: 'Subjective performance assessment of digital processes using the modulation noise reference unit (MNRU)', Annex C to Supplement No 14, Red Book, V (1985).

11 CCITT: 'Intermediate reference system (IRS)', Recommendation, p48, Red Book, V (1985).

12 Gostling C D: 'Examining the ability of the BTRL 9.6 kbit/s Skyphone codec to pass DTMF signalling tones', Internal Memorandum (1988).

AN EFFICIENT CODING SCHEME FOR THE TRANSMISSION OF HIGH QUALITY MUSIC SIGNALS

S M F Smyth and P Challener

ABSTRACT

This paper reports on the development of two very high quality music coding schemes suitable for a wide range of uses including ISDN, broadcasting and other low capacity digital applications. These schemes compress hi-fi music, band-limited to 15 kHz and sampled at 32 kHz, to just 4 bits per sample, leading to a total channel bit rate of 128 kbit/s. This represents a substantial reduction in bit rate compared with currently available techniques, but despite this coding efficiency, subjective testing has shown that the quality of the coded music is essentially identical to that of the original material. It is thought that these results are of major importance, not only for telephony-compatible music transmission, but also for digital audio in general.

1. Introduction

In digital telephony, speech signals are normally encoded into 64 kbit/s bit streams by means of pulse code modulation (PCM). This coding technique requires input analogue speech signals to be band-limited to the frequency range 300-3400 Hz, prior to sampling at an 8 kHz sampling rate. Subsequently, each sample is quantized to one of 256 logarithmically spaced levels, which is transmitted to line in the form of an 8-bit code word. The major factors affecting the quality of such transmissions are the restrictions in bandwidth at the input to the system and the limited dynamic range offered by the 8-bit quantizer; however, these restrictions are considered acceptable for telephony applications. Nevertheless, in more critical applications, such as conferencing, broadcasting and entertainment services, this quality is certainly not sufficient and higher specification solutions are required. Many of these are in fact analogue circuits, which are maintained to high technical standards, but the alternative has been to use high bit rate digital systems, operating at data rates in excess of 300 kbit/s. Such systems are expensive to install and operate and must be specially provided for each application; until recently, the idea of using signal processing to compress high quality audio signals into telephony-rated channels was little more than a dream.

The first reported attempt to code high quality music signals for telephony applications [1] involved the compression of 7 kHz bandwidth audio signals using a relatively simple 2-band sub-band differential PCM scheme, DPCM.

Using 3.5 bits to code each sample, the resulting transmission rate was in the region of 56 kbit/s (configured for the North American ISDN). Subsequent to this work, investigations into alternative 7 kHz audio coding schemes have been reported [2,3]. These have included techniques such as adaptive differential PCM, (ADPCM), sub-band DPCM and harmonically time scaled PCM. The most recent work in this area has involved a detailed evaluation of the CCITT G.722 wideband speech coding recommendation using music signals [4]. This coding scheme, while primarily intended for speech signals, allows for the first time the provision for 7 kHz music transmissions over ISDN type circuits at 64 kbit/s.

In comparison to the exisiting consumer type music facilities such as dial-a-disc, the subjective superiority of this 7 kHz bandwidth system is indisputable. Not only is the high frequency rendition clearer, but the coder's ability to reproduce bass frequencies down to 50 Hz is perceptually more life-like. Nevertheless, a distinct disadvantage of even 7 kHz audio is its inability to reproduce the very highest audio frequencies, i.e. those between 7 and 15 kHz. By raising the coding bandwidth to approximately 15 kHz, this form of band-limiting can no longer be perceived, despite the fact that the auditory response of the human ear will often exceed 18 kHz [5]. In fact 15 kHz has been used for some time by broadcasting companies for their high quality FM broadcast networks [6].

The immediate disadvantage of transmitting high bandwidth audio signals digitally, however, is the very high data rates which are required. For example, using linear PCM, the per channel bit rate will lie in the region of 512 kbit/s without inclusion of error correction or concealment. In recent years, a number of schemes have been developed which reduce the overheads involved with these transmissions. The most popular systems operate at bit rates of around 300-400 kbit/s [6,7,8,9]. As the maximum channel capacity for ISDN has been standardised at 128 kbit/s (2 x 64 kbit/s), this degree of compression is clearly inadequate. The excessive data rates of existing music coders have been due primarily to their adherence to relatively simple digital companding or adaptive delta modulation techniques (ADM). These systems, unlike their 7 kHz counterparts, exploit little of the natural redundancies associated with the sound signals of interest. The inefficiency of coding music is due partly to the higher sampling overheads involved and, until recently, the absence of high speed digital signal processing (DSP) hardware.

A promising medium-complexity candidate scheme which appears particularly suited to high quality music coding and which does exploit the considerable natural redundancies of music is sub-band ADPCM [5,10]. A high coding efficiency is ensured in this system, as it not only incorporates the benefits of digital companding but also takes advantage of both time and spectral redundancies through the use of linear prediction and sub-band coding respectively.

The purpose of this paper is to report two new sub-band ADPCM music coding schemes, of differing complexity, and to document their performance. Both compress music signals band-limited to 15 kHz into bit rates of only 128 bit/s or 4 bits per Nyquist sample.

While the work described here is primarily concerned with high quality music coding for ISDN, applications are to be found in other bandwidth conscious environments, e.g. music distribution for land and satellite-based broadcasting [9]. Moreover the implications of high quality music coding are also very significant in the continuing development of the domestic digital audio media.

2. Characteristics of music

To improve the music coding efficiency beyond that possible with linear PCM, the utilisation of known characteristics, or redundancies, within music signals is necessary. Due to their entertainment value, it is possible for music, or sound signals, to exhibit any number of characteristics. The techniques described make use of three predominant characteristics of normal music which, when correctly utilised, provide significant coding gains over PCM; these are listed below. To complement this list, examples of typical 1024 point discrete Fourier transform (DFT) sound spectra and their associated waveforms are shown in Fig 1. In each case, the upper plot consists of 1024 samples in the time domain, (covering a total time duration of 32ms), which corresponds directly to the spectra shown below.

- A considerable downward spectral tilt is exhibited by the majority of sounds, Figs 1(a), (b), (c), (e) and (f). This is also true for a longer term analysis of music.

- In the time domain, waveforms are highly predictable, Figs 1(a), (b), (c) and (f) and in the short to medium-term, stationary, Figs 1(b) and (f). To quantify this fact, typical 10-tap linear prediction gains (Gp) are tabulated for each sound, Table 1.

- Sound spectra can become highly resonant, implying that music has a sinusoidal tendency, although this is usually restricted to the lower frequencies, Fig 1(b). This form of redundancy is generally unknown in speech coding but is unfortunately associated with the more subtle music sounds.

The variation of the average symmetrical DFT (SDFT) transform gain (Gt) with transform block size is illustrated in Fig 2, for the sound sources depicted in Fig 1. Since the SDFT gain is simply a measure of the coefficient deviation across the music spectrum, the gains shown for the larger block sizes will include the exploitation of all three characteristics outlined above. Using a generalized scaler

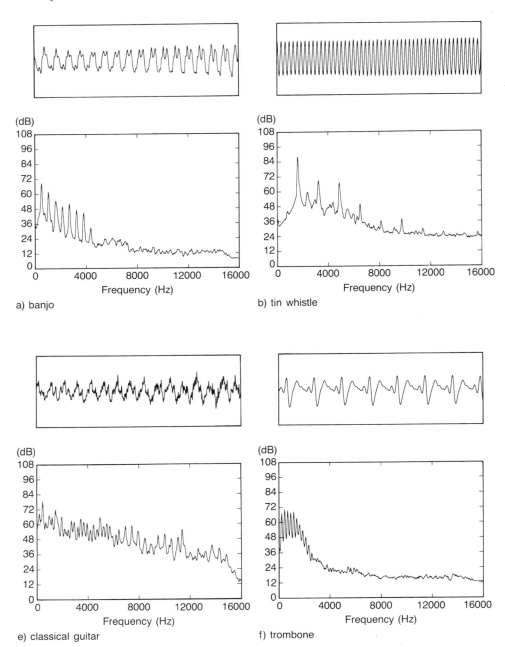

Fig 1   Examples of music spectra and waveforms (32 ms window).

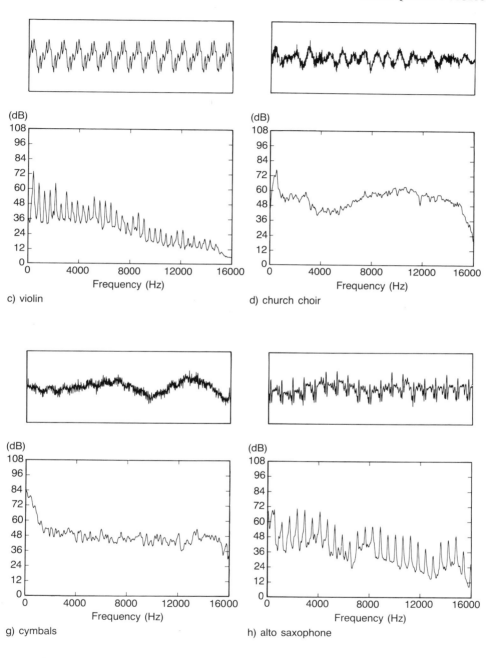

c) violin

d) church choir

g) cymbals

h) alto saxophone

Fig 1   continued (see Page   for detailed explanation).

Table 1   Typical linear prediction gains (Gp) for music signals (Fig 1).

		Gp (dB)
a)	Banjo	25
b)	Tin whistle	27
c)	Violin	18
d)	Choir	17
e)	Classical guitar	19
f)	Trombone	31
g)	Cymbals	6
h)	Alto saxophone	10

quantizing split-band coder, the greatest gain likely to be achieved over PCM is therefore in the region of that shown for the 4096 transform block size. For example, the peak transform gain over PCM for a trombone signal approaches 45 dB. For a 4-bit per sample coding allocation, the effective short-term coding SNR may be approximated to $24 + 45$ dB or 69 dB.

From these results it is clear that substantial short-term redundancies exit. However in practice, even with adaptive transform coding techniques, the full potential of these are difficult to grasp.

3. Perceptual issues of music coding

The foremost requirement of hi-fi music coding is the maintenance of a high coding transparency. This implies that the quality, the bandwidth and distortion/noise levels, of the coded audio should not be subjectively different from that of the original analogue signal. The minimum coding bandwidth to satisfy this criterion has been shown [12] to be approximately 15 kHz. By relying on the inherent redundancy of music for the maintenance of signal quality, it would, at first, appear that this process might not always prove satisfactory, especially for non-redundant signals. While this is true to some extent, practically, the problem is substantially offset by the intervention of a number of perceptual phenomena. For example, a noisy signal exhibits little redundancy and cannot therefore provide any coding gain. The theory of auditory masking, however, indicates that coding noise becomes increasingly inaudible (or masked) as the harmonic content of the signal rises. This suggests that noise-like signals are perceptually more tolerant to coding error than, say, a resonant monophonic signal. The latter signal, however, is inherently more redundant, which will in effect result in a lower noise floor. The tendency for sound spectrum to resemble noise at higher frequencies may also allow for an increase in the acceptable distortion levels in these regions, Figs 1(a), (b), and (f). Rapidly changing signals are another example of non-redundant sounds, but these too are perceptually tolerant, due to, among other things, the existence of temporal masking.

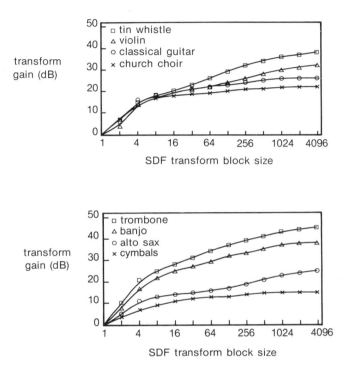

Fig 2   Symmetrical discrete Fourier transform gain versus block-size.

With the knowledge of these masking properties a re-examination of the signal characteristics reveals a class of perceptually redundant features. Additional information on such features may be obtained from existing literature [13,14,15,16].

4. Sub-band ADPCM music coding

A major limiting factor of low bit rate PCM for music coding, is the occurrence of audible noise or distortion modulation in the presence of monophonic signals. With these schemes even the processes of digital companding and fixed spectral emphasis cannot adequately suppress this phenomena for word lengths below 11 or 12 bits [6,8]. While split-band coding schemes potentially face the same problem, the exploitation of certain redundant features of music signals, however, allows sub-band ADPCM to operate successfully with very much smaller word lengths. Before introducing the technical details of the new sub-band coders, it is appropriate at this stage therefore to discuss the various mechanisms by which the removal and exploitation of these redundancies is achieved. In the following sections the operation of the new coding schemes are related to the characteristics of music, and, where possible, also to the deficiencies of digital companding. This will provide an indication as to the reasons for the excellent performance of the new schemes, which code music at 4 bits per sample, as opposed to 12 or more bits per sample, with essentially no loss in quality.

4.1   Sub-band coding

Split-band techniques, such as sub-band coding, are used primarily to exploit the short and long-term spectral redundancies within the music spectrum. The mechanism of sub-band coding is to split the signal into a number of independent bands and to vary the accuracy of the quantization in each band according to the input signal energy. The effect of this process is to allow high energy regions of the music spectrum to be coded more accurately leading to a lowering of the coding noise floor on that achieved in PCM. This improvement is commonly referred to as the sub-band gain.

It will be appreciated that even with the most basic 2-band scheme, significant sub-band gains will be achieved as a result of the long-term spectral tilt of music. Nevertheless, by increasing the number of sub-bands, the coder's ability to resolve the finer components of the signal spectrum, and hence to exploit the potential sub-band gain, is further improved. This fact is clearly demonstrated in the transform gain variations shown in Fig 2. Practical considerations such as implementation complexity, inter-band leakage, sub-band delay and an adequate energy classification procedure, however, tend to offset the immediate advantage of this approach.

An important subjective by-product of sub-band coding is the reduction in the perceived noise modulation over PCM. Since the music signal is split into several frequency bands prior to quantization, modulated quantization noise developed at each quantizer is constrained to that band and cannot interfere with signals in any other band. As a result, noise masking by the modulating spectral component is much more effective than in the broadband case.

4.2   Backward adaptive quantization

Incorporated into each sub-band, backward adaptive quantization provides a near optimal range match over a much wider dynamic range than is possible with instantaneous or block companding, and without the need to transmit gain settings as side information. The backward range matching is particularly effective for adaptive quantizers with large numbers of levels. As a result of the fixed signal-to-noise operation of these quantizers, sub-band background noise under idle conditions is non-existent. Moreover bandwidth limiting effects from their sluggish adaption characteristics are considerably reduced by the sub-band approach, which allows for parameter optimisation based on the characteristics of individual band signals.

By maintaining a constant signal-to-noise ratio (SNR), adaptive quantization seeks to exploit the masking properties of the human auditory system. As already mentioned, this process is very much enhanced with its incorporation into a sub-band coding structure.

4.3   Linear prediction

An alternative approach to the exploitation of the spectral redundancy in the frequency domain is the application of linear prediction prior to quantization. The appropriateness of linear prediction for the coding of speech has in the past been well documented. In the work reported here, it has been shown that substantial prediction gains exist for the vast majority of music sounds (Table 1). A significant advantage of linear prediction is that its efficiency rises dramatically with an increase in the signal periodicity or spectral purity, i.e. the ability to directly attentuate, prior to quantization, those signals which normally promote audible noise modulation. The combination of linear prediction and sub-band coding thus avoids the need to resolve the spectrum in order to code the resonant components preferentially. In addition, by operating with 2 or 4 sub-bands, the stationary characteristics of the sub-band signals are such that backward adaptive prediction has been found to provide an almost optimal performance. This is particularly true for sinusoidal-type signals whose predictability is largely unaffected by sub-band decimation.

Therefore, the overall effect of linear prediction is to attenuate predictable signals, of which the most subjectively critical are characterized by highly resonant spectra. In the presence of noise-like signals the prediction process is, however, incapable of providing any coding gain, but the inherent noise masking which accompanies these signals lessens the significance of this.

4.4   128 kbit/s sub-band ADPCM music coding

From the outset, it is the aim of low bit rate music coding to exploit as many of the redundant features of music as is conveniently possible. Two 128 kbit/s coding schemes are presented here which, by combining the processes of sub-band coding and ADPCM, are capable of coding high quality music signals to just 4 bits per sample. This combination is referred to as sub-band ADPCM music coding. It is thought that this system represents a very computationally efficient solution to the problem of music compression. The diversity of redundancy removal processes involved not only reduces its sensitivity to uncharacteristic signals but also collectively takes advantage of the best properties of each.

Two 128 kbit/s sub-band ADPCM music coding schemes have been developed. This was done in order to establish the range of performances possible for a low to medium complexity 4-bit sub-band system. The first consists of a 2-band 24 tap quadrature mirror filter (QMF) tree structure, shown in Fig 3, which employs a 2 pole, 6 zero gradient adaptive predictor and backward adaptive Laplacian quantizer in each band [5], as illustrated in Fig 4. This system is similar to the CCITT wideband coding recommendation [11], apart from the higher sampling rate which is demanded by the high quality music signals. In addition, the predictor coefficients are modified to accommodate the more sinusoidal-type signals encountered in music [4]. The bit allocation however is fixed with 5 bits in the lower band and 3 bits in the upper. This fixed allocation has proven to be the most appropriate for music signals, both in terms of its redundancy exploitation and subjective performances. This coder represents a fairly simple implementation, requiring no side information and exhibiting a coding delay of only 22 samples of 0.7 mS.

The second coder, illustrated in Fig 5, uses a 4-band 64 tap QMF tree structure as shown in Fig 6, where each band incorporates an 8 pole backward block adaptive (BBA) predictor (updated using the autocorrelation method) and a backward adaptive Laplacian quantizer. The BBA predictors have been shown to out-perform the CCITT gradient adaptive predictors used in the 2-band coder for typical music sounds [4]. In this coder however, the bit allocation is allowed to adapt in a backward mode, according to the short-term energy distribution of the predicition error signal across the four bands. The liberal use of backward adaption in this coder also avoids the need to transmit side information. However the coding delay is now 192 samples, and 6.1 ms and the overall complexity approximately four times that of the 2-band scheme.

While the 2-band scheme is tailored to some degree for the characteristics of music, a more efficient utilisation of the known redundancies may be expected with the latter 4-band scheme. This is because the process of redundancy removal hinges on both the coder's ability to resolve the signal spectrum and the accuracy to which bits can be allocated according to the error energy distribution. The resolving power, in the case of a QMF based coder, is ultimately limited by the number of sub-bands, and, to a lesser degree, by the extent of leakage between the sub-bands.

5. Subjective evaluation of 4-bit music coding

In order to establish the musical performance of the new sub-band ADPCM music coders, testing of each coder using critical music signals has been undertaken. It is at this stage only that the non-quantitative aspects of their redundancy exploitation, such as noise making, can be reliably evaluated.

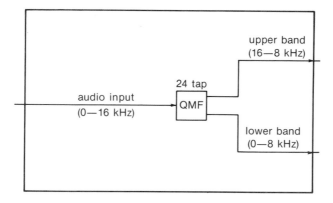

function table

Q   backward adaptive quantizer
1/Q   inverse backward adaptive quantizer
$P_{(PZ)}$ pole-zero gradient adaptive predictor
Δ quantizer step-size adaptor
QMF   quadrature mirror filter

Fig 3   2-band 24 tap QMF tree structure.

5.1   Audio equipment

Vitally important to the successful evaluation of any high quality coding scheme is the maintenance of signal fidelity throughout the audio acquisition, coding and playback processes. This is necessary if delicate coding imperfections are to be reliably revealed and their effects assessed. All of the source material used in the subjective assessments was obtained from either a CD player or a Sony PCM-F1 digital recorder. Digitization of the music signals was achieved using a purpose-built data acquisition unit, employing 16-bit stereo A to D and D to A converters. Anti-aliasing and reconstruction filtering was performed with 9th order, 15 kHz roll-off active filters. To evaluate the success of each coding arrangement, coded music was compared to the original (band-limited to 15 kHz) by listening to both passages through high quality loudspeakers. Tests were conducted using four 100 W reference mono power amplifiers, driving a pair of active bi-amped monitor quality loudspeakers. These were placed in a room considered to be representative of a good domestic environment.

5.2   Evaluation procedure.

The music passages used for the evaluations were grouped under four headings (see Table 2,) and encompass a broad range of instruments and arrangements. The listening panel consisted of 10 males aged between 23 and 35, the majority of whom are involved in speech related research. Each test involved a comparison of two music passages, A and B, each of 18 seconds duration, one representing the original (A) and the other the original coded at four bits per sample (B). The two passages were played back in the sequence A B A B and listeners were asked to grade the quality of the sound according to a seven point comparison scale, Table 3. The $+/-1$ scores were included to allow listeners to register a perceived difference rather than a preference, indicating therefore which passage they thought might be the original. On the other hand listeners were advised to score higher to indicate a preference.

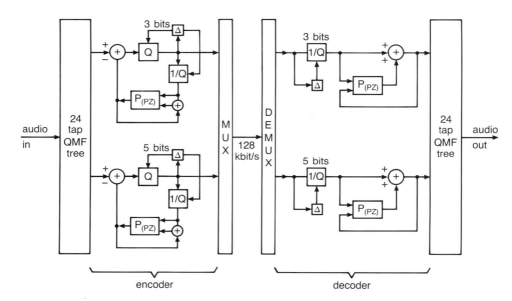

function table

Q	backward adaptive quantizer
1/Q	inverse backward adaptive quantizer
$P_{(PZ)}$	pole-zero gradient adaptive predictor
Δ	quantiser step-size adaptor
QMF	quadrature mirror filter

Fig 4   2-band sub-band ADPCM music coder (128 kbit/s).

5.3   Evaluation results

The averaged scores obtained from the listening panel for the coder performances, as delivered by the loud-speakers and headphones, are displayed to the right of each title in Table 2. An average coding SNR is also shown for each passage.

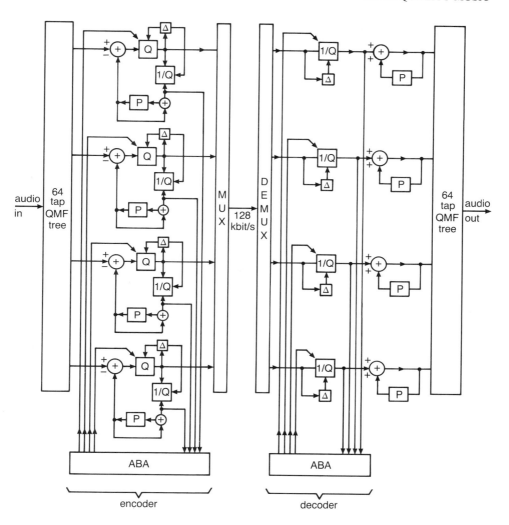

function table

Q   backward adaptive quantizer
1/Q   inverse backward adaptive quantizer
Δ   quantizer step-size adaptor
P   all-pole backward adaptive predictor
ABA   adaptive bit allocation

Fig 5   4-band sub-band ADPCM music coder (128 kbit/s).

Table 2   Averaged scores and SNRs for both coding schemes (A = original).

		2 Band Coder			4 Band Coder		
		SNR (dB)	speaker average score	phones average score	SNR (dB)	speaker average score	phones average score
Popular							
1.Peter Gabriel 'So'	(Bass, Guitar)	21.8	+ 0.6	+ 0.3	23.1	0.0	0.0
2.Thomas Dolby 'Flat Earth'	(Elect' percussion)	23.4	+ 0.4	+ 0.1	25.2	− 0.1	0.0
3.Phil Collins 'Face Value'	(Alto Sax, piano)	26.6	+ 0.5	+ 0.3	32.7	0.0	0.0
4.Joan Armatrading 'Track Record'	(Percussion, cymbals)	24.7	0.0	− 0.1	27.0	0.0	0.0
Miscellaneous							
5.CD Test Demo, Diapason	(Indian Harp)	28.4	+ 0.7	+ 0.2	30.9	+ 0.1	+ 0.1
6.CD Test Demo, Diapason	(Percussion-Drum)	37.6	+ 0.5	+ 0.3	43.8	0.0	0.0
7.CD Test Demo, Diapason	(Provence music)	27.7	+ 0.3	0.0	31.0	0.0	0.0
8.Live PCM-F1 recording	(Tin Whistle)	35.4	+ 1.4	+ 0.9	49.2	+ 0.3	+ 0.1
Classical							
9.Denon Audio Technical CD	(Orchestra)	29.3	− 0.1	+ 0.1	34.5	0.0	0.0
10.Denon Audio Technical CD	(Piano)	37.0	0.0	+ 0.1	45.1	0.0	0.0
11.Denon Audio Technical CD	(Concerto)	25.6	+ 0.4	0.0	29.8	0.0	0.0
12.CD Test Demo, Diapason	(Organ & Orchestra)	29.5	− 0.2	− 0.1	36.1	+ 0.1	0.0
Folk and Jazz							
13.CD Test Demo, Diapason	(Big Band)	24.8	+ 0.2	0.0	28.2	− 0.1	0.0
14.CD Test Demo, Diapason	(Banjo)	27.0	+ 0.5	+ 0.1	32.2	+ 0.1	0.0
15.Denon Audio Technical CD	(Jazz, piano, sax)	27.8	− 0.1	0.0	31.6	0.0	0.0
16.Live PCM-F1 recording	(Trombone)	40.2	+ 0.2	+ 0.1	53.9	0.0	0.0

Table 3   ABAB 7 point score table.

+ 3	A better than B
+ 2	A slightly better than B
+ 1	A virtually identical to B
0	A same as B
− 1	B virtually identical to A
− 2	B slightly better than A
− 3	B better than A

Testing began with the evaluation of the 2-band sub-band coded music, played through the loudspeakers. This gave the listening panel a certain degree of training in the techniques of evaluation, since these tests were to provide the greatest perceptual differences. It was generally found that for both coders, listeners could perceive little, if any, difference over the vast majority of material. For example, over 50% of the 160 scores recorded for the 2-band loudspeaker test (subjectively the worst) were in fact zero. For the 4-band loudspeaker test the zero count rose to just under 93%. Such were the difficulties experienced in distinguishing between passages, that when listeners did perceive a difference, quite a number of scores actually indicated a preference for the 4-bit music. This occurred more frequently with the 2-band coder than for the 4-band coder. In fact in the latter it was found that listeners were much less willing to score at all. Surprisingly the headphone delivery was consistently less revealing than that given by the loudspeakers — despite the fact that headphones provide much better isolation and are unaffected by environmental acoustics. The result perhaps re-emphasises the fact that the level at which distortion and noise is perceived, is not only influenced by the quality of the source material, but also by the faithfulness of the playback equipment.

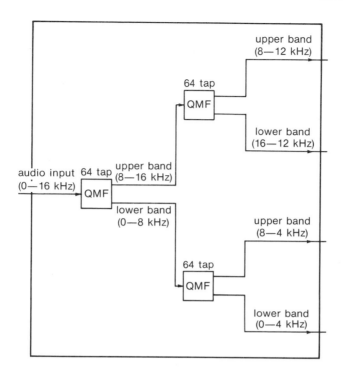

function table

Q   backward adaptive quantizer
1/Q   inverse backward adaptive quantizer
Δ   quantizer step-size adaptor
P   all-pole backward adaptive predictor
ABA   adaptive bit allocation

Fig 6   4-band 64 tap QMF tree structure.

6. Discussion

Of all the passages evaluated, only the 2-band coded tin whistle (Table 2, track 8) could be consistently identified by the listening panel as being inferior to the original (i.e. A was better than B). The problem while slight, was in the form of audible noise modulation at the extreme excursions of the passage. The 4-band coding did however remove this problem entirely. Since this was the only form of recognisable distortion noted during the course of the tests, it is appropriate at this point to examine the phenomena objectively; a spectral analysis of the coding performance, using the tin

115

whistle, is shown in Figs 7(a), (b) and (c). These graphs compare the input signal spectra and the resulting coding error spectra for not only the 4-band and 2-band coders, but also for a typical full-band coding scheme.

From Fig 7(b), the presence of error components whose amplitudes exceed that of the input signal suggests that audible noise modulation is likely to occur predominantly in the 6 to 10 kHz region. Informal re-trials of the 2-band coder using the same signal have confirmed this finding. The dramatic lowering of the error levels on moving to the 4-band scheme (Fig 7(c)) explains the equally impressive improvement of the subjective scoring of this signal (Table 2). Fig 7(c) also demonstrates the near-optimal bit allocation of the coder for this particular segment. In contrast to the two sub-band manipulated spectra, Fig 7(a) illustrates the destructive nature of wideband modulated noise. This unmasking phenomena is perceived as a high level of background hiss — analogous to a conventional tape recorder.

While audible noise modulation was not perceived in any of the trombone signal tests, the inherently low bandwidth of this signal is typical of those which promote audible noise modulation in low bit rate digital companding schemes. It is of interest therefore to briefly analyse the 2-band coding performance using this signal. A spectral plot of the coding error is shown in Fig 8. From this it would seem that the subdued resonant structure of this signal does not produce the same noise excursions in the lower band, as is witnessed for the tin whistle. As a result, noise components are not found to exceed the signal in any region, reducing the likelihood of audible noise. This would explain the excellent subjective scores obtained for the trombone signal irrespective of the number of coding bands.

As with the tin whistle, the notable lack of high frequency noise in Figs 7(c) and 8, demonstrates the importance of the new sub-band coding method in containing the effects of noise modulation. The results obtained would most certainly have been impossible to achieve using existing digital companding techniques, at this bit rate or higher.

Since both the tin whistle and trombone passages used for the subjective tests were monophonic in their entirety and contained no silence, the coding SNR figures shown in Table 2 for each sound may be considered for comparison with the SDFT gains shown in Fig 2. On doing so, the 4-band coding performance, in terms of redundancy removal, for these signals is approximately equal to the theoretical SDFT gain for a 128 sample block. These transform gains assume a perfect coefficient energy distribution classification for each block transmitted to the receiver (rarely achieved in practice). Under these circumstances it is interesting to note that for both signals, the combined sub-band and prediction gains achieved amount to just 10 dB below that of the 4096 block SDFT.

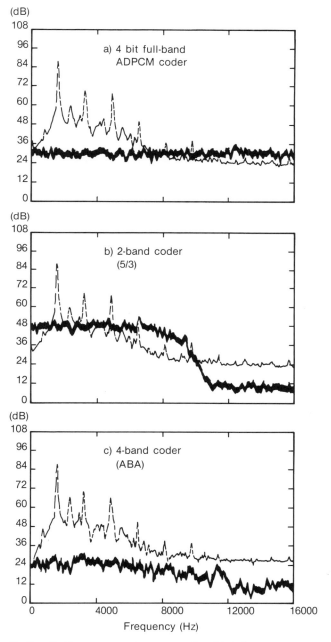

Fig 7   Coding error spectrum versus tin whistle input spectrum.

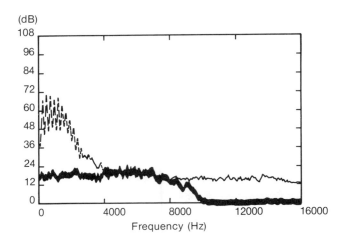

Fig 8   Trombone spectrum versus 2-band coded noise spectrum (fixed bit allocation 5/3).

To summarise then, the following can be drawn. Firstly, the results show that very little difference could be detected between the coded music and the original. Secondly, both a substantial objective and subjective gain may be achieved by moving from a 2-band fixed bit allocation scheme to a fully adaptive 4-band coder. Finally, the most revealing sounds were found to be resonant monophonic, Table 2 track 8, as expected. However noise modulation was completely masked by the 4-band coder for this and all other program material used in the tests.

7. Conclusion

The results obtained clearly demonstrate the very high coding efficiency of sub-band ADPCM in comparison with digital companding or adaptive delta modulation schemes when coding music signals. In particular, the new 4-band coding arrangement shows that high quality digital audio can be represented by split band ADPCM words approaching one quarter that of linear PCM, and still remain essentially indistinguishable. It is believed that these findings are very significant and represent a major advance in digital audio techology, having immediate implications for ISDN, broadcasting and DBS (digital broadcast by satellite) hi-fi distribution. Furthermore, ADPCM is known to offer bit error immunity down to 1 in 1000 without any form of protection or concealment — 4 or 5 orders of magnitude better than most PCM based systems. With future professional digital audio standards looking beyond 16 bits per sample as a means of improving dynamic capability, it is thought that the continuing viability of PCM as a reliable and economic means of storing or transmitting high quality digital audio should be seriously questioned.

Acknowledgements

The authors gratefully acknowledge the continuing financial assistance for this research, from the Department of Education for Northern Ireland.

References

1   Johnston J D, Crochiere R E: 'An all-digital commentary grade subband coder', J Audio Eng Soc 25(11) , (November 1979).

2   Cox R V et al: 'Testing of wideband digital coders', IEEE Proc ICASSP (1984).

3   Combescure P et al: 'ADPCM algorithms applied to wideband speech encoding (64 kbit/s 0—7 kHz)', IEEE Proc ICASSP (1982).

4   Smyth S M F, McCanny J V, Challener P: 'An independent evaluation of the performance of the CCITT G.722 Wideband Coding Recommendation using Music Signals', IEEE Proc ICASSP, New York (April 1988).

5   Smyth S M F, McCanny J V: 'High quality music coding at 4 bits', submitted to IEE Electronic Letters (January 1988).

6   Cain C R et al: 'NICAM3: near instantaneous companding digital transmission for high-quality sound programmes', REE, 50(10) (October 1980).

7   Grundy K T et al: 'Recent developments in digital audio techniques', Audio Eng Soc Preprint no. 1956(b5) (March 1983).

8   Soumagne J et al: 'A comparative study of the proposed high-quality coding schemes for digital music', IEEE Proc ICASSP (1986).

9   Rhode and Schwarz: 'Audio coder DCA for digital sound broadcasting', III(1986).

10 Smyth S M F, McCanny J V: '4-bit hi-fi: high quality music coding for ISDN and broadcasting applications', IEEE Proc ICASSP, New York (April 1988).

11 CCITT Study Group XVIII Report R 26(C), Recommendation G.72X (August 1986).

12 Muraoka T, et al: 'Examination of the audio-bandwidth requirement for optimum sound', J Audio Eng Soc, 29 ,2—9 (February 1981).

13 Zelinski R, Noll P: 'Adaptive transform coding of speech signals', IEEE Trans ASSP, 25 , No 4 (August 1977).

14 McNally G W: 'Digital audio in broadcasting', IEEE ASSP Magazine (October 1985).

15 Bloom P J: 'High-quality digital audio in the entertainment industry', IEEE ASSP Magazine (October 1985).

16 Wacker G: 'Music transmission using CVSD digital coders', Inter Elect and Elect Conf (October 1981).

NOISE REDUCTION USING FREQUENCY-DOMAIN NON-LINEAR PROCESSING FOR THE ENHANCEMENT OF SPEECH

E Munday

ABSTRACT

Broadband additive noise is a common source of corruption in speech signals and often limits the effective operation of speech-signal processors. This paper presents a frequency-domain noise reduction technique which has low complexity and, since it uses only a single input, is well suited to a wide range of applications in speech processing systems, either as a pre or post-processor. Computer simulation of this noise-suppressor has been used to test its effectiveness on white-noise corrupted speech. The indications from informal listening tests are that significant noise reduction is achievable whilst speech quality is maintained substantially unaffected. This fundamental noise-suppression method is extended to give three alternative noise suppressors which are, to varying degrees, better matched to the spectral characteristics of speech.

1. Introduction

The spoken word is the natural and, consequently, by far the most common form of human communications. Unlike all other electronic means of communication, speech systems offer the untrained user the simplest and most natural access. It seems highly improbable that, in the forseeable future, even the impact of sophisticated computer technology will change peoples' preference for speech as the medium of human-to-human communications, whether direct or for message storage.

Enhancing speech signals is an important growth area within digital signal processing (DSP). This trend is likely to continue since major performance improvements to DSP microprocessors are being made which encourage the use, and progressive development, of sophisticated signal processing algorithms for real-time applications. The enhancements to speech signals facilitated by such algorithms may improve speech perception by improving speech quality, increasing the intelligibility and/or reducing listener fatigue. Noise reduction is one important area of speech enhancement which is primarily intended to achieve the latter two of these goals. A wide range of applications exist for good noise reduction techniques which avoid introducing unacceptable levels of distortion into the speech signal. Implementation of this type of algorithm may be in the form of either a stand-alone pre- or post-processing device, or as an integrated part of a larger system. Examples of application areas are speech coding and the analysis or recognition of speech signals.

1.1   Research review

Many different approaches have been used to cancel or reduce additive noise in speech signals. Noise-cancelling microphones are sometimes very effective in acoustic environments, but tend to be of little use in combating noise above 1 kHz. In contrast, processing the electrical noise corrupted signal offers considerable potential for broadband reduction of noise and is the most common approach to general problems of noise reduction. Much work has been done by other researchers into noise reduction (NR) techniques based on time-domain (t-domain) and frequency-domain signal processing. Systems with one, two or more input signals have been considered. Adaptive t-domain filtering based on FIR transversal or lattice digital filters, using least-mean-square adaptation algorithms, have been used to very good effect in cancelling periodic additive noise [1,2]. This approach most often addresses the two-input noise cancellation (NC) case.

Broadband additive noise presents a different challenge to the NR system. Here, the typically random nature of the noise reduces the potential for accurately predicting the magnitude and phase of the noise components to be subtracted from the corrupted speech signal, to effect NR. Frequency-domain (f-domain) processing is well suited to this type of noise environment and so has attracted quite a lot of attention from researchers, particularly for military applications, in which very low signal-to-noise ratios are commonplace. Short-time Fourier analysis (STFA), whether viewed as t-domain processing, or as an alternative implementation of finite period Fourier transformation, provides the benefit of spectral feature extraction. An interesting short-time basis representation of the voiced parts of speech used by some researchers, is a linear combination of narrow-band signals with harmonically related instantaneous frequencies [3].

Single input NR systems are often better suited to broadband noise applications than are dual input systems. Many of the more interesting single input f-domain NR techniques depend on some form of estimation of the noise spectrum and so often rely on accurate detection of silence periods in speech. A popular approach in stripping off the noise is direct subtraction of the estimated noise spectral components from the corrupted speech signal. One such method which operates on power spectra, sets to zero any negative components produced at the subtraction stage. For input signal-to-noise ratios (SNR) of less than 5 dB the reconstructed t-domain signal is said by the authors to suffer from 'an annoying musical noise' [4]. The same researchers report elimination of this annoyance by including two additional features — subtraction of an overestimate of the noise power spectrum and setting a minimum-level noise spectral floor. Having good noise-spectral estimation is an important requirement of this method.

Investigations of several different f-domain processing techniques aimed at enhancing the intelligibility of speech distorted by wide-band noise are described by Curtis and Neiderjohn [5]. The techniques examined are categorised by the authors as:

- minimum mean square filtering,
- spectrum squaring,
- pitch frequency analysis,
- spectral subtraction.

Although the performance of some of these single input techniques tested with SNR values between − 6 to 6 dB were poor, the authors conclude that 'all the successful techniques investigated are similar in that they are an attempt to emphasise spectral components as a function of the amount by which they exceed the noise'.

In another study, suppression of stationary noise from speech was effected by subtracting the 'noise bias' calculated during non-speech activity [6]. Four augmenting procedures were then tested with the aim of reducing the residual noise left after subtraction. Test results were gained using speech recorded in a helicopter, in what are taken to be severe noise conditions. The author indicates that overall significant improvements in intelligibility were achieved when the best combination of processing techniques were used as a single input pre-processor to an LPC speech analysis-synthesis vocoder. The system philosophy adopted has a number of disadvantages when considered for application to less severe noise conditions. High complexity results because of the need for dependable selection of silence periods and for accurate noise spectrum estimation during these periods. Further practical complications occur because the noise is assumed to be stationary during periods of speech and because a 300 ms speech-free gap is assumed to exist if the noise becomes non-stationary.

In a paper on speech enhancement using a soft-decision noise-suppression filter McAulay and Malpass [7] describe how use of a speech detector and a maximum likelihood estimator of the speech spectrum magnitude result in a class of suppression curves which permit a trade-off of noise against speech distortion. It is reported that the additive noise can be made imperceptible by proper choice of a parameter known as the suppression factor.

1.2   NR by spectral attenuation

The new noise suppression techniques described in this paper are single-input f-domain signal processing methods aimed at enhancing speech by providing reduced listener fatigue and increased intelligibility. The fundamental technique, upon which the three latter methods are based, is conceptually very simple. The essence of this approach is to apply a non-linear transfer characteristic (TC) to each component of the short-time spectrum, to reduce the contribution of those likely to be noise dominated, and then reconstruct the t-domain signal. Since processing is performed in the f-domain this NR scheme has the property of feature extraction; that is the periodic pitch components prevalent in speech are emphasised relative to random broad-band noise. Additional feature extraction is utilised in the extended NR methods, the most sophisticated one being capable of adapting to the time-varying formant structure of the speech signal. There is evidence that the human ear is less sensitive to distortion introduced in the short-time spectrum of a speech signal than to distortion in the t-domain signal [8]. Consequently, the disturbance effect of using a non-linear TC in the NR system outlined above, is less severe than might initially be expected.

Many current f-domain NR schemes are intended for extremely harsh noise environments. The f-domain perspective described here is different to previous approaches in several fundamental aspects:

- the intended operational range is for SNRs of better than 6 dB;
- the processing is not spectral subtraction, but magnitude-dependent spectral attenuation;
- no speech detector nor noise estimator is required in the simplest form of this NR device;
- in its basic form this NR device has low complexity.

In section 2 of this paper an overview is given of the f-domain signal processing concepts relevant to this NR work. The basic single transfer-characteristic NR is described in section 3, and the assessment of its performance is presented in the fourth section. Three extensions to the basic noise suppression technique are discussed in section 5, with concluding comments being given in the final section.

2. Frequency-domain signal processing

For some applications, processing signals in the frequency-domain (f-domain) is an attractive alternative to time-domain (t-domain) processing, offering potential advantages such as block processing, increased operational speed and signal feature extraction. Consequently, an extensive body of knowledge has been formed on f-domain signal processing.

The fundamental principles relevant to the f-domain noise suppressor (NS) described in section 3 are presented in this section. The concept of non-linear attenuation of spectral components is also introduced and the resulting degree of distortion typically incurred in processing speech signals is illustrated by example.

2.1   Signal enhancement

Spectral feature extraction from a noise corrupted signal is a well proven method of enhancing a wanted signal relative to background noise. This is particularly effective for periodic signals in random (uncorrelated) broad-band noise. Short-time Fourier spectra (STFS) are commonly provided by one of the forms of discrete approximations to the Fourier transform, such as the fast Fourier transform (FFT) for either complex or real signals, or the discrete cosine transform (DCT) for real signals. These are block processing algorithms which can provide a good approximation to the true Fourier transform if the length of the transform block is sufficiently long. This segmentation of the t-domain signal is referred to as truncation or rectangular windowing.

As an example of the degree of enhancement achievable using short-time Fourier transformation (STFT), consider a case where a wanted sinusoidal signal is severely degraded by additive white noise. Merely performing an FFT on the composite t-domain signal enhances the periodic sinusoid relative to the uncorrelated random noise. Theory predicts that the degree of this enhancement (gain), for rectangular windowing, is:

$$\text{Gain} = 10 \, \text{Log}_{10} \, N \, \text{(dB)}$$

where N is the number of samples in the FFT. The t-domain and spectral plots of Fig 1 illustrate such a case for which the sinusoid frequency is 500 Hz, a very low SNR of 0 dB is used and the window block length is 1024 samples. It is evident from the f-domain plot that the single spectral line of the sinusoid has been extracted from the noise; a difference of 20 dB exists between the signal and the highest peak 'white' noise magnitude in this STFS. This feature extraction property may be put to effective use in NC or NS devices.

In a second simple example of this property, the t-domain and f-domain plots of which are given in Fig 2, the periodic signal is now a bi-polar square wave with a fundamental frequency of 250 Hz; again uncorrelated noise is added. The resulting SNR is 10 dB. Although severe distortion of the time signal has resulted, the well known odd harmonic structure of this square wave is clearly visible. For either this example or the previous one, it is evident that use of a suitably positioned threshold on the spectral magnitudes will cancel the additive noise. This thresholding is equivalent to adopting a non-linear input-output transfer characteristic (TC) which passes all spectral components above the designated value with constant gain and infinitely attenuates those below the value. This non-linear TC performs a hard-decision operation, which is exactly what is needed for the examples shown, but a less harsh TC is preferred in cases where not all the wanted signal spectral components are extracted from the noise. Practical examples of noise corrupted speech signals almost exclusively fall into this category and are better treated using noise-reducing 'soft- decision' TCs.

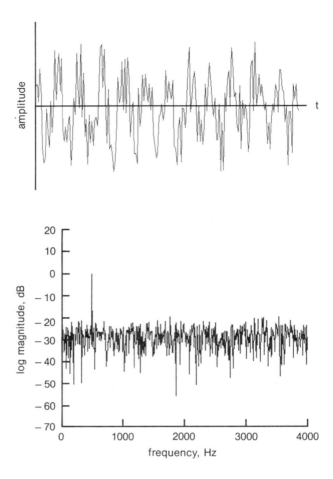

Fig 1   Sinusoid corrupted by additive white noise.

2.2   *Feature extraction accuracy*

To extract the desired f-domain features of a signal using a STFT, such as an FFT, may involve a compromise between spectral resolution and dynamic range of spectral components. Windowing the t-domain signal with a rectangular function can result in an unacceptably high degree of spectral distortion even for moderately large window lengths. This problem arises because the transformed window shape is a sinc function, which has high sidelobes, and its convolution with the Fourier transform of the signal generates relatively large erroneous spectral lines around the true components. As a result the dynamic range of true components existing near to larger neighbours may be severely limited. This smearing effect is sometimes called 'frequency leakage'. However, rectangular windowing offers the benefit of good spectral resolution — that is closely spaced signal spectral components can be resolved.

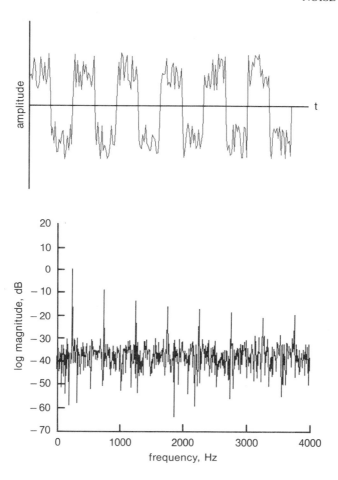

Fig 2   Square wave corrupted by additive white noise.

Many alternative windowing functions have been devised. They offer different compromise solutions to the resolution/frequency-leakage problem. The windowing function used in the NR methods described later in this paper is the Hanning window. Although its resolution performance is inferior to that of the rectanglar function it offers far lower frequency leakage. A spectral comparison of the performances of these two windows is provided in Fig 3 (see Page   ). These are rectangular and Hanning windowed 1024 point FFT plots of a noise-free signal, consisting of two equal-amplitude, closely spaced sinusoids with frequencies of 1000 Hz and 1015 Hz. High frequency leakage occurs for the rectangular window. At no frequency are the erroneous spectral lines more than **75 dB** below the level of the two spectral lines of the sinusoids, and at a spot frequency of 1250 Hz the level of the frequency 'leaked' by the rectangular window is 20 dB higher than the level for the Hanning window.

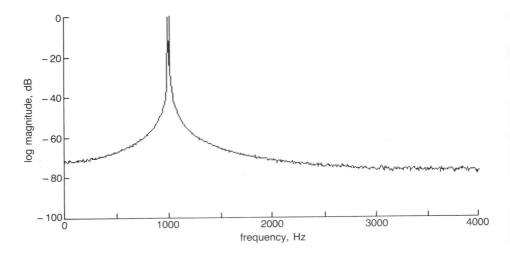

Fig 3a   Performance of 1024 point rectangular windowing.

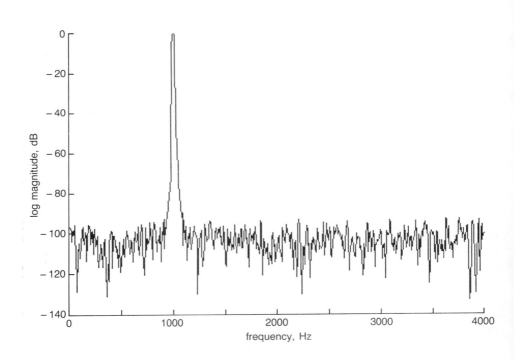

Fig 3b   Performance of 1024 point Hanning windowing.

In contrast the Hanning window transform is incapable of resolving the two tones, which are clearly separated by use of the rectangular window.

The penalty paid in using the Hanning window for its superior frequency-leakage performance, is the need to overlap-sample the t-domain blocks before they are transformed. An illustration of the 50 per cent overlap Hanning windowed case is given in Fig 4. Here the raised cosine form of this time-windowing is overlapped by half a frame so as to exactly compensate for the reduced contribution from time samples away from the centre of the window. This 'equalization' operation is completed when, after inverse transformation, the processed t-domain blocks are 50 per cent overlap added in a coherent sample-pair form. One consequence is an increase in required processing since each t-domain sample is used twice.

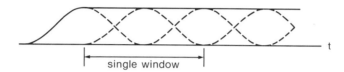

Fig 4   Constant envelope given by 50% overlapped Hanning windowing.

2.3   Non-linear spectral processing

The schematic diagram given in Fig 5 shows the sequence of operations of one form of NR system based on non-linear TC processing of the signal spectral components. If each spectral component were processed using a purely linear TC and 50 per cent overlapped Hanning windowing then, for the reason explained in the previous section, the reconstructed output signal would be undistorted (note the constant envelope shown in Fig 4). To illustrate this point the original speech input and linear TC processed output of a short segment of speech signal are shown superimposed in Fig 6a. Although this is a zoomed plot, which looks at a very low level speech segment at the onset of voicing, it is clear that no appreciable distortion has been introduced.

In applications where the SNR is not too severe and the wanted signal has some reasonable degree of periodicity, discrimination against the lower magnitude spectral components of random broad-band noise can be effected by adopting a non-linear TC. The shape of this TC is chosen to selectively attenuate these low-level noise components whilst passing the majority of the signal components substantially unchanged. Logically, the TC will have two regions; firstly a linear region, and secondly a non-linear region, which, being positioned below the linear part, introduces a progressive increase in attenuation of the input component for decreasing magnitude (see Fig 8 in section 3). This is then a NR technique based on magnitude-dependent attenuation of the signal plus noise spectral components.

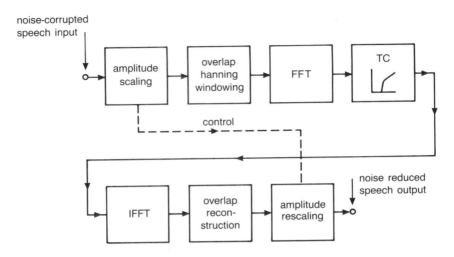

Fig 5   Fundamental noise reduction system.

For speech applications, some harmonic distortion of the signal will result due to low-level spectral components falling into the non-linear region. To reduce this effect the interface between the linear and non-linear regions may be made continuous — that is a smooth knee transition region will reduce the harshness of distortion to moderately low-level speech components.

When a non-linear TC is used on 50 per cent overlap, Hanning windowed noise-free signals, the correctly reconstructed t-domain signal will, in contrast to the equivalent linear TC case, be distorted. This happens because the balance between the t-domain sample pairs in the compensatory overlap reconstruction has been upset. The effect is that the processed signal envelope is modulated by a (typically small) distorting waveform of complex shape; this shape being dependent upon the particular shapes of the windowing function and the non-linear TC, and on the noise-free signal waveform within the t-domain window. In Figs 6b and 6c two examples of this envelope distortion on noise-free speech signals are presented, and compared (by superimposition) with the corresponding output signal segment obtained using linear TC processing. Figure 6b shows a segment of large amplitude, voiced speech. Very little distortion has been introduced by the non-linear TC — this characteristic having been chosen for its good performance with speech. To examine in detail the resulting distortion, Fig 6c presents a zoomed plot of a very low-level segment at the onset of voicing. Here it is clear that small amounts of distortion have been introduced into this low-level speech.

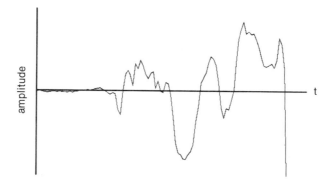

Fig 6a   Comparison of low-band and original linear-TC processed speech signals.

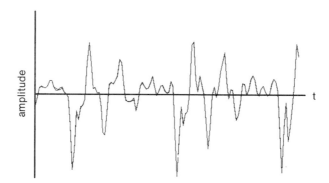

Fig 6b   Comparison of high-level speech signals processed using linear and non-linear TCs.

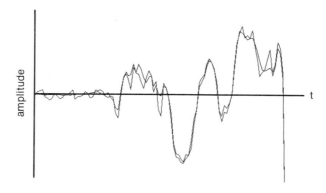

Fig 6c   Comparison of low-level original and linear-TC processed speech signals.

3. A novel speech noise suppressor

The fundamental speech noise reduction (NR) technique is described in this section. Figure 5 showed the components of a system based on this technique. Essentially, the technique is one of suppressing or reducing broadband noise by:

- extracting important features of speech from the noise using an overlap time-windowed, discrete Fourier transformation technique;

- attenuating each spectral component of the transformed noisy speech signal to an extent dependent upon its magnitude using a single non-linear transfer characteristic (TC);

- reconstructing the processed t-domain signal by overlap adding the complementary sample pairs,

- aligning the noisy signal to the TC to effect good NR by either t-domain (or f-domain) signal amplitude scaling or by repositioning the TC to suit the signal conditions.

The rationale behind this NR technique is as follows. If the speech signal is corrupted by broadband, random noise and has a SNR in excess of about 6 dB, then significant noise attenuation may be exacted, with relatively little perceived distortion to the speech signal, given that the major speech spectral components are maintained on the linear part of the TC and the noise spectral components are depressed onto the steeply attenuating non-linear region.

Extraction of speech spectral components from the noise is obviously crucial to the effectiveness of this technique. The forward transform, in performing this enhancement, lifts the spectra of the resonant and periodic parts of speech from the noise. Since the major part of speech exhibits one or both of these facets [9], then good enhancement is achievable. Voiced speech (when the vocal chords are vibrating) consists of a strong, low frequency pitch component and many of its harmonics, and is therefore enhanced particularly well. An example of a noise-free male voiced part of speech and its short-time Fourier spectrum (STFS) is given in Fig 7. This is the centre segment (of duration 0.128 s) of the word 'cell' and is obviously rich in pitch harmonics. Even for this short segment the STFS gives an indication of the formant structure.

Without loss of generality, the transform method adopted throughout the remainder of this paper is the FFT which, in its various forms, is widely available. Hanning windowing of 50 per cent overlapped t-domain blocks has been used exclusively in the computer simulation of the NR system described in this section.

The FFT block or window size chosen for the NR device is an important parameter. The choice is a compromise between several conflicting operational aspects such as: processing gain (enhancement), processing speed and spectral smearing of dissimilar parts of speech. For broadband noise, enhancement of speech is increased with the block size, but processing time is also increased at a greater than proportional rate. It is desirable that the block time span be matched to the duration of distinct components of speech and yet minimise the probability of spanning the voiced/unvoiced transition periods (since smearing of the STFS results). It is also important to provide adequate frequency resolution to permit discrimination between adjacent harmonics of the pitch component, even for the deepest male voice (which may have its fundamental at about 80 Hz). Clearly, there is a range of acceptable FFT block sizes, the particular choice being dictated by the specific constraints of the applications. However, it is unlikely that this window length will fall outside the range of 128 to 1024 time samples for a speech sampling rate of 8 kHz.

The non-linear spectral TC introduced in section 2.3 is an essential feature of the NR system described above. The logarithmic plot of the spectral input-output TC presented in Fig 8, shows the linear and non-linear regions of an example TC which has a smooth or soft knee. This TC is an extreme example which introduces harsh speech distortion even for moderately high SNR conditions. It is interesting to note that spectral thresholding is performed if the non-linear part of the TC is a vertical line below a hard knee and so it is clear that excessive speech signal distortion will result from its use. The opposite upper extreme of the 'non-linear' part of the TC is shown in Fig 8 to be a straight-line downwards extension of the linear part. An acceptable performance compromise, between the degree of NR and the extent of speech distortion introduced, is struck using a TC with a non-linear locus which is at neither of these extremes, having a maximum slope less than the TC of Fig 8.

Analytical methods may be used to determine the shape of good TCs, but such an approach is difficult and time consuming. In this work the required shapes of the TC have been determined heuristically using both male and female speech in the computer simulated NR system. Two examples of moderately successful TCs are given in Fig 9(a) and 9(b). The performances of these and a preferred TC (Fig 10) are discussed in section 4.

Good performance of the NR system is strongly dependent upon accurate alignment of the soft knee at the base level of the speech spectral components of perceptual importance. If this is achieved then the lower level spectral components of the noise will, as required, be depressed onto the steeply attenuating, non-linear slope of the TC. A typical example of these overlapping spectral-magnitude ranges of speech and noise, suitably aligned, is indicated on the TC of Fig 10.

133

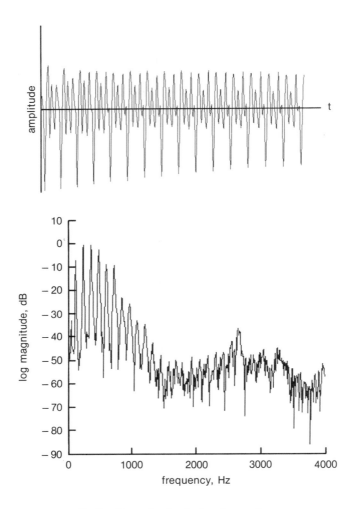

Fig 7   Example of voiced male speech.

In practical situations this alignment operation will need to be performed continuously. There are several ways of positioning these components on a single fixed-scale TC, one being the speech detector and noise estimator method favoured in spectral subtraction NR systems.

A lower complexity alternative solution is to magnitude scale either the t-domain or f-domain input signal to effect a quasi-optimal positioning on the static TC. The scaling factor used in this operation may itself be derived in either the f-domain or the t-domain. In the f-domain the necessary 'instantaneous' average-level measurement may be taken across all spectra, or a subset selected to match important known speech-signal characteristics. Depending on the windowing size, it may prove necessary to perform some inter-block averaging.

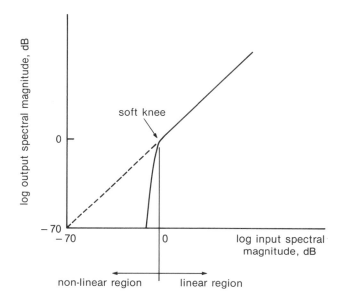

Fig 8   Example of harsh TC.

If the scaling factor is derived in the t-domain, then a suitably wide time-averaging frame will be required to prevent rapid changes in scaling which would arise due to the short-term variations that occur naturally in speech. For the majority of applications, corresponding re-scaling will be required to provide appropriate signal level consistency between device input and output.

Another method of aligning correct signal and TC positions is, of course, to reposition the TC. Although simple in concept this is likely to require greater computation than the equivalent methods described above.

Validation of this fundamental NR technique has been carried out by computer simulation. Some of the results of this study are presented and discussed in the next section.

4. Single TC NR system performance

Results presented in this section are based on an NR system simulation which used a 1024 point FFT and processing in the f-domain was performed on the magnitude information only, the phase information remaining unmodified for the inverse FFT. Additive broadband noise-corrupted male and female speech has been processed. Noise reduction performance is illustrated by means of output-against-input plot comparison in both the t-domain and f-domain for a short segment of speech. The degree of noise reduction and quality of speech were assessed in informal listening tests, the results of which are discussed.

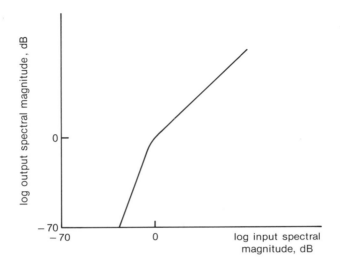

(a)

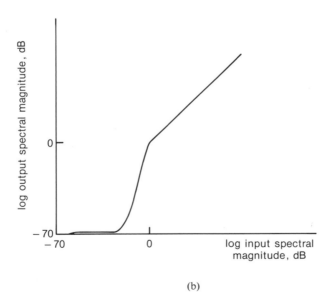

(b)

Fig 9   Examples of text.

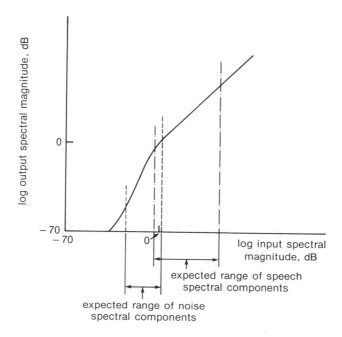

Fig 10   Example of a good TC for speech.

Consider the example of a white-noise corrupted square wave which is described in section 2.1 and illustrated in Fig 2. Originally this was offered as a prime example for noise cancellation by simple spectral thresholding. If instead the TC given in Fig 10 were used to attenuate (rather than eliminate) the noise then this NR device would increase the 10 dB input SNR to approximately 22 dB, which cleans up the square wave signal considerably. Obviously this performance is inferior to that for thresholding, but in practice the wanted speech signal spectrum is hardly ever completely lifted above the noise and so severe speech distortion is likely to result if thresholding is employed.

Using a predominantly voiced male-speech segment, consisting mainly of the word 'call', a set of t-domain and f-domain plots are presented to demonstrate the degree and nature of both the noise reduction and the distortion introduced into the speech. The average SNR across this segment is approximately 14 dB and the noise is 'white' additive. Figure 11 shows a 386 ms segment of this noisy speech and its STFS. Broadband noise is most obvious in the low amplitude part of the t-domain signal immediately before the onset of voicing, and in the higher frequency range of the spectrum above 1.3 kHz. Since the noise reduced output signal in the t-domain looks remarkably similar to the noise-free original, Fig 12 compares the low-amplitude segment of these two waveforms, immediately proceeding the high-amplitude voiced part. These superimposed plots show that the t-domain distortion introduced by the

NR system, when using the TC of Fig 10, is low, the peak amplitude of this segment being 16 dB below that of the voiced part. Spectra comparing the original noise-free 'call' utterance and the NR output of the noise corrupted version of this speech is presented in Fig 13. There is evidently a strong resemblance between the output and input f-domain signals, particularly below 1.3 kHz. Figure 14 illustrates a similar spectral comparison, but here it is between the noise-corrupted signal STFS and that of the NR device output signal STFS; this shows that the higher frequency components of the white noise are depressed by approximately 11 dB at the NR device output, relative to the noisy input.

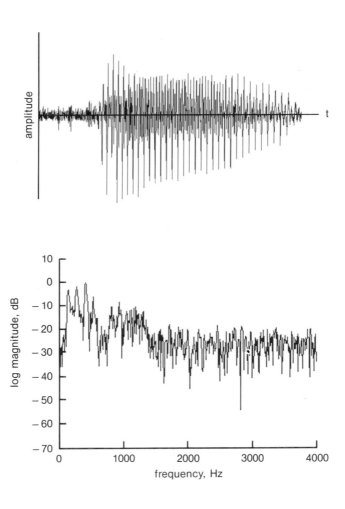

Fig 11   Voiced speech corrupted by broadband noise.

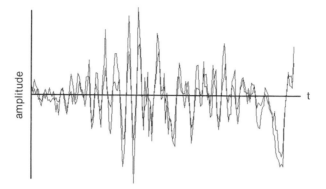

Fig 12   Comparison of low-level noise-free original and NR-processed noisy speech signals.

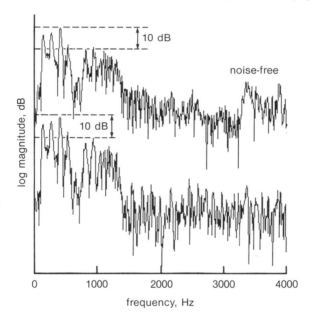

Fig 13   Speech comparison of noise-free and NR-processed noisy speech signals.

Generally, only small improvements in output-to-input SNRs were achieved thoughout the speech processing tests even for carefully selected and accurately positoned TCs, irrespective of whether male or female speech was used. As an example, the approximate improvement in segmental SNR for the case cited above was only 3 dB. Listening tests on realistically long speech segments, for which the SNR improvements were not appreciably better than this example, highlighted the point that the perceived improvement in speech quality is not reliably indicated by the small increase in SNR.

139

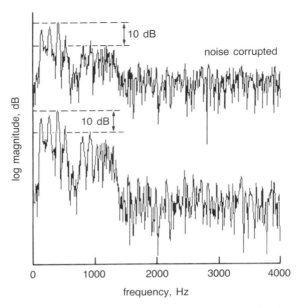

Fig 14   Spectral comparison of noise-corrupted and NR-processed noisy speech signals.

Informal listening tests have been conducted on the single TC NR system for a range of TCs having different slope gradients below the soft knee. The noise environment was that of additive broadband noise for which short segmental SNRs varied from around 7 dB up to 22 dB. Of the four TCs shown in Figs 8 to 10 the speech harshness introduced by the TC of Fig 8 excluded it as a viable option. Performance assessments for male and female speech, relating to the other three TCs, differed on the competing issues of degree of noise reduction and perceived added distortion in the speech. Generally, the TCs of Fig 9 were both considered to be good for high noise reduction, but they did not perform well on speech quality. The TC shown in Fig 10 was deemed to be the best choice, offering very significant reduction in broadband noise levels with low, unobtrusive speech distortion. Experiments with the relative position of the input speech plus noise signal about the soft knee of this TC indicated that audible increases in distortion result from shifts of around 3 dB. This distortion was judged to have a 'short-term echo'-like sound.

5. Multiple TC NR schemes

The ideas presented below are extensions to the single TC NR technique described in section 3 and are aimed at better spectral shaping in the noise reduction process, based upon fundamental or learned characteristics of speech signal spectra. These proposed methods discriminate in the point of onset and rate of attentuation offered to noisy speech spectral components by selective use of two or more different TCs across the audio band of interest.

In Fig 15 an example is given of the typical formant structure of speech [9]. Significant increase in NR performance coupled with improved speech quality can result from using multiple TCs, rather than a single 'blanket' TC, only if the majority of speech contained the form of resonances depicted here. Fortunately, speech has a predominant formant structure, since all voiced and most unvoiced utterances are filtered by the vocal tract. If the formant bandwidths are known then quite accurate delimitation of the high SNR spectral bands is possible, assuming the noise to be broadband in nature (whether white or pink). Similarly, the frequency ranges of low SNR parts of the signal are also known. A 90° rotated sketch of two extreme forms of TCs are also included in Fig 15. This is to exemplify how regions of different expected SNR may have purpose-selected TCs, which are matched to the specific spectral features. Matched selection of TCs for the designated regions is based on the regional expected SNR. The aim is to choose a TC which has its soft knee positioned at the lowest expected level of speech component in that frequency band and also has a non-linear region with a slope that reflects the likely degree of noise.

Three strategies which make use of this multiple TC technique are:

- fixed TCs permanently assigned to pre-specified frequency bands,

- allocation of matched TCs to either pre-specified or dynamically estimated frequency bands during the initial operational phase of the NR device,

- continuous adaptive-allocation of matched TCs to dynamically specified frequency bands.

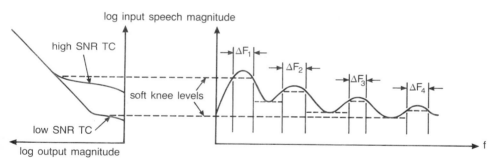

Fig 15   Spectral band selection of TC based on formant structure.

All of these methods require that alignment of each input-signal spectral-component and its TC be performed. Several ways of performing this alignment are described in section 3 for the single TC NR scheme. However, for multiple TC processing amplitude scaling in the f-domain is preferred.

The effectiveness of the first technique relies on careful delimiting of the spectral bands, and on selection of the best TCs for good matching to the most probable speech and noise conditions within these bands. Inevitably, major design compromises must be made for this fixed TC approach, since the detailed formant matching can only be an approximation to the time-varying, speaker-dependent formant structure found generally in speech.

The second method is a logical extension of the fixed multiple TC approach. The primary aim is to tailor the spectral attenuation of noise to the approximate time-averaged formant structure of the individual speaker, estimated during the initial period of operation, and so enhance the NR performance.

The final fully-adaptive multiple TC NR technique is a further progression from the previous methods. This is a form of 'matched filter' noise suppressor. That is the soft knee of each purpose-selected TC is, during detected periods of formant speech, maintained at a level just below the expected level of speech. As before each TC is also selected to provide the best rate of attenuation based on the estimated SNR and noise level conditions existing for each spectral component. Tracking information used in the adaptation process may be derived from a line spectral pair (LSP) analysis or by spectral estimation using the f-domain signals already available within the noise suppressor. Best performance of this type of NR system is obtained using formant frequency tracking control signals and TC selection control derived from temporal changes in the processed-signal spectral magnitudes. With adequate control this non-linear matched-filter process may even be usefully continued during fricative and other non-resonant parts of speech, and should still provide some degree of NR for these broad-band speech segments given that the instantaneous SNR across the spectrum is sufficiently high.

This fully-adaptive scheme should effect a considerable improvement in noise reduction and provide even better speech quality (and therefore reduce listener fatigue) than the alternative non-linear TC NR techniques described previously. It is conceivable that this matched-filtering approach will, for some civil applications, increase speech intelligibility. Such improvements arise from maintaining the speech-dominated spectral components on the linear part of their respective TCs for the vast majority of time, thereby minimising the perceived distortion. This feature is in strong constrast to the inflexible operation of the single TC NR device which, despite the limitations, is capable of providing good noise reduction with low levels of distortion.

6. Conclusion

Cancellation of additive noise in speech and other signals is often difficult to achieve. For many applications it is sufficient to reduce the noise level and reshape its form so that it is perceptually unobtrusive.

A new single-input frequency-domain method of noise reduction in speech has been presented. It is founded on the principle of selective attenuation of signal-plus-noise spectral components. For the simplest form this approach avoids the cost and complexity of implementing the speech detection and noise estimation required in other f-domain NR systems which instead perform spectral subtraction. The selectivity in attenuating the spectral components of the speech-plus-noise signal is simply achieved by using a single non-linear input-output transfer characteristic across all components. Computer simulation of this NR technique has been used to process speech signals corrupted by broadband additive noise, for which segmental SNRs of the input signal varied in the range 7 to 22 dB. Informal listening tests using both male and female speech, indicate that the perceived noise level can be considerably reduced whilst maintaining speech quality.

Three interesting extensions to the fundamental NR technique have been described. All of these are aimed at improving the overall performance of the NR system by use of multiple non-linear transfer characteristics; each characteristic being matched to the expected or monitored properties of the input signal. These improved techniques use either fixed, semi-adaptive or fully-adaptive spectral-band positioning of the selected TCs. The fully-adaptive NR system performs a type of speech signal 'matched filtering' in the f-domain. The ultimate aim of this approach is to extract the speech from the noise corrupted signal with no perceptible distortion of the speech and no audible noise.

The single-input f-domain NR techniques described are for stand-alone pre-processing or post-processing speech applications. Their general flexibility of operation and potential for inexpensive implementation suggests a range of applications, such as speech coding, speech analysis and synthesis, voice communication systems, speech recognisers and speech authentication systems.

Patent

The range of new noise-suppression techniques described in this paper are the subject of a patent application.

Acknowledgements

The author is grateful to B Prescott for assisting in proving the correctness of the fundamental concept described in this paper. Thanks are also due to P Challener and to D Musker for the technical discussions and suggestions which helped refine the techniques described.

References

1   Widrow B et al: 'Adaptive noise cancelling: principles and applications', Proc IEEE, $\underline{63}$, pp 1692—1716 (December 1975).

2   Griffiths L J: 'An adaptive lattice structure for noise-cancelling applications', IEEE Proc ICASSP, pp 87—90, Tulsa, Oklahoma, USA (April 1978).

3   Portnoff M R: 'Short-time Fourier analysis of sampled speech', IEEE Trans ASSP, $\underline{29}$, pp 364—373 (June 1981).

4   Berouti M, Schwartz R and Makhoul J: 'Enhancement of speech corrupted by acoustic noise', IEEE Proc ICASSP, pp 208—211 (April 1979).

5   Curtis R A and Niederjohn R J: 'An investigation of several frequency-domain processing methods for enhancing the intelligibility of speech in wideband random noise', IEEE Proc ICASSP, pp 602—605, Tulsa, Oklahoma, USA (April 1978).

6   Boll S F: 'Suppression of acoustic noise in speech using spectral subtraction', IEEE Trans ASSP, $\underline{27}$, pp 113—120 (April 1979).

7   McAulay R J and Malpass M L: 'Speech enhancement using a softdecision noise suppression filter', IEEE Trans ASSP, $\underline{28}$, pp 137—145 (April 1980).

8   Portnoff M R: 'Time-scale modification of speech based on short-time Fourier analysis', IEEE Trans ASSP, $\underline{29}$, pp 374—390 (June 1981).

9   Schroeder M R: 'Linear predictive coding of speech: review and current directions', IEEE Communications Magazine, $\underline{23}$, pp 54—61 (August 1985).

FORMANT BASED SPEECH SYNTHESIS

P M Hughes

ABSTRACT

Working at data rates of under 6 kbit/s, formant based synthesisers can produce speech output which is virtually indistinguishable from natural speech over the telephone. In order to produce speech of this quality it is necessary to analyse natural speech and thereby obtain the sets of synthesis parameters used to describe the speech. This paper deals with the problems associated with automatic formant based analysis-for-synthesis and some of the methods which can be used to overcome these problems.

1. Introduction

Increasingly, good quality stored speech output is being considered as an essential part of many new systems and services. Applications for voice output include voice guidance messages which can help customers to make the best use of newly installed equipment or services, speech output interfaces for remote test equipment which needs to be accessed over the telephone network, and large automatic or operator assisted database enquiry systems. An important constraint in such applications is that the coded speech should occupy only the minimum amount of computer memory. For example, in smaller systems, where the design limitations often include the size, number and power consumption of the circuit cards (or integrated circuits used), it is important to maximise the use of available memory. Correspondingly, in larger systems, it is found that by using a highly compressed representation of speech the speech data may be stored using semiconductor memory rather than magnetic disks. The ability to compactly and accurately describe a speech signal is central to the development of such systems. As a result, there is great interest in techniques which allow speech signals to be re-generated from the minimum amount of stored information.

The process examined in this paper is that of formant based synthesis of natural sounding speech. In particular, the paper deals with the problems of obtaining sets of synthesis parameters which, when used in conjunction with a formant based model of the human vocal tract, allow accurate synthesis of any given segment of natural speech. This process, which is more commonly known as synthesis-by-analysis, has been shown to produce speech output which is virtually indistinguishable from natural speech over the normal telephone band.

2. The formant synthesis concept

Formant synthesis is based upon the premise that the human vocal tract can be thought of in terms of a source-tract model; that is a source, which is responsible for generating the basic excitation signals, and a tract which imposes various resonances, or formants, upon the source signal [1]. In general terms, the source signal is thought of as being either periodic and impulse-like for the voiced sounds (these are sounds such as the vowel sounds which are produced by vibrating the vocal folds), or noise-like. The latter corresponds to the unvoiced sounds such as 'ss', 'sch', 'th' etc., which are caused by forcing expired air through a constriction in the vocal tract. As the shape of the vocal tract is changed, by moving the articulators such as the tongue etc., then the spectral position and intensity of the formants which are imposed on the excitation signal also change. A formant synthesiser can be used to try and copy the formant structure and the changes in the formants which occur in natural speech. As these changes occur relatively slowly, it is possible to use one set (or vector) of synthesiser parameters to specify a short segment (frame) of the speech signal. This feature can be used to considerably reduce the amount of data needed to represent the signal. Generally, it is found that frames of about 10 ms (i.e. 100 synthesiser vectors per second) are needed to reproduce natural sounding speech.

The excitation source and the spectral shaping network which make up a formant synthesiser have to be varied dynamically in response to the control signals supplied. Both the low order digital filters, which form the basis of spectral shaping network, and the numerical processes needed for generation of the excitation signals, can be implemented relatively easily on the high speed programmable digital signal processing (DSP) devices which are now available.

3. Formant synthesis models

At present, there are two commonly used formant synthesis models, the cascade/parallel synthesiser developed by Klatt [2] and the 'versatile parallel formant synthesiser' developed by Holmes et al [3,4]. Although there has been dissent about which of the two systems is the better [5], it is generally agreed that in terms of the capabilities of the two systems to synthesise a given speech sound, there is little to choose between them [6]. In spite of this, the Klatt model has, in the main, been favoured for text-to-speech synthesis, whilst the Holmes model tends to be used for synthesis-by-analysis systems. The reasons for this are probably related more to the way in which the different synthesis models are controlled, rather than the inherent capabilities of the synthesisers themselves.

The most obvious advantage of the parallel formant synthesiser for the synthesis-by-analysis application, is that fewer parameters are required to specify each frame of synthesised speech. As one of the direct aims of this approach is to minimise the effective data rate of stored speech messages, this clearly makes the Holmes synthesiser the preferred choice. A further advantage of the parallel formant approach, is that the synthesiser is designed such that each formant is independent of the others (i.e. changes made to one of the formants in a synthesised speech signal will have only a minimum effect on parts of the signal spectrum away from that formant). This orthogonality, which is not a feature of the Klatt model, greatly simplifies the testing and development of formant-by-formant optimisation techniques. It also allows straightforward hand editing techniques to be used for production of the high quality reference data needed for assessment of new automatic analysis algorithms.

As can be seen in Fig 1, the spectral shaping network (i.e. the tract part of the model) which gives the parallel formant synthesiser its name, consists of a number of formant

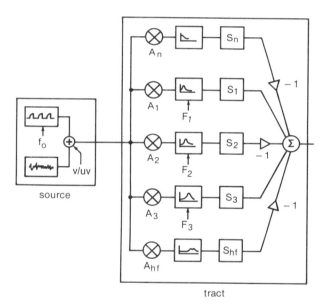

Fig 1   The parallel formant vocal tract model showing formant resonators and spectral shaping filters.

generators connected in parallel. The formant generators themselves consist of two stages; a resonant filter followed by a spectral correction filter. The spectral correction filters are required in order to eliminate potentially catastrophic signal cancellation which might otherwise occur between the skirts of the different resonant filters. A smooth interpolation of the spectrum between the formant peaks is achieved by alternating the polarity of the formant generators prior to the output summing node. The centre frequencies of the formant resonators F1, F2 and F3 are individually controlled by externally specified parameters, as is the amplitude of the excitation signal applied to each of the formant generators. These variable frequency resonators (F1, F2 and F3) are implemented as second order all-pole networks. Since the frequencies at which the formants F4 and F5 occur has little perceptual effect on the quality of the synthetic speech, a fixed filter is used to simulate the action of the higher formants. In this particular implementation, a fixed frequency fourth order resonator is used. This provides a double peaked response which can be thought of as an 'average' setting for formants F4 and F5. The low frequency correction filter, Fn, which is used to adjust the spectral energy of the synthesised signal at frequencies below the first formant, also has a fixed frequency characteristic with a resonant peak at about 250 Hz. This very roughly corresponds to the resonance which is introduced into some sounds by the nasal cavity.

Within each pitch period in segments of voiced speech, it is possible to identify two different mechanisms at work in the vocal folds. For part of each pitch period, the vocal folds are open, effectively coupling the lungs into the vocal tract (Fig 2). The lungs act as a damping network and absorb sound energy from the vocal tract. In order to simulate this action in the synthesiser, the bandwidth of the resonators is

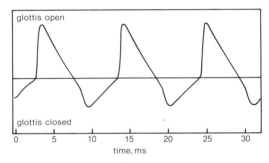

Fig 2   Typical laryngograph trace showing glottis open and glottis closed phases for 30 mS of male speech.

increased (pitch synchronously) towards the end of each pitch period. The formant bandwidths are also significantly widened when the unvoiced excitation signal is used as there is no glottis-closed phase to produce the undamped narrowband formants which appear in voiced speech.

The data required by the synthesiser consists of the formant amplitudes An, A1, A2, A3 and Ahf, the formant frequencies F1, F2 and F3, the pitch, F0, and voicing, V/UV. Since the speech signal can be regarded as being quasi-stationary over short periods, each vector of synthesis parameters is used to represent a 10 ms frame of speech. In practice, it is found that the individual synthesiser parameters may be quantised quite coarsely. Currently a linear quantisation strategy is used, in which each of the parameters is represented by a six bit binary number. The resulting equivalent data rate for formant coded speech is, therefore, 6 kbit/s. This rate can be reduced further by noting that the differences between parameters in successive time frames of data are rarely greater than ±16 steps. The data can, therefore, be coded differentially using only five bits for each parameter. The voicing parameter can be further restricted to three bits (fully unvoiced, fully voiced and six intermediate levels of mixed voicing) without any loss of quality, giving a reduced data rate of 4.8 kbit/s sec.

Although the parallel formant synthesiser is relatively complicated in terms of the signal processing tasks which have to be performed, it can be implemented in hardware using the current generation of single chip digital signal processors (7). A number of systems have been produced using this technology ranging from a four-channel double Eurocard sized unit to a 'matchbox-sized' synthesiser which can be powered from a small battery. The latter, a photograph of which may be found elsewhere in this journal [8], includes a system controller and sufficient memory to store over a minute of speech.

4. Development support tools

In order to develop and refine a speech analysis/synthesis system, it must be possible to assess the quality of the synthesised speech produced. Such an assessment should highlight where and why any analysis errors occurred and allow successful developments to be identified and retained. The first step is to listen to the speech produced. Unfortunately, if the analysis problems have resulted in erroneous synthesis vectors, it is often difficult to determine the exact nature and location of the errors simply by listening. This applies even in the case of gross transient errors which give rise to clicks or pops in the synthesised speech and which are notoriously difficult to isolate by means of listening tests alone. The need to establish a more analytical and systematic approach to assessing the quality of newly developed analysis algorithms and to the diagnosis of analysis errors, has led to the development of the BT speech and graphics editor (SAGE) system. Based on a high resolution graphics terminal, this system allows spectrograms (or spectrogram-like plots) of speech signals to be displayed and compared.The basic format of the display is shown in Fig 3. In order to highlight differences between the natural and synthesised speech, the spectrograms of the natural and synthetic speech signals are plotted one above the other. The quality of the formant frequency data specified in the synthesis vector may be checked by overlaying the estimated formant frequency tracks (in colour) on the spectrogram of the natural speech. The central panel between the two spectrograms can be used to display the sampled speech data, the pitch track, the voicing parameter or the formant amplitude parameters (but only one at a time). In addition to the monochrome display, which is suited to formant identification and tracking, it is possible to select a colour option which uses a false colour 'heat scale' for the spectrograms rather than the standard grey scale. This is particularly useful for identifying some of the more subtle differences in the spectral energy between natural and synthetic speech spectrograms. The major use of the colour display is, therefore, to check that the formant amplitude parameters have been estimated correctly. As the system is software based, it is a simple matter to produce alternative displays such as the LPC spectrogram shown in Fig 7 and discussed later in this paper.

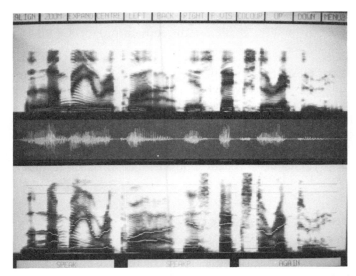

Fig 3   Basic system display showing spectrograms of natural speech (lower) and synthesised speech (upper).
Central panel shows source speech waveform. Formant tracks are overlaid on the natural speech
spectrogram.

As well as the basic display system, an extensive menu driven editor has been developed
which allows any of the synthesiser parameters (formant frequencies, formant
amplitudes, pitch and voicing) to be changed interactively. The editing is performed
simply by drawing the required parameter track onto the screen using a graphics tablet
and puck. As the operator of this system will generally wish to listen to the effects
of any changes made, the synthesised speech (as represented by the parameter tracks
currently shown on the display) can be generated in full or in part at any time using
a hardware synthesiser under the control of the SAGE system. As such, in addition
to using the SAGE system to assess the performance of the automatic analysis
procedures, careful manual editing allows any analysis errors to be removed and so
provides a means of obtaining high quality 'truth data'.

5. The formant analysis problem

In order to synthesise a given speech message, it is first necessary to analyse it.
The formant analysis problem can be considered either in an abstract sense as a feature
estimation and extraction problem (Fig 4a), or in a more closed form as a parametric
optimisation problem (Fig 4b). The former starts with the premise that in segments
of voiced speech there exist continuously identifiable features which can be classified
as formants. Given that it is possible to construct a formant synthesis model which
is an accurate representation of the human system, it should be possible to use data
obtained from natural speech signals to drive the synthesiser. Provided that the
formant identification and extraction processes are accurate and that the synthesiser
is an accurate model of the human vocal tract, the synthetic speech produced should

closely approximate the original natural speech. Unfortunately if there are imperfections in the vocal tract model, which is almost inevitable, then the synthetic speech produced may only be a poor approximation of the natural speech.

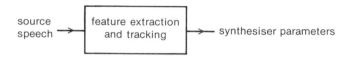

Fig 4a   Formant analysis by direct feature extraction.

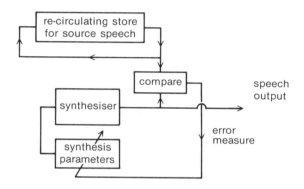

Fig 4b   Formant analysis viewed as a parameter optimisation problem.

The alternative approach is much more directed towards the synthesis-by-analysis problem. Given the practical synthesiser described above, there are 2^6 different choices for each parameter in the synthesis vector. As the vector consists of 10 parameters, it is possible to construct a total of 2^{60} different parameter vectors. Within this exceedingly large set there should exist one parameter vector which, when used to drive the synthesiser, produces a frame of synthetic speech which in some sense is closest to the corresponding natural signal under analysis. The problem is now transformed into one of selecting the optimum multi-dimensional parameter vector from this very large set. It is not sensible to propose an exhaustive search technique which steps through each parameter vector in turn, synthesising each possible speech frame and comparing it with the natural speech. Even if trial synthesis and comparison with the natural speech could be performed one million times faster than real time, to select the optimum vector for one 10 ms frame of speech would take in the region of 40 000 years. Fortunately, by using iterative techniques, whereby an initial guess of the synthesiser parameters is made and then gradually refined by comparing the results of a trial synthesis with the natural speech (analysis-by-synthesis), it is possible to devise analysis procedures which require relatively few synthesis/comparison cycles.

A major advantage of the analysis-by-synthesis approach to formant analysis is that as the analysis process contains information about the synthesis model (i.e. the trial synthesis and comparison with the natural speech segment), differences between the model and the human speech production system will ultimately have much less of an influence on the quality of the synthesised speech. This awareness of the synthesis model is also of value for analysis of unvoiced sounds, where the formant description of speech is not such a good approximation to the natural speech production process.

The solutions currently under study, and discussed in the following section, involve a combination of the direct feature extraction methods for obtaining an initial guess for the parameters followed by an iterative stage where that guess is successively refined. Although analysis times are for the present rather long (approximately 27 seconds for each 10 ms segment of speech) it is hoped that in the future formant analysis-for-synthesis will be possible in near real-time or even real-time.

6. Algorithms for speech analysis

As noted above, analysis-by-synthesis consists of two phases: initial estimation of the synthesis vector and successive refinement of that vector. The exact nature of the iterative processes which work most effectively and reliably is currently under study and will be reported at a later date, however, by making a reasonably accurate initial guess, the time taken to perform the iterative refinement can be considerably reduced. A number of techniques are available for obtaining initial estimates of the pitch and voicing parameters [9]; however, accurate estimation of the formant frequencies and amplitudes is less easy. Methods which have been tried in this application include linear prediction (LP) based spectral estimation, line spectral pair (LSP) analysis [10] and adaptations of the discrete Fourier transform (DFT).

A problem which arises with DFT based techniques is illustrated by the narrowband spectrogram of Fig 5. In this spectrogram, it is relatively easy to identify the broader dark bands which correspond to the formants. However, as well as the formants, a series of regularly spaced bands of energy which occur at harmonics of the pitch frequency is also apparent. These smaller bands occur because the analysis window used is sufficiently long to reveal the periodic nature of the glottal excitation. Automatic formant identification and tracking algorithms are often confused by this pitch banding and hence, it is necessary to use curve fitting algorithms to try to identify the overall spectral envelope and eliminate the pitch harmonic structure. This tends to reduce the reliability of the technique, by producing spurious formant peaks. Reducing the length of the analysis window can help (Fig 6), but as can be seen, this also tends to smear the formant detail over a wider frequency band making accurate identification of the centre frequencies more difficult.

An advantage of LP based analysis is that an estimate of the spectral envelope of the signal is a direct result of the analysis process [11]. The effects of this can be seen in the LP spectrogram in Fig 7. In this spectrogram, the display data has been modified so as to highlight local maxima in the short term estimates of the speech spectrum. Ideally these maxima should correspond to the formant peaks. However, as can be seen, there are a number of spurious points which do not coincide with the expected formant positions (as would be identified by eye). This will give rise to errors in the estimation of the formant frequencies unless further processing is performed to identify and remove erroneous points.

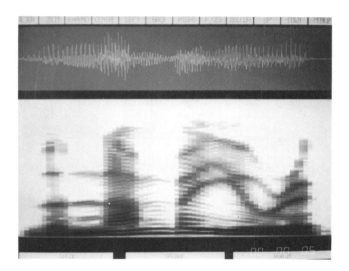

Fig 5   Narrowband spectrogram of natural speech showing formant peaks and pitch harmonics.

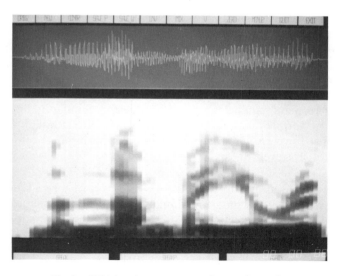

Fig 6   Wideband spectrogram of natural speech.

153

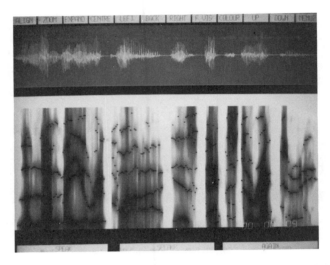

Fig 7   LPC based spectrogram of natural speech with local spectral maxima highlighted to emphasise possible formant positions.

As LP analysis helps to reveal the short term spectral envelope of a speech signal, it is tempting to assume that the heights of the peaks in the LP spectra can be measured and used to derive formant amplitude data for the synthesiser. Unfortunately, there are a number of fundamental differences between the LP and formant synthesis models; the LP analysis model has no equivalent of the Fn low frequency correction for example. It is also known that LP analysis is prone to errors which result in incorrect estimates of the overall gain of the LP spectral envelope. As a result, estimates of synthesiser formant amplitudes obtained from LP spectra are generally rather inaccurate. This is illustrated in Fig 8, where hand corrected synthesiser amplitude values for formant F2, are plotted against the heights of the F2 formant peak obtained by LP analysis. Whilst there is a broadly linear relationship between the two parameter sets, there is also a significant unpredictable variability between the two sets of measurements. This variability can lead to the LP based estimate of the synthesiser formant gain being up to 50% in error. Similar difficulties arise with measurement of formant amplitudes A1, A3 and Ahf, although the problem is compounded for formant F1, where the basic relationship between the two sets of measurements is not even linear.

The difficulties noted above preclude the development of direct DFT or LP based analysis-for-synthesis algorithms and similar problems can be shown to exist with other apparently viable strategies. The advantage of these techniques, however, is that although relatively inaccurate, the necessary computations can be performed quickly and easily using standard DSP hardware. Initial results also indicate that whilst the data produced in this way is not good enough for producing synthesised speech, it is sufficiently accurate to be used as a starting point for subsequent analysis-by-synthesis techniques. A number of synthesis-by-analysis schemes which are capable of producing an optimised set of synthesis vectors from such starting estimates are currently under investigation.

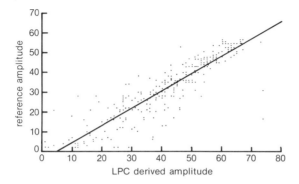

Fig 8   Scattergram showing the relationship between reference amplitudes and LPC derived amplitudes for formant F2.

7. Conclusion

Formant analysis is, without doubt, a very difficult problem; real-time formant analysis even more so. Formant analysis can, however, be viewed more as an optimisation process whereby the output of a model of the human vocal tract is adjusted to give the best fit to the speech under analysis. Although complicated, the re-defined problem is at least computationally viable. If the problems associated with these formant analysis procedures can be solved, then by using such techniques as vector quantization and variable frame rate synthesis, it is not unrealistic to propose effective data rates approaching 2 kbit/s for formant coded speech. The full potential, however, of formant based synthesis-by-analysis lies not just in the reproduction of fixed messages at very low data rates, but in the scope for development of high quality extended concatenation systems.

Adopting the optimisation concept outlined in this paper significantly changes the philosophy of the formant analysis process; initially, the formant parameters are regarded simply as a set of controls which are adjusted so as to minimise an error criterion. The formant information which results, is produced almost as a by-product of the analysis process. Subsequent exploitation of the direct relationship between the synthesiser parameters, the human vocal tract and features which can be observed in spectrograms of natural speech, opens up many new avenues. For example, there are many applications in which the spoken output messages are for the most part fixed and contain only a few variable fields which can be filled with a finite number of alternative words (e.g. talking timetables, share prices, telephone numbers etc). Currently, only very basic word concatenation techniques are used to produce such messages and in general give an unnatural and hesitant sounding output. By studying and then accurately modelling the process of segmental concatenation in natural speech, it may be possible to develop a system when concatenated short segments (probably of sub-word length) of analysed speech are used to produce high quality, variable content messages which retain the naturalness of fluent human speech. Such a system relies heavily on the fact that the parameters used to synthesise formant encoded speech can be modified to change the sound of the synthesised speech (and thereby match the natural speech) without unduly affecting its natural quality. Further work will, however, be needed if the potential of techniques such as this is to be exploited to the full.

Acknowledgement

The author would like to express his thanks to M C Hall (speech and language processing division) and J R Crombie (computer applications and software development division) for their work on developing and programming the SAGE editing system, and R B Underwood, currently attending York University, for her work on the relationship between formant synthesis and LP model.

References

1 Gibson D L, Gillott T J and Helliker L A: 'Textalk: the BT text to speech system', Br Telecom Technol J 6 , No 2 (April 1988).

2 Klatt D H: 'Software for a cascade/parallel formant synthesiser', J Acoust Soc Amer, 67(2) , pp 971—995 (March 1980).

3 Rye J M and Holmes J N: 'A versatile software parallel formant speech synthesiser', JSRU Research Report, No 1016 (1982).

4 Holmes J N: 'Avoiding unwanted low-frequency level variations on the output of a parallel formant synthesiser', J Acoust Soc Amer, 68 , p S18 (1980).

5 Holmes J N: 'Formant synthesisers: cascade or parallel?', Speech Communication, 2 , pp 251—273 (1983).

6 Klatt D H: 'Review of text-to-speech conversion for English', J Acoust Soc Amer, 82(3) , pp 737—793 (September 1987).

7 Quarmby D J and Holmes J N: 'Implementation of a parallel-formant speech synthesiser using a single-chip programmable signal processor', IEE Proceedings, 131 , Pt F No. 6 (October 1984).

8 Wheddon C: 'Speech communication' Br Telecom Technol J, 6 , No 2 (1988)

9 Rabiner L R, Cheng M J, Rosenberg A E and McGonegal: 'A comparative study of several pitch detection algorithms', IEEE Trans Acoust Speech, Signal Processing, ASSP—24 , pp 339—417 (October 1976).

10 Cheetham B M G and Hughes P M: 'Formant estimation from LSP coefficients', Proc Int Conf on Digital Processing of Signals in Communications, pp 183—190 (September 1988).

11 Rabiner L R and Schafer R W: 'Digital processing of speech signals', Prentice Hall (1978).

TEXTALK: THE BRITISH TELECOM
TEXT-TO-SPEECH SYSTEM

D L Gibson, T J Gillott and L A Helliker

ABSTRACT

Text-to-speech systems are now being increasingly used as essential components in a new range of office automation and telephone-based services which enable people to obtain information from computers.

This paper outlines the various processes by which this conversion of unrestricted English text to speech is achieved in the BT text-to-speech system.

1. Introduction

With the growing interest in information technology, there is an increasing demand for systems which enable people who are not expert computer users to obtain information held on remote computer systems. The telephone system provides an obvious channel for such communication, and consequently British Telecom has a direct interest in such developments as they offer an opportunity for further exploitation of voice communication networks.

If the remote user does not have a computer terminal at his/her disposal, an alternative means of interacting with the remote computer system is required. Speech is man's most natural means of communication and ideally speech recognition and synthesis systems would be used by the remote computer system to process the caller's request. With present speech recognition technology this approach may be satisfactory for some applications, such as games, but inappropriate in other areas, where isolated words can be used successfully, for example. In other situations the sending tones from a tone-sender or a touch-tone telephone may offer a better solution. However, speech is the only practical method for the computer to convey information back to the caller and it is therefore necessary to provide voice output facilities to enable the remote computer to communicate over a telephone line. Often, the information which is required to be passed on to the caller is in a textual form already (or can easily be converted to text), and so the necessary machine-man interface can be provided by a device which converts text to speech. However, a wide range of information can be held on computer databases and this information can be output in many different formats. The text-to-speech system must be sufficiently general to enable it to process and convert into speech text which is unrestricted in format.

2. Human production of speech

In order to be able to produce intelligible and natural-sounding speech, the text-to-speech (TTS) system must be able to simulate human processing of text and the mechanics of speech production.

2.1 Human text processing

Very little is known about the cognitive processes involved in human text processing; it is still the subject of fundamental psycholinguistic research [1]. The components of the TTS system which convert text into a phonetic representation are based on rules which have been developed through logical, conscious examination of the British English orthographic system. They therefore do not, necessarily, reflect the rules which a fluent reader applies sub-consciously when processing a text. Work is currently progressing on neural networks; these are software systems which simulate the neurological functioning of the brain [2]. When exposed to suitable data, they can learn to perform the mapping from text to phonetic representation just as a child learns to read. These systems are still embryonic, however, and require further work before they will be accurate enough for use as a front-end to a speech synthesiser. In the future, they should be more accurate than the type of rules used at present, as their theoretical basis is far sounder; they have the potential to equal human achievement in this task.

2.2 The human vocal tract

A sagittal section of the head indicating the human speech production organs is shown in Fig 1. Prior to the beginning of speech, air is drawn into the lungs through the nose or mouth via the open vocal folds. During speech production, the lungs are progressively contracted by the chest and diaphragm muscles. This forces a flow of air back up through the vocal folds. The speaker generally takes another breath where a punctuation mark would occur in writing, to ensure that the sub-glottal air-pressure does not fall too low. Air can be expelled through the oral or nasal cavities, or both, depending on the position of the velum and the lips.

In the production of a voiced sound, for example a vowel or a sound such as 'M' or 'L', the vocal folds are brought together by muscular force, and the flow of air between them causes them to vibrate in a manner and at a frequency which are both characteristics of the speaker's voice. This is known as the Bernouilli Effect. The pharynx, and the oral and nasal cavities act as resonators, the nasal cavity is of fixed geometry for a particular individual and thus resonates at fixed frequencies. (The nasal congestion associated with colds and flu temporarily alters the resonating frequencies of the nasal cavity and therefore the characteristics of the sufferer's voice.) The oral tract, however, is of highly variable volume and shape due to the variable positions of the tongue, lips and jaws and it can therefore resonate over a wide range of frequencies. The different speech sounds are formed by varying the positions of the articulators and creating a continuously varying set of resonators.

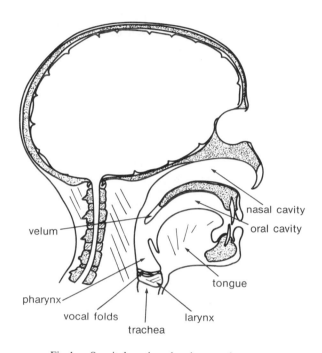

Fig 1   Saggital section showing vocal organs.

The spectrum of a short segment of a vowel is shown in Fig 2. It shows a number of spectral peaks, known as formants, which is the expected characteristic of this combination of resonant cavities.

In an unvoiced sound (eg, 'SH', 'T'), the vocal folds are not brought together and no vibration occurs. Instead, the sound heard is the result of turbulent air-flow in the oral cavity. This is produced either by the air passing through a narrow gap between two articulators, e.g. the tongue and the roof of the mouth, or by the bringing together and rapid release of two articulators. Examples of these types of sounds are the consonants 'S' and 'P' respectively. Figure 3 shows the spectral characteristics of a voiceless sound, which has very little formant structure.

Some sounds, for example 'V' and 'Z', involve simultaneous vocal fold vibration and turbulent air-flow through the oral cavity.

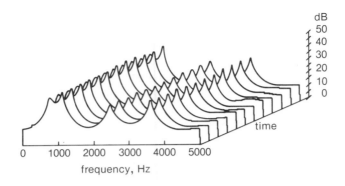

Fig 2   Spectrum of vowel segment.

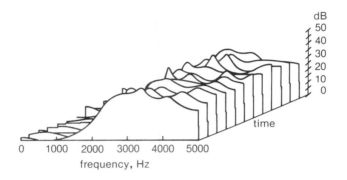

Fig 3   Spectrum of voiceless sound.

Natural speech is smooth and flowing; one sound merges into the next with no break or detectable boundary. This is because the articulators have to move from the configuration necessary to produce one sound into the configuration for the next sound. During this movement, air continues to flow through the glottis and sounds will continue to be produced. For example, if the sound 'EE' is produced, followed by an 'AA' (see Table 1 for a key to the phonetic notation), with no interruption of the vocal fold vibration, the intervening sounds, 'I' and 'E', will also be produced. In natural speech, these movements have to occur quickly, and the vocal tract often does not have sufficient time to achieve the ideal position for a sound. This has the effect that sounds are changed slightly by those adjacent to them, for example, the 'AA' in 'man' is slightly nasalised due to its position between two nasals; the velum is unable to move quickly enough to make the 'AA' totally non-nasal. Some sounds are more susceptible to this type of alteration, for example, there are two distinct realisations of 'L', according to phonetic context. (This is described in some detail in Section 3.1 below.) This phenomenon is known as co-articulation and a model of the vocal tract must be able to duplicate it in order to sound natural [3].

3. Conversion of text-to-speech

The major difficulty faced when attempting to model speech by rule is the above-mentioned continuously varying nature of the speech waveform. How can events within that waveform be captured and used in a synthesis system?

One solution which has been adopted as a model for natural speech is to build up a phonological inventory based on recognisable events in the speech waveform. These events can be characterised either on an articulatory or acoustic basis, or more usually both. The aim of either method is to produce static units which can be proved to have some reality at the phonological level, and whose phonetic realisation accurately reflects the acoustic events mentioned above. Thus a continuously varying phenomenon (the speech waveform) can be represented discretely as a series of segments. These segments are referred to as 'phonemes'. The phonological taxonomy of English contains 40—50 phonemes.

Table 1 TEXTalk phonetic notation.

Symbol	Example
NG	sing
TH	thin
SH	shin
CH	chin
DH	the
ZH	pleasure
J	just
Y	youth
EE	seed
EY	Sheffield
I	sit
E	set
AA	sat
A	above
ER	bird
U	but
OO	book
AR	father
UU	soon
O	hot
AW	bought
IA	beard
AI	bake
OA	boat
OU	about
IE	bite
OI	boy
EI	their
UR	poor *

P, T, K, B, D, G, M, N, F, S, V, Z, H, L, R, W: as in normal orthography.

* Not found in all versions of Standard British English.

TEXTalk uses this discrete model to produce a simulation of the speech waveform from text. However, forty phonological units are not on their own sufficient for natural pronunciation of English. Consider the example below:

- litter --≫   L I T A
- milk --≫   M I L K

Both of the above transcriptions are adequate at the phonological level. However, before the words can be pronounced, an additional stage of processing must be performed in order to produce an adequate phonetic realisation. This is due to various time-domain phenomena, such as the co-articulation discussed in 2.1 above.

To illustrate this further stage, consider the phoneme /L/ in both transcriptions. In the first example, /L/ occurs at the beginning of the word and is followed by a high front vowel. In the second, however, it occurs between a high front vowel and a velar plosive. In the latter case, the velar will affect the quality of the preceding lateral. The qualities of the laterals in each utterance will differ noticeably as a result.

A discrete model must take account of these differences. They must be characterised acoustically in a similar fashion to the phonemes mentioned above. Characterisations of the variations of phonemes are referred to as 'allophones'. The difference between the two varieties of /L/ would be expressed by saying that the phonological unit /L/ could be realised on the phonetic level by two allophones, one of which is velarised (traditionally known as a 'dark' L). TEXTalk uses a phonetic inventory of 120 allophones.

As well as considering speech as a sequence of sounds, it is important to note that it has other aspects to its structure. The segmental model must take account of the rhythm and duration of sounds. Thus phonemes are grouped into syllables, which have notional stress assigned to them. The acoustic correlates of stress which are altered in each allophone in response to the stress values assigned to syllables are pitch, duration and intensity.

The algorithms employed in TEXTalk reflect the model outlined above. The complex process is shown diagrammatically in Fig 4. It can be divided into four main processes, each of which will now be described in outline.

3.1   Text restriction module

The role of the text restriction module is to take as its input unrestricted English text and produce from it a pronounceable version of that text for use by the pronunciation module. To do this it makes use of two different types of table:

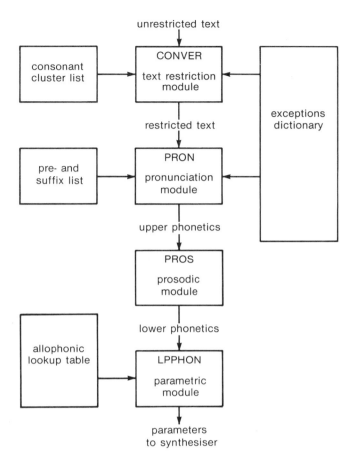

Fig 4   Diagram of text-to-speech system.

- Dictionary — each word passed to the text restriction module is looked up in the main dictionary: if an entry for the word is found, its phonetic form picked up from the dictionary will be used in subsequent processing. The dictionary is mainly used at this point to identify the correct pronunciation of standard abbreviations and common acronyms.

- Use of consonant cluster lists — in the English language only certain combinations of consonants are used. The module contains a list of these allowable consonant clusters; should a word contain a group of consonants which are not in this list then the word is deemed to be unpronounceable in which case it will be spelled. Thus, 'BTRL' will be rendered as 'bee tee arr ell'.

The text restriction module also carries out other text preprocessing functions, notably in the way in which numbers are handled. For example, a number string is considered to be a word whose first character is a digit or a currency symbol. If the number string consists of a two digit triad with separating colons it is treated as a time, if the numbers are separated by the solidus symbol '/' the string is treated as a date. Alternatively, if the string is terminated by a suffix such as 'th' or 'st' it will be treated as an ordinal number, or if prefixed by '£' will be treated as a sum of money. Thus, '£25.02' will be spoken as 'twenty five pounds and two pence' whilst '25/10/87' will be spoken as 'twenty fifth of October, nineteen eighty seven'.

This module also provides facilities for the user to influence the machine's treatment of the input text. For example, assume that a certain word has not been pronounced to the user's satisfaction and for some reason is unlikely to be contained in the dictionary. The user can enter the word in phonetic text in order to force the system to pronounce it correctly. However, to do this the text-to-speech system must have a signal passed to it that the text coming in must be treated differently from normal text (in the case of phonetic text, it is passed through the text restriction module without being processed). Special character sequences are reserved for this purpose; they are referred to as trip sequences. The trip sequences to signal the beginning and end of phonetic text are {P and }. Thus a typical input text containing trip sequences might look like this:

This is an example of a {P 'T R I P } sequence.

Other trip sequences might be used to control speech rate or loudness.

3.2 Pronunciation module

All text to speech systems need some means of converting the conventional orthographic text to the set of phonemes used in the language. This is because the orthographic system rarely reflects the pronunciation accurately. In English, this divergence is marked for historical reasons, and thus an efficient module to perform this conversion is needed. Two main methods are used.

Firstly, it is possible to formulate a set of rules to express knowledge of how some letters are represented as sounds. These rules are called grapheme to phoneme rules as they convert the written representation (graphemes) to the phonological one (phonemes). These rules are a much expanded version of the set originally proposed by the Joint Speech Research Unit [4].

Secondly, to deal with those words which form exceptions to the rules, a so-called exceptions dictionary is employed. This is the same one as is used in the text restriction module. It contains a list of words and their phonological transcriptions. The list is scanned, and if a particular word is found, it is replaced wholesale by its transcription and no more processing is carried out by the pronunciation module.

The above two processes are not sufficient to deal with many of the words that occur in English, which, like many Germanic languages, has a tendency to build up words by agglutination of morphological units. For the purposes of the program, the significant morphological units are designated as stems and affixes. Affixes collectively comprise prefixes (such as 'un-', 'con-', 're-'), and suffixes (such as '-ation', '-ity'). The stem is the 'core' word left after any affixes have been removed.

The pronunciation module must also segment a word into syllables, and make sure that each syllable has a stress. This is vital for later use in pitch and duration assignment. All the areas mentioned will now be dealt with in more detail, with examples.

3.2.1   Dictionary lookup.

The pronunciation module performs this twice. If the text restriction module itself has not found a word in the dictionary, it will pass that word to the pronunciation module. The first look up is performed on the whole word. If it is present, the phonetic representation will be picked up and passed on to the prosodic module without any subsequent processing. If it is not, then affix stripping will be performed as described below, and the stem will be looked up.

3.2.2   Affix stripping.

This part of the program will try to reduce a word to its component prefixes, suffixes and stem. This is done to cut down on the enormous size of dictionary that would result if every derived word was inserted. It does this using separate prefix and suffix lists which act as auxiliary dictionaries. The search is done repeatedly to deal with the commonly found phenomenon of concatenated prefixes or suffixes. The lists consist of the pre- or suffix plus their phonetic transcriptions, plus any stress information introduced by the affix in question. An example of the latter would be elEctric vs electrIcity (stress moved to the I by addition of the ITY suffix). As an example, 'unwittingly' would be segmented as follows:

1st pass: PREFIXES

unwittingly --≫ un + wittingly   un --> U N

No more prefixes found

165

2nd pass: SUFFIXES

wittingly --> witting + ly   ly --> L EY

witting --> wit + ing   ing --> I NG

    No more suffixes found
    Stem 'wit' looked up in dictionary

This section of the program also deals with pronunciations hidden by the orthographic representation of the stem plus suffix. For example, the word 'tonal' is comprised of the word 'tone' + AL. 'Tone' is an open syllable whose pronunciation is indicated orthographically by the presence of a word-final 'E'. However, in the derivation 'tonal', when the affix is stripped, the final 'e' is not visible. Rules in the affix-stripping section of the code decide when this e is re-added to the stem in order to guarantee correct pronunciation (T OA N instead of T O N).

3.2.3 Grapheme to phoneme conversion.

This process converts the text stem from graphemes to phonemes using a set of ordered context-sensitive production rules, i.e. rules of the format 'A goes to B in the environment C'. An example of this type of rule is given below for the grapheme 'A'.

    A --> AR/__ TH#

This is read by the program as 'A goes to the phoneme AR when it is found before TH at the end of a word'. An example of this would be the word 'path', which would be represented as the phoneme string 'P AR TH'.

The final stage in this conversion will be to add on the phonetic transcription of any affixes that have been stripped off. The example in section 3.2.2 above will by this stage have a representation similar to the following:

    U N W I T I NG L EY

3.2.4 Lexical stress and syllabification.

Words must be stressed at the syllabic level. There are several tasks that must be performed in order to do this correctly. Firstly, the behaviour of words within a sentence must be modelled. Some words very rarely take stress; they form a small closed class which is termed function words. Examples of these are 'the', 'a', etc. All function words are in the dictionary and do not usually take stress in a sentence.

All other words are termed content words and are the usual candidates for word-level stress. The pronunciation module must mark all words as one or the other. Content words are marked at the beginning with a colon, function words with a slash.

Secondly, once the content words have been identified, they must be syllabified. This is done using a simple phonetic algorithm.

Thirdly, the lexical (i.e. word level) stressing is performed. Each syllable is assigned primary, secondary or zero stress for use by the prosodic module. This is done using various criteria, some syntactic, some phonotactic. The example used in section 3.2.3 will now be represented as

:U N "W I T -I NG -L EY

The double quotes represent primary stress, and the hyphens represent syllable boundaries.

3.3   Prosodic module

The input to the prosodic module is a stream of phonemes produced by the pronunciation module, and the output is a stream of allophones with values for pitch and duration assigned. Various processes are carried out and these are briefly described below.

3.3.1   Allophone selection.

This process decides how to realise a phoneme as its appropriate allophone. Various criteria determine this in the program; not all of them are linguistic in nature.

An important phenomenon occurring in natural speech is that of co-articulation, mentioned in section 2.1 above. This can be represented in a synthesis by rule program to a certain extent by specifying certain allophones which contain idealised acoustic characteristics generated by co-articulation, the so-called 'intrinsic' allophones. Rules are specified which determine when a certain phoneme should be replaced by one of these intrinsic allophones; they take the form of context-sensitive production rules.

Some selection rules work in a different way. For example, the phonological unit of a plosive has a complex phonetic realisation which can be regarded as being made up of three discrete segments. Firstly, there is a period of silence due to increasing air pressure behind an occlusion produced by the articulators, e.g. the lips in the case of /P/; secondly, the compressed air is released explosively due to sudden removal of the occlusion, producing a burst of white noise of short duration but high amplitude; thirdly there is a period of lower amplitude white noise for a longer duration as the remaining air is released and pressure returns to a normal level. The three acoustic stages are represented in the synthesis by rule program as three separate allophones. The types of rule described in this paragraph decide which of the three components are to be selected under which conditions.

3.3.2 Durational assignment.

Notional values for the duration of each allophone are stored in look up tables. They are then modified, according to certain criteria: lexical stress (assigned by the pronunciation module), the structure of each syllable, the number of content words in the breath group, etc. A set of ordered context-sensitive rules carries out the modification process.

3.3.3 Pitch assignment.

Pitch is assigned on a syllabic basis, depending on the punctuation at the end of the breath group. A breath group, as its name suggests, is a unit of speech roughly corresponding to the amount of speech a speaker will output in one breath. The punctuation will dictate the type of pitch contour used, and the pitch will be assigned accordingly. The greatest rise or fall, denoting the greatest stress, will be assigned to the stressed syllable of the final content word of the breath group.

By the end of the processing performed in the prosodic module, the output begins to look much less like text and more like control parameters. Each allophone is annotated with its duration and pitch value. The output of the prosodic module can thus be seen as a halfway point between text and parameters. A portion of the example used above, 'unwittingly', is shown:

```
 U   4   25
 N   3   25
 W   4   23
 I   8   28
 T   1   27
TY   2   26
 .   ..
 .   ..
```

3.4 *Parameter generation module*

This module forms the final stage in the processing chain, and its purpose is to take the information provided by the prosodic module and produce from it a set of parameters to drive the hardware model of the vocal tract.

The vocal tract model used by TEXTalk was devised by Holmes, Mattingley and Shearme [5], based on the source-and-filter model first proposed by Gunnar Fant

[6]. Basically, such a model consists of two excitation sources, one periodic to emulate quasi-periodic vocal fold vibration, the other aperiodic to simulate random fricative noise. These sources excite four filters connected in parallel. Three of these filters are variable in terms of both amplitude and frequency, and are used to emulate the spectrum produced by the oral tract. Each cavity in the vocal tract produces a characteristic formant in response to vocal-fold vibration. Hence a synthesiser that attempts to model the spectrum in terms of its formants is called a formant synthesiser. The same filters are excited by the aperiodic source to produce voiceless sounds. More details of the model of a parallel-formant synthesiser used by the TEXTalk system are given by Golfin et al [7].

A frame of eleven control parameters is provided to this hardware model every 10 ms. Raw parameters for each allophone are obtained by look up from a data table, but these values need to be modified to allow for the co-articulatory interaction between allophones. Each allophone has an associated internal and external duration, and these values are used to control the way in which the formant frequencies, amplitudes and pitch are allowed to vary on allophone boundaries. Thus, it is possible that for allophones of short duration the idealised formant frequency targets specified in the table might be missed, a situation which commonly occurs in natural speech due to rapid movement of articulators.

4. Current performance and further development

The current version of TEXTalk is adequate in terms of voice quality. However, in order to perform well in BT services it must be improved. In general, it is recognised that systems of this type benefit from linguistic knowledge encoded in the form of rules. Formulation of machine-usable rules from this knowledge is a vital part of the development of the TEXTalk system.

For example, much perceptual information is conveyed by intonation, an important component of the prosody of speech. At present, TEXTalk has only a simple model of intonation. This limitation can be overcome by adoption of a more sophisticated prosodic model and a suitable means of controlling this model. A suitable phonologically-based model has now been identified and has been found under test to be capable of producing speech of greater intelligibility using only a simple control strategy. It is thought that an improved control strategy will derive from a (necessarily limited) parse of the incoming text. Similar rules will be applied to duration of segments, another important acoustic component of prosody.

Another limitation to the speech quality is the adoption of the current Holmes model and data tables to permit control of more sophisticated systems are in preparation. The improvements to the quality of speech stemming from wider bandwidth, linguistically more accurate filter configurations, enhanced glottal pulse control and faster parameter update rate are most encouraging.

Other techniques, such as database analysis to improve the grapheme to phoneme ruleset, and alternative formant transition algorithms, are also being investigated.

References

1   Allport A, MacKay D G, Prinz W and Scheerer E (eds): 'Language perception and production: the relationships between listening, speaking, reading and writing', Academic Press, London (1987).

2   McCulloch N, Ainsworth W and Linggard R: 'Multi-layer perceptrons applied to speech technology', Br Telecom Technol J, 6, No 2 (April 1988).

3   Ladefoged P: 'A course in phonetics', Harcourt, Brace and Jovanovich, USA (1975).

4   Edward J A: 'Pronunciation rules for English text', JSRU Research Report No. 1014 (1982).

5   Holmes J N, Mattingley I G and Shearme J N: 'Speech synthesis by rule', Language and Speech 7, pp 127—143 (1964).

6   Fant C G M: 'Acoustic theory of speech production', Mouton, The Hague (1960).

7   Golfin N G, Challener P and Millar P C: 'A single card text-to-speech synthesiser', Br Telecom Technol J, 3, No 2 (April 1985).

PHONE-IN COMPETITIONS: A DEVELOPMENT AND EVALUATION TOOL FOR VOICE-INTERACTIVE SYSTEMS

P C Millar, I R Cameron, A J Greaves and C M McPeake

ABSTRACT

The importance of testing speech systems under realistic operating conditions is discussed. Application areas for telephone-based speech systems are considered, and it is concluded that a telephone competition would serve as a good vehicle for collecting data to be used for evaluation and development for many of these applications. The implementation and running of a fully automated voice-operated telephone competition is described. Finally, results are reported and examples are given to illustrate the usefulness of obtaining speech data in this way.

1. Introduction

Machines with a voice input and output capability offer a simple method of delivering information technology (IT) services to the general public over the telephone network. They make direct communication between a user and a machine possible, without the need for any extra equipment such as modems, keyboards or display units.

The voice-interactive systems required for these applications need three elements: speech recognition to interpret commands from the user, voice output to respond to the user, and a dialogue structure to control the interaction. Developing systems incorporating these features and evaluating their performance can be costly and time consuming. So it is important to ensure that the test conditions are valid for the target applications.

It is relatively easy to evaluate the component parts of voice products in isolation rather than as part of a system, but there are dangers in relying too heavily on such methods for anything more than comparative assessments. This can be particularly true in the case of word recognition subsystems, where the performance can depend a great deal on the practical operating environment. For example, speech engineers are well aware that an utterance given by a speaker during a training session can be acoustically quite different from the speaker's normal delivery. For this reason, recognition performance results are less meaningful if the subjects merely read words from a list than if they give responses in the context of a human/machine voice interaction. Similarly, dialogue structures and error recovery techniques need a realistic, task-oriented scenario in order to test their true effectiveness.

With these points in mind, a new approach was sought for gathering development and performance data relating to interactive speech systems capable of operating over the telephone network. In particular, it was important that the test subjects comprise a representative cross-section of the general public, and that they interact with the voice response system in a manner that would be typical of a real application.

2. Choice of test conditions

Applications for telephone-based voice input/output systems are numerous, e.g. intelligent answering machines, database inquiry services, telephone shopping, job notification for field staff, telephone marketing, telephone competitions and telephone banking.

These applications have system requirements that are essentially similar. Any one would serve as a good model to develop and test the required techniques. A phone-in competition is, however, an ideal choice, because those participating would be motivated to complete the voice interaction successfully.

2.1   Aims

By making telephone banking the theme for the trial competition, data relating to banking and telephone marketing could also be collected. In this way it would be possible to obtain information about these specific applications, as well as demonstrating and testing more general techniques and principles relating to voice-interactive systems. The main aims of the exercise could, therefore, be listed as follows:

- to assess a voice-interactive service operating under realistic conditions,

- to obtain data that could be both relevant to telephone banking and of general use in improving recognition accuracy,

- to assess the effectiveness of dialogue control techniques,

- to demonstrate the principles of automated phone-in competitions,

- to assess the accuracy of automated capture of speech messages,

- to demonstrate the principle of using phone-in competitions for market research.

2.2   Publicity and instructions

To attract entrants to the competition, an article was published in a British Telecom staff newspaper which has a readership throughout the whole of the United Kingdom. The article briefly outlined some of the potential uses of voice-interactive technology, highlighting telephone competitions and automated telephone banking as typical application areas. Specific information about automated telephone banking was given, and readers were invited to enter a phone-in competition, which involved answering questions on this topic. The competition entry procedures were given on a form and entrants were advised to fill in their answers prior to making their telephone call. It should be noted that written instructions were purposely kept to a minimum. The entrants were merely informed that their telephone calls would be answered by a machine, and that this machine would only be able to interpret single-word utterances. They were also told that a tone (beep) would sound to indicate when the machine was ready to accept a response from the caller.

2.3   Competition structure

The competition was structured into three parts. After being given a welcome message, the callers first had to go through a semi-formal template training routine, which involved speaking the digits 0-9, YES, NO, and 15 other words. In the second part of the competition the entrants had to give their answers to four factual questions, followed by their assessment of the order and level of usefulness of six proposed telephone banking services. The callers' responses during this section should all have been drawn from the set of words given in the template training session. The entrants were then requested to record a slogan along with their name, address and telephone number. Finally, the system informed each caller of their unique six-figure call reference number, and terminated the call after giving a goodbye message.

This format was chosen so as to demonstrate as many features of automated telephone competitions as possible. It was realised from the start that a commercially run competition would only comprise a shortened subset of these features, because participants could be deterred if call times are too long. The time for a typical caller to complete their entry in this trial competition was 12 minutes, and it was apparent that some callers were not going through to the end because of this. Whilst it was desirable for as many callers as possible to complete their entries, multiple entries were undesirable, since they would bias the data obtained. The length of the dialogue, therefore, had the useful effect of discouraging repeated calls in this case.

In an attempt to keep the level of interest high throughout the long interaction, an impressionist recorded the utterances that were to be delivered by the system, using a number of voices. In this way, the machine was able to take on the personality of four different television characters during the various stages of the dialogue.

3. Equipment

A system as shown in Fig 1 was used for the competition. The 14 telephone lines were connected via a hunting group facility. Thus it was sufficient to quote a single telephone number on the competition entry form.

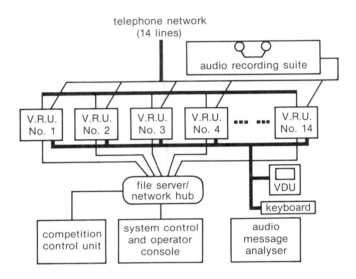

Fig 1   Automated voice-operated telephone competition system.

The telephone lines are terminated in voice-response units (VRUs). In addition to performing voice input and output functions these units also supply the appropriate line conditions for call answering and clear-down.

Each VRU comprises a personal computer (PC) and a voice card. The voice card performs word recognition and is able to produce output messages from pre-stored coded speech samples. It can also generate and store templates from speech input signals. The PC runs the applications program, interprets the recognition events and selects the voice output messages accordingly. A single switchable display and keyboard is provided so that an operator can interrupt normal running of any of the VRUs. A network also enables the PCs to communicate with the system console and the competition control unit, so that data collected on the individual VRUs can be collated centrally.

The competition control unit (CCU) automatically adjudicates each completed competition entry, by comparing the entrants' responses with a pre-judged set of model answers. It then orders the entries according to their scores. In addition, the CCU also keeps a running tally of the statistical distribution of the answers — information that could be useful for market research applications. A typical CCU screen display is shown in Fig 2.

```
┌────────────VOTEC competition control unit V1.06────────────┐
│                                                             │
│     service statistics:    Fri Oct 02 12:06:07 1987         │
│                                                             │
│            1st 2nd 3rd 4th 5th 6th       total rating        │
│ Balance:       131 59  43  36  21  15         2210           │
│ Statement:      25 49  49  62  60  29         1648           │
│ Transfer:       43 55  65  52  44  29         1759           │
│ Help:           26 15  19  48  54 139         1333           │
│ Cheque Book:    31 26  46  55  73  47         1568           │
│ Mini statement: 32 34  66  35  36  29         1810           │
│                                                             │
│ Last call ref. 020240   Question score: 4   Total score: 4089034 │
│                                                             │
│ Low score: 3096043   High score: 4126050   Winners: 200     │
│                                                   Limit: 200 │
├─────────────────────────────────────────────────────────────┤
│ Current activity: Incoming answer file 12 Files processed: 000321 │
├─────────────────────────────────────────────────────────────┤
│ Status: Incoming                       Disc Space: 15420 kB  │
│ Error count: 000000  Last error: (WARNING ONLY) answer file busy │
└─────────────────────────────────────────────────────────────┘
```

Fig 2   Typical competition control unit display.

The system control console (SCC) monitors the status of the VRUs and the CCU, and gathers statistics relating to the performance of the system. A record is kept of the key events of each telephone call. These are time and date stamped and saved for subsequent analysis. As shown in Fig 3, certain information is extracted and displayed on a screen so that an operator can monitor the activity of the system.

```
┌─────────────────────────────────────────────────────────────┐
│               VOTEC network supervisor V2.1                  │
│ Network status: Running │ system time: Fri 2 Oct 1987 — 11:25:11 │
├─────────────────────────────────────────────────────────────┤
```

Note	Status	OK	Total	Time	Max	Aug	CRN
VRU01	INCOMING CALL	121	278	5:23	20:04	6:39	010342
VRU02	INCOMING CALL	60	165	3:08	18:40	7:21	020204
VRU03	INCOMING CALL	41	105	1:07	20:19	6:46	030122
VRU04	INCOMING CALL	19	41	11:06	14:02	7:17	040063
VRU05	AWAITING CALL	4	14		13:28	6:56	
VRU06	INCOMING CALL	1	11	9:15	10:52	3:34	060023
VRU07	AWAITING CALL	0	2		1:55	1:48	
VRU08	AWAITING CALL	0	1		1:49	1:49	
VRU09	AWAITING CALL	4	10		11:22	5:22	
VRU10	AWAITING CALL	1	6		9:30	3:34	
VRU11	AWAITING CALL	0	2		1:59	1:53	
VRU12	AWAITING CALL	0	2		1:43	1:30	
VRU13	AWAITING CALL	0	0		0:00	0:00	
VRU14	AWAITING CALL	1	19		9:06	2:59	
CCU01	Winners: 200/252		655				

```
├─────────────────────────────────────────────────────────────┤
│ Console disk: 18676 KBytes free. Statistics file size: 62.45 KBytes │
│ Operator available? NO           Printer Status: OK          │
└─────────────────────────────────────────────────────────────┘
```

Fig 3   Data displayed on the system control console.

The audio recording suite was necessary to record all conversations so that dialogue faults and caller's problems could be identified. The recordings also had to be of a high quality so that they could be used later to generate accurate speech sample data. For these reasons a customised digital audio recording system was assembled using video-8 tape recorders. This system comprised nine dual-track machines and gave 24-hour coverage with only one tape-changing session per day.

4. Recognition considerations

Prior to the start of the competition, a stock set of representative templates was generated by processing speech from a sample group of 10 speakers (5 male, 5 female). These stock templates were then used for comparison during the template training stages of the competition proper. In this way it was possible for the VRUs to identify cases when there was a significant probability that the caller had spoken an incorrect word or that the received signal had been corrupted by noise. In such cases, the callers were asked to speak their last utterance again. By careful use of this type of control, it was possible to obtain very good template sets from each caller's training session.

These personal templates were then used throughout the remainder of the telephone call so as to maximise the recognition performance. They were also saved in a session record file, which was time and date stamped, so that they could be further processed if required at some later time.

For the caller to complete a competition entry successfully, the voice response unit had to perform a minimum of 26 correct recognition events. In order to achieve this level of recognition performance, without making the interaction too tedious, a robust confirmatory dialogue routine was used. This used soft decision logic to identify cases when mis-recognition was likely to occur [1]. If the input utterance was found to have a similar degree of match to two different templates then confirmatory questions were asked to establish which word had in fact been said. This technique was found to be particularly useful when the received signals were accompanied by a high level of noise.

An example of how part of the interaction might have proceeded is as follows:

Machine: What telephone banking service do you consider to be most useful? — [beep] — **Caller:** Transfer. **Machine:** And what usefulness rating have you given it? — [beep] — **Caller:** Six { signal partially masked by line noise}. **Machine:** Did you say, two? — [beep] — **Caller:** No. **Machine:** I see, then did you say, six? — [beep] — **Caller:** Yes.

Note that this confirmation routine speeds the caller's progress through the dialogue. The routine is only invoked when there is significant uncertainty about the accuracy of the recognition event. When the confidence in the match is high the dialogue proceeds without confirmation. There is, therefore, little need for re-cap or other error recovery routines to be invoked [1].

5. Operation

The applications programs for the competition are written in the C programming language, and use library functions to send and interpret messages from the voice card. The programs are loaded into each VRU via its own floppy disk drive. This means that the individual VRUs are all capable of running different versions of the application at any given time. This not only enables comparative tests to be performed, but also demonstrates that the system configuration permits separate applications to run concurrently. It also allows program up-dates to be fed onto the system without any noticeable interruption to the service.

The equipment needs very little human intervention in its normal operating mode. The most labour intensive tasks during the running of the competition was the changing and archiving of the audio recording tapes. The equipment ran for 24-hours-a-day throughout October 1987. During this time the only major operational problem was the occurrence of a complete power failure, but when power returned the VRUs automatically resumed operation, and continued to take calls.

Two sets of statistics files were saved, one containing data relating to the individual telephone calls (details of each recognition event and the progress of the call), and the other contained the answers recorded for each completed competition entry. These files, along with the template data files, were held in the individual VRUs as well as the CCU or SCC, but back-ups were also taken once a week to safeguard against catastrophic loss.

Additional files containing the digitally coded voice messages left by the contestants were also stored on the CCU. These were later accessed to find the names, addresses and telephone numbers of the winners, and also to hear their slogans.

6. Results

The exercise proved extremely productive in collecting information relating to the implementation of voice-interactive systems. A full breakdown of the data obtained would be too detailed for this paper. However, the following examples illustrate the usefulness of the method.

6.1 Speech data collected

The phone-in competition proved to be a very effective vehicle for collecting speech data from a wide range of speaker types using a variety of telephone channels. Caller classes roughly matched the staff distribution throughout the company. Approximately 12% of the callers were female, and about 90% of the calls were over long distance routes.

177

The fact that the complete interaction takes place between a telephone caller and a machine means that true human-machine response mode utterances were obtained. The training procedure at the beginning of the call enabled speaker specific templates to be gathered, and these were used to increase the recognition success rate throughout the subsequent parts of the competition. They were also saved for post-competition analysis purposes. It may be the case that the caller's utterances during the template gathering phase of the competition are of the less natural 'training mode' form, but the deliveries given in the question phase are likely to be typical of the subjects' normal 'response mode' speech.

All the callers' speech signals were stored so that a very large database of speech collected from a representative cross-section of the population could be assembled. Whilst part of the data collected during this exercise is specific to a telephone banking application, much of it will also be of general use.

Over 1100 callers completed their entries to the competition successfully, and a further 400 spoke a significant proportion of utterances before terminating their session. This has resulted in a database of around 90 000 words.

There were more than 1550 complete sets of words spoken in 'training mode' form (29 words per set), and approximately 1350 complete or nearly complete sets of utterances given in 'response mode' (10 words, 6 digits and a minimum of 11 YES/NO responses per complete set).

In all, approximately 40 000 words have been recorded in response mode. Of these, about 7500 were digits, 14000 were YES, 2500 were NO, and the remaining 16000 were words particular to telephone banking.

The template data from the training sessions can be archived and processed directly by a computer. Further processing can then be performed to classify the utterances. This can be useful for quantifying the recognition performance of the system, or, for example, in finding a more representative set of standard templates. This was in fact done for the words used in the competition, and a significant improvement in the speaker-independent recognition accuracy was achieved. Table 1 shows the relative performance of the reference template sets used in the competition and new sets generated using a template sifting routine. (The '% correct' sub-categories are: 1st choice correct without confirmation, 1st choice correct but triggering the confirmation routine, and 2nd choice correct using the confirmation routine. The '% failed' column shows the utterances that had scores beyond the acceptance threshold, and the '% misrec' column shows the utterances that were incorrectly classified).

Table 1   Recognition performance results.

A — Old sets (Acceptance threshold = 45, confirmation threshold = 7)

Word Set	No. of tests	% correct (1st, 1st c, 2nd c)	% failed	% misrec
Digits (M)	7425	81.75 (34.92, 32.77, 14.06)	13.47	4.78
Digits (F)	945	73.44 (30.05, 29.84, 13.54)	21.27	5.29
YES/NO (M)	990	89.49 {No confirmation possible}	10.11	0.40
YES/NO (F)	182	79.12 { with YES/NO responses }	20.33	0.55

B — New sets (Acceptance threshold = 45, confirmation threshold = 7)

Word Set	No. of tests	% correct (1st, 1st c, 2nd c)	% failed	% misrec
Digits (M)	7425	86.67 (42.65, 31.58, 12.43)	10.24	3.10
Digits (F)	945	84.23 (39.05, 30.26, 14.92)	12.38	3.39
YES/NO (M)	990	96.36 {No confirmation possible}	3.13	0.51
YES/NO (F)	182	96.15 { with YES/NO responses }	3.30	0.55

M = Male
F = Female

Unfortunately, the template feature data used in the above example are machine/algorithm specific. The competition audio recordings are the source of the more generally useful data. The signals on this medium have, however, to be extensively processed to get them in a form that can be easily manipulated on a computer. Firstly, the caller's utterances have to be stripped from the rest of the dialogue and stored in a compacted form. This has been done automatically by identifying the beep response cue preceding each utterance and recording the following 1.8 s of received signal. Markers have to be associated with this compacted data to label the event intervals. The utterances also need to be categorised according to: the word spoken, the sex of the speaker, whether it was a response or training mode delivery and the quality of the recording. Unfortunately, although labour intensive, it was considered that using human listeners for this task is the only reliable method of classifying this data, if a high level of confidence in the integrity of the final database is to be achieved.

6.2   Human factors

The human factors considerations can be classified under the headings — subjective opinions of the participants, and man/machine interface problems. A full human factors evaluation of the system has not yet been performed, but there were several points that became apparent throughout the course of the competition and as a result of some follow-up questionnaries given to 239 of the participants [2].

Although this particular competition had been designed to fulfil objectives that would not normally be addressed in a commercially-run exercise, the user- reaction feedback has been generally encouraging for a service of this type. This was apparent from the following statistics:

- users who found the competition enjoyable 66%

- users who felt comfortable talking to a computer 75%

- users who liked the voices used by the computer 67%

and of particular interest was the fact that 70% of those questioned said they would be likely or very likely to take part in a similar competition in the future.

The practical human factors problems that were discovered during the operation of the competition were mostly connected with the dialogue. They had a minor effect on the performance of the service in this instance. However, the fact that they occurred highlights the need to test systems under practical operating conditions. The following two examples were the ones that appeared to cause the most difficulty.

- After the entrants spoke the slogans, the machine would say, 'I have recorded your slogan as follows ...' { It would then play back a recording of the slogan so that the caller could hear that it had been received correctly}. It then asked the caller, 'Would you like to record your slogan again?' The dialogue designers had originally expected a YES/NO response at this point. Unfortunately, a substantial number of users interpreted this as a request for them to re-record their slogans, and immediately began re-reading their message. This, of course, caused problems for the recogniser, and to overcome them the dialogue had to be changed to the less ambiguous message, 'Your slogan sounded like this ...{ }... Are you happy that your slogan was complete and correct?'

- During the question phase of the competition callers were asked to rank the telephone banking services in an order of preference and give them a usefulness rating score. The machine would then confirm the caller's responses by saying, 'You have chosen (service X), with a rating of (score N), is that correct?' About 10% of callers replied with, 'CORRECT', to this question, causing difficulties because the machine could only interpret a YES/NO response at this node. No modification was made in this case, however, as the error recovery dialogue was usually able to cope.

The main lesson appears to be that the dialogue must be made robust to non-standard responses and that particular care should be taken to avoid the possibility of ambiguity in any requests by the machine.

6.3   Market research

The competition demonstrated the principle of using automated interactive telephone services for collecting market research information. Because the callers are interacting directly with a computer system the data that they are supplying can be processed automatically. The adjudication facility effectively illustrated that manual transcription of data is unnecessary when using this type of equipment. Similarly, the automated routines for recording the caller's slogan, name, etc demonstrated that machines can successfully gather and compose free-text messages from untrained users.

The raw data from the competition can, however, be processed further to generate additional statistics. This, of course, is one of the main reasons why promotional competitions are run. The plots in Figs 4 and 5 are given as examples of the type of information that might be extracted for market research purposes.

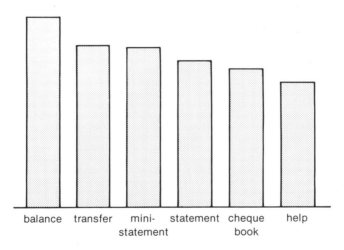

Fig 4   Relative popularity of the proposed telephone banking services.

Figure 4 was generated from an aggregation of the entrants' usefulness rating scores. This clearly shows that the balance enquiry service was the most popular choice with the contestants.

The call holding time statistics, displayed in Fig 5, illustrate the kind of data that can be further extracted from files stored on the SCC. They show the positions in the telephone call at which the entrants hung up, or the time it took them to complete their entries. From this it may be possible to infer the length of time that certain callers are prepared to interact with a machine for this type of application. Alternatively, it may be that the peaks correspond to the parts of the call that caused particular difficulty to some entrants.

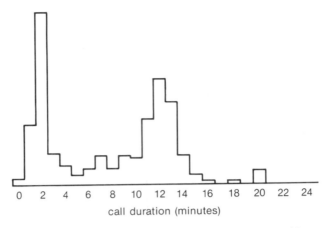

call duration (minutes)

Fig 5   Distribution of call holding times for the competition.

As well as being difficult to interpret, it should also be noted that statistics of this sort can be sensitive to the method of collection of the raw data, so caution must be taken in attaching any absolute significance to these particular results. The principles involved in this type of automated data collection are, however, demonstrated.

7. Conclusion

The phone-in competition proved to be a useful vehicle for evaluating a speech system operating in a real-life environment. The data obtained has already been used to improve the technical performance of some sub-systems. In addition, general principles of operation have been demonstrated and user-reaction to the technology has been tested.

Acknowledgements

Acknowledgement is given to our colleagues S McKinty, J Reah, K Silburn and J Crackett, for their part in developing the software, and to A Bennett and B Taylor for organising the publicity and commercial aspects of the exercise.

References

1   Millar P C, Cameron I R and Chaplin D J: 'A robust dialogue control strategy to improve the performance of voice-interactive systems', European Conference on Speech Technology, Edinburgh (September 1987).

2   'Reactions to BT competition using voice recognition computer', Harris Research Centre Report (November 1987).

MACHINE TRANSLATION OF SPEECH

F W M Stentiford and M G Steer

ABSTRACT

The automatic translation of speech between different languages would allow peoples of all nationalities to communicate freely over the international telephone network. Until recently there appeared to be no prospect of such systems for many years to come.

Research at British Telecom Research Laboratories has been successful in overcoming fundamental problems in the recognition, synthesis and translation of speech through the use of carefully selected keywords [1]. This paper describes a prototype speech translation system and how it is designed.

1. Introduction

Research in the field of machine translation (MT) began in the 1950s but was brought to a virtual standstill by a very critical report from the National Academy of Sciences in 1966 [2]. There is now a resurgence of interest throughout the world with major MT projects underway in Europe, Japan and the US [3,4]. In addition there are now several computer based products for text translation which are commercially available for assisting human translators [5,6]. The vision of high-speed high-quality automatic translation has always been the motivation behind MT research but even today there is no off-the-shelf solution for arbitrary texts [7,8,9].

The use of speech recognition and speech synthesis technologies together with MT now offers the possibility of automatically translating speech [10]. The increasing opportunities for spoken communication between countries having different languages suggests that there is a clear need for such a system. In Japan especially there are great pressures to provide an automatic translation facility to aid overseas communications, and the Automatic Interpreting Telephone Research Laboratories were established in April 1986 with just this objective in view [11].

Difficult problems specific to speech translation lie in the handling of recognition errors and the parsing of disfluent speech. Many parsers are extremely fragile in the sense that a failure in the search for potential parses is taken to mean that an incorrect path has been selected rather than an indication of erroneous input. Such parsers will yield solutions only if the input conforms precisely to the grammar and will reject input deviating even by one word [12]. A process which controls the dialogue can restrain the form that possible user utterances can take. However, the user normally has to be already aware of the general form of acceptable grammatical structures [13,14].

Considerable effort has been applied to the processing of both spoken and written natural language, and several approaches have been investigated which are capable of negotiating the vague and fragmented nature of human dialogue. Conceptual parsers attempt to extract key ideas from the input and ignore other parts which perhaps may contain errors and omissions. They are thus immune to many errors but not to those associated with the key ideas themselves [15].

Pattern matching is another analysis technique which matches the input against a set of patterns of words. This approach was first exemplified in ELIZA [16] which appeared to cope with a wide range of human dialogue if only at a very shallow level. Again this approach is unaffected by errors occurring in parts of the input not involved in the matching process [17,18]. An advantage of pattern matching is its ability to handle idioms which by definition can only be recognised and interpreted as a whole.

The principal limitation of pattern matching lies in its failure to analyse much of the redundant material present in natural language. The regularities reflected by auxiliary verbs, for instance, are more easily represented by grammar than by an exhaustive list of word patterns.

This paper describes a pattern matching technique which handles dialogue regularities in a non-redundant fashion. A procedure for the extraction of information-bearing key words is defined which enables a large set of phrases to be maximally distinguished from each other. This provides immunity to recognition errors even if they occur in critical parts of the utterance. At the same time it allows the identification of phrases to be quite tolerant of ungrammatical and fragmented input. The set of phrases used in this work has been translated into several European languages. This together with the appropriate synthesisers provides the basis for a multilingual speech driven phrase-book.

2. Problems of spoken dialogue

The informal and non-grammatical nature of normal language is a fact of life [18]. The problems which arise are especially severe in the case of spoken dialogue, which usually contains a much greater variety of unpredictable expressions than text [19]. The introduction of errors by speech recognition when communicating with computers imposes an even greater handicap on any automatic mechanism which attempts to extract meaning from a spoken utterance.

The performance of speech recognisers is influenced by the size and content of the vocabulary. In every application an acceptable compromise must be reached between the cost of handling recognition errors and the vocabulary size. In the context of speech translation no recogniser exists which is capable of handling a suitably large vocabulary at a level of accuracy which would retain the original grammatical structure for subsequent processing [20].

If existing speech recognisers are to be used for the input and translation of more than a few awkwardly constructed word combinations, then such recognisers must be operated in a word spotting mode. The limited vocabulary can then be confined to a carefully selected set of keywords which effectively extract necessary information. It should then be possible to process a very wide range of utterances without the problem of very large vocabulary recognition or a heavy dependence on syntactic analysis for error recovery.

When communicating within a limited domain of discourse, it is nearly always possible to specify all the required message concepts likely to be transmitted. Such phrase books have been written for example, for international telephone operators [21], international business correspondence [22] and international trade [23]. Difficulties arise when the user cannot remember the precise contents of a large phrase-book and wishes to access one of the messages using his own natural speech.

3. Phrase separation

Language may be usefully regarded as the creation of distinctions [24]. The selection of keywords from the total vocabulary spanned by a phrase-book is therefore governed by the contribution which that keyword makes towards the distinction of each phrase from all others. In this sense a word which is merely present in one phrase and found nowhere else may be of less importance than a word which occurs in 50% of the phrases. Furthermore the performance of a keyword is dependent on the set of keywords already selected. In an ideal case maximum information is extracted when each keyword is present in orthogonally different binary partitions of the set of phrases. In practice this is usually not possible but it does indicate a useful criterion for keyword selection. A similar approach has been used elsewhere [25,26] to extract features for pattern recognition where it is a prime requirement that such features should act independently of each other.

For example, consider the three phrases:

A. Who do **you** want to **speak** to?
B. **I** cannot hear **you**.
C. May **I** **speak** to Mr Smith please?

The occurrence of three keywords, 'you', 'speak' and 'I' is displayed in Fig 1. Each word occurs in two phrases and each pair of phrases differs by at least two keywords. This is an optimal solution in the simple case of three phrases and three keywords.

	you	speak	I	
A.	1	1	0	
B.	1	0	1	1 = word present
				0 = word absent
C.	0	1	1	

Fig 1   Word occurrence matrix.

The phrase 'To whom do **you** want to **speak**?' would be identified with A because of the similar pattern of occurrence of the keywords, **you** and **speak**.

4. Linguistic feature selection criterion

More formally, consider a set of H phrases P_i and a set of K linguistic features. Let each phrase P_i correspond to a feature vector F_i where

$$F_i = (f_{i1}, f_{i2}, ..., f_{iK}) \qquad i = 1,2,...,H$$

where

$$f_{ij} = 1 \qquad \text{if the } j\text{th linguistic feature is present in the } i\text{th phrase.}$$
$$f_{ij} = -1 \qquad \text{otherwise.}$$

Let $f_j = (f_{1j}, f_{2j}, ..., f_{Hj}) \qquad j = 1,2,...,K$

In the task of distinguishing the P_i in noise the best discrimination is achieved when the F_i are all separated from each other by a maximum angle. It can be shown [27] that the largest angle β, such that the angular distance between any pair of F_i is at least β, is given by

$$\beta = \cos^{-1} \left(\frac{-1}{H-1} \right) \text{ for } K \geq H-1.$$

It is to be noted that β is independent of K and that as H increases, an orthogonal arrangement of the F_i becomes very close to the optimum.

A measure of a feature's performance is required which when changed guarantees an improvement in the separation or the orthogonality of a set of feature vectors F_i.

It can be shown that given $[f_{ij}]$ is a square matrix ($H = K$) then a necessary and sufficient condition that the row vectors F_i are mutually orthogonal is that the column vectors f_j are mutually orthogonal. This means that any tendency for the f_j to become mutually orthogonal is similarly reflected in the F_i. Measures of angles between the f_j therefore have a direct bearing on the separation in feature space of the feature vectors F_i corresponding to the phrases P_i.

The independence (mutual orthogonality) of the F_i is given by

$$M = \sum_{i,j} (F_i.F_j)^2 = \sum_{i,j} \left(\sum_k f_{ik}.f_{jk} \right)^2$$

$$= \sum_{i,j,k,m} f_{ik}f_{jk}f_{im}f_{jm}$$

$$= \sum_{i,j,k,m} f_{ki}f_{mi}f_{kj}f_{mj}$$

$$= \sum_{i,j,k,m} f_{ki}f_{kj}f_{mi}f_{mj}$$

$$= \sum_{i,j} \left(\sum_k f_{ki}f_{kj} \right)^2$$

$$= \sum_{i,j} (f_i.f_j)^2$$

$$= \sum_{i \neq a} \sum_j (f_i.f_j)^2 + \sum_j (f_a.f_j)^2$$

$$= \sum_{i \neq a} \sum_{j \neq a} (f_i.f_j)^2 + 2 \sum_{j \neq a} (f_a.f_j)^2 + (f_a.f_a)^2.$$

which decreases towards zero as the mutual orthogonality of the F_i increases.

Hence for M to improve and decrease with f_a, it is only necessary that M_a decrease where

$$M_a = \sum_{j \neq a} (f_a.f_j)^2$$

since other terms are constants. The measure M_a provides an easily computed assessment of candidate feature a for its inclusion in a set for the optimal separation of phrases.

5. Phrase recognition

The linguistic features used in this work consist of keywords and combinations of keywords called **operators** [25,26] which are identified by isolated word speech recognisers. Consider the set of phrases P_i where

$$P_i = (w_{i1}, w_{i2}, \ldots, w_{iN_i}) \qquad i = 1, 2, \ldots, H$$

and w_{ij} is the jth word in the ith phrase. An operator o_j is defined as a set of pairs

$$o_j = (x_{ij}, r_{ij}) \qquad\qquad i = 1,2,\ldots,n_j$$

where

$$1 \le x_{ij} \le N_{max},$$

r_{ij} is a keyword

and N_{max} is the number of words in the longest phrase.

The operator o_j fits the phrase P_i if there exists an offset a_j such that

$$w_{i(x_{kj} + a_j)} = r_{kj} \qquad\qquad k = 1,2,\ldots,n_j$$

An unknown phrase Q produces a feature vector

$$(q_1, q_2, \ldots, q_K)$$

by the application of K operators.

Let

$$D_i = \sum_j |f_{ij} - q_j|$$

Q is identified with reference phrase P_m where

$$D_m = \min_i D_i$$

6. Phrase variation

Although the basic structure of phrases may be identified using the mechanism described above, many phrases require additional analysis to determine further information. To this end, careful attention has been paid to the handling of certain variables such as dates, times, prices, people's names and other proper nouns. For example:

I would like to book a room for the night of *8th December 1987*.
I expect to arrive about *7 pm*.
A single room with bath will cost *£55*.
My name is *Mr Steer*.
This is the *Royal* Hotel.

In the examples above the dates, times and prices require translation before synthesis in the target language; the proper nouns do not. It would be incorrect, for example, to translate 'Mr White' as 'Monsieur Blanc' in French rather than as 'Monsieur White'.

The prototype system handles these parameters by simultaneously recognising and storing each individual word in the spoken phrase. Then, assuming that the correct phrase has been selected by the system, two processes may take place.

- Proper nouns can simply be coded and transmitted to the receiving end for embedding in the foreign speech output.

- Other parameters requiring translation can be handled by a second recognition pass. Having already chosen the phrase, the location of a parameter is known, or can be deduced. New speech templates corresponding to that parameter can be loaded into the recogniser and the appropriate stored words re-recognised.

This two-pass process effectively increases the recognisable vocabulary of the system without degrading its recognition performance.

Additionally, these sub-vocabularies may be easily increased to include any other type of parameter appropriate to a particular phrase-book.

Although the system is phrase-book orientated it is extremely robust to errors. These may arise from the speech recogniser itself, but equally may originate from the user. It should be emphasised that the system does not require the user to know the **exact** contents of the phrase-book; provided the spoken phrase is close enough to one of the stored phrases then a phrase containing the intended meaning will be chosen. An example of this is:

Spoken phrase (keywords in bold):

Please would you reserve me **a** single **room with** bath.

Closest phrase in phrase-book:

I **would** like **to** book **a** single **room with** bath **please**.

which translates into French, German and Spanish as:

French: Je voudrais réserver une chambre pour une personne avec salle de bains.
German: Ich möchte ein Einzelzimmer mit Bad reservieren.
Spanish: Desearía reservar una habitación individual con baño.

Although the spoken English phrase differs from the stored phrase by two keywords **(to, you)**, it is still the closest, and a phrase with the intended meaning is therefore selected.

A further example is:

Spoken phrase:

> I **am sorry all our rooms are** occupied.

Closest phrase in phrase-book:

> I **am sorry, we are** fully **booked** then.

Here, the spoken phrase differs from the chosen phrase by five keywords.

7. Results

The performance of this translation system is to a large extent dependent on the separation of phrases achieved with the chosen set of keywords.

A set of several hundred phrases related to hotel booking has been analysed and it has been found that virtually all of the phrases differ from each other by three or more words taken from a subset of just 100 keywords. This gives the translation system as a whole a high immunity to errors resulting from speech recognition or the mode of expression. In practice it has been found that as many as half of the words in any given phrase can be mis-recognised before the wrong phrase is selected. It has also been found that the most useful keywords are found high on the frequency-ordered word list for that particular phrase-book.

As an example, the 20 most useful keywords in English, French, German, Spanish, Italian and Swedish for the hotel booking phrase-book are given in Table 1.

An example of the high immunity to speech recognition errors is shown below:

Spoken phrase:

> I **wish to** reserve **a** single **room with** bath.

Recognised phrase:

> **By wish to served a** * **room with are** (where * indicates that a word was detected but not identified).

Despite three recognition errors ('By' for 'I', 'served' for 'reserve', 'are' for 'bath'), the correct phrase was selected.

Table 1   The 20 most useful keywords for the hotel-booking phrase-book.

	ENGLISH	FRENCH	GERMAN	SPANISH	ITALIAN	SWEDISH
1	to	vous	Zimmer	el	di	hotellet
2	a	le	sind	tiene	desidera	har
3	has	l'hôtel	ist	habitación	il	vi
4	by	chambre	für	que	l'albergo	ni
5	is	à	an	una	per	rum
6	hotel	nom	sie	su	sono	och
7	it	les	Hotel	hotel	una	bilparkering
8	the	est	ein	a	che	service
9	that	je	haben	servicio	arrivare	ett
10	situated	la	und	aparcamiento	camera	erbjuder
11	room	nous	wir	reserva	è	för
12	how	personne	ihr	para	si	en
13	accept	quel	hat	esta	dispone	det
14	for	de	einen	me	quanto	kan
15	facilities	il	es	facildades	a	på
16	rooms	ce	Parkplatz	de	parcheggio	önskar
17	car	bonjour	ich	usted	persone	jag
18	you	arrivé	das	gracias	c'è	ar
19	of	parking	die	adiós	accettate	alla
20	yes	pense	vom	llegar	o	ligger

8. Prototype system

The prototype system is based on two BT 5200 personal computers (PC) linked via a simple datalink. Each PC contains commercially available speech recognition and speech synthesis hardware, and will handle one language at any one time. The serial datalink between the two computers could equally be a connection over the public switched telephone network with a data modem connected at each end.

Figure 2 shows the prototype hardware as demonstrated at Telecom '87 in Geneva in October 1987 and at the Royal Society in May 1988. The central monitor displays the phrases passed from one language to the other. A simplified block diagram of the hardware is shown in Fig 3.

One PC is initialised to recognise and synthesise one language, the other computer a different language. At present these languages may be any pair chosen from English, French, German, Spanish or Japanese, but in principle any number of computers and languages may be linked at the same time.

Assume for example that English and French have been selected. To use the system an English speaker enters a phrase into his computer, uttering each word clearly and in an isolated word fashion. The phrase is terminated by saying 'enter'. The computer then selects a phrase, processes any parameters, and echoes the chosen phrase to the user via the screen and speech synthesiser with a 'Do you mean ...'. If the phrase has been correctly identified, or is similar in meaning to the original spoken phrase, then the user can accept it by replying 'yes'. If the phrase did not convey the user's intended meaning then the user can reject it and make another attempt.

Fig 2   Prototype hardware as demonstrated at Telecom '87.

If the reply was acceptable the relevant phrase information is transmitted to the receiving end. There the corresponding French phrase is selected, any parameters inserted and the complete phrase is displayed on the screen and synthesised. The French recipient then has the option of having the synthesised output repeated if required.

The process is repeated in the opposite direction and a dialogue can take place. The overall system operation is shown in block diagram form in Fig 4.

9. Applications

Speech translation can be potentially applied to virtually any spoken communication across international boundaries. The research reported in this paper, however, is restricted to domains of discourse in which a set of message concepts can be defined and pre-translated into target languages. Suitable applications include the translation of spoken communication in specific business areas such as stockbroking, holiday booking and international car-hire. There is also a need to improve communications between international telephone technicians.

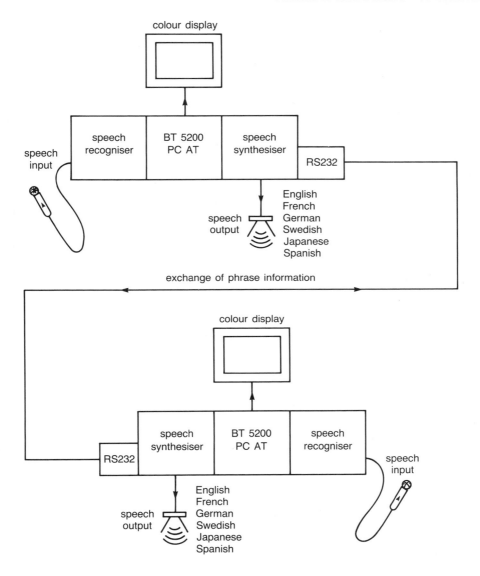

Fig 3   Simplified block diagram of prototype hardware.

Speech translation technology may be applied to the teaching of foreign languages where it could provide valuable assistance to students by automatically correcting their attempts at spoken translation.

It is hoped that the analysis of larger domains of discourse will demonstrate the feasibility of an increasing range of applications for speech translation.

193

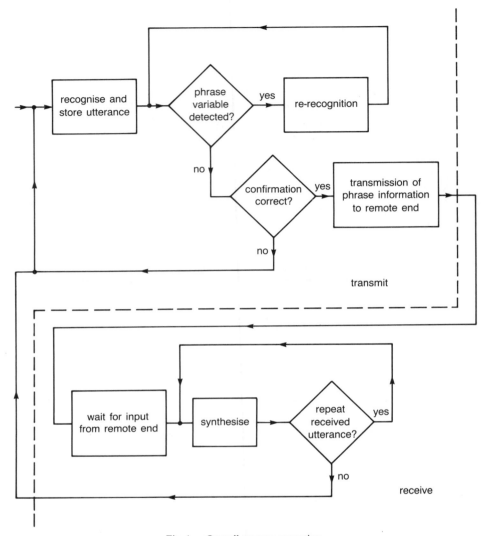

Fig 4   Overall system operation.

10. Future developments

The current equipment employs isolated word speaker dependent technology. That is, the user must train the recogniser to his voice before using the system, and when speaking to the recogniser must pause between words. Further developments in this area will allow the input of continuous speech and a much more natural flow of dialogue. Speaker independent recognisers will remove the need for tedious training procedures and offer the possibility of an automatic speech translation service on the public switched telephone network.

There is also research into developing better, more natural sounding, speech synthesisers, the ultimate goal here being to match the speech output to the voice of the originator or any other speaker for that matter!

11. Conclusions

A speech driven language translation system has been developed which allows the translation of spoken phrases between a number of different languages. The system is phrase-book based and overcomes many of the difficulties presented by recognition errors and disfluent input. Additional flexibility has been provided by the special handling of phrase parameters such as dates, times and names.

The system has been designed to make full use of existing technology whilst possessing immunity to errors from both the speech recogniser and the speaker.

There are several immediate applications for this system and it has potential for many more.

References

1 Stentiford F W M and Steer M G : 'A speech driven language translation system', 1st European Conference on Speech Technology, Edinburgh (1987).

2 'Languages and machines. Computers in translation and linguistics', Report by the Automatic Language Processing Advisory Committee, National Academy of Sciences, National Research Council, Washington (1966).

3 'Machine translation and natural language processing: opportunities for artificial intelligence in Canada', Cognos Inc., Reference DOC-CR-84-048 (February 1985).

4 Slocum J: A survey of machine translation: its history, current status, and future prospects', Computational Linguistics, 11 , No 1 (January—March 1985).

5 Johnson T: 'Natural language computing: the commercial applications', Ovum Ltd, 7 Rathbone Steet, London (1985).

6 Balfour R W: 'Machine translation: a technology assessment', BMT Consultants, Acomb Court, 23 Lansdowne Way, London (1986).

7 Nagao M: 'Current status and future trends in machine translation', Future Generation Computer Systems, 2 , pp 77—82 (1986).

8 Pigott I M: 'Essential requirements for a large-scale operational machine-translation system', Computers and Translation, 1 , pp 67—71 (1986).

9 Lawson V: 'The background to practical machine translation', Computers and Translation, 1 , pp 109—112 (1986).

10 Fujisaki H: 'Interpreting telephony as the ultimate goal for telecommunication', International Symposium on Prospects and Problems of Interpreting Telephony', Sponsored by Telecommunications Advancement Foundation of Japan, Tokyo (April 1986).

11 Kurematsu A: 'Research on automatic telephone interpretation', ATR Interpreting Telephony Research Laboratories, TWIN 21 Bldg, MID Tower, 2-1-61 Shiromi Higashi-ku, Osaka 540, Japan (March 1987).

12 Hayes P J and Reddy D R: 'Steps toward graceful interaction in spoken and written man-machine communication', International Journal of Man Machine Studies, 19 , pp 231—284 (1983).

13 Bobrow D G, Kaplan R M, Kay M, Norman D A, Thompson H and Winograd T: 'GUS, a frame-driven dialog system', Artificial Intelligence, 8 , pp 155—173 (1977).

14 Young S J, Russell N H and Thornton J H S: 'Speech recognition in VODIS II', Proc ICASSP-88, New York (April 1988).

15 Schank R C, Lebowitz M and Birnbaum L: 'An integrated understander', American Journal of Computational Linguistics, 6 , No 1, pp 13—30 (1980).

16 Weizenbaum J: 'ELIZA — a computer program for the study of natural language communication between man and machine', Communications of the ACM, 9 , No 1, pp 36—45 (1966).

17 Hayes P J and Mouradian G V: 'Flexible parsing', American Journal of Computational Linguistics, 7 , No 4, pp 232—241 (1981).

18 Parkison R C, Colby K M and Faught W S: 'Conversational language comprehension using integrated pattern-matching and parsing', Artificial Intelligence, 9 , pp 111—134 (1977).

19 Hayes P J, Hauptmann A G, Carbonell J G and Tomita M: 'Parsing spoken language: a semantic caseframe approach', Proc 11th International Conference on Computational Linguistics, pp 587—592, Bonn (25—29 August 1986).

20 Schmandt C: 'Problems in the design of speech interfaces using large vocabulary recognisers', Proc Speech Tech '86, pp 157—159, New York (28—30 April 1986).

21 'List of phrases used in the international telephone service', CCITT, published by UIT (August 1965).

22 'The multilingual business handbook', Pan Books Ltd (1983).

23 'Trade data elements directory', United Nations publication, Geneva (1983).

24 Winograd T and Flores F: 'Understanding computers and cognition: a new foundation for design', p 174, Ablex Publishing Corp., New Jersey (1986).

25 Stentiford F W M: 'Automatic feature design for optical character recognition using an evolutionary search procedure', IEEE Trans Pattern Anal Mach Intell, 7 , pp 349—355 (1985).

26 Stentiford F W M: 'Automatic feature design for speech recognition', Int Conf on Speech Input/Output; Techniques and Applications; IEE Conf Publication No. 258, pp 15—20 (24—26 March 1986).

27 Flores I and Grey L: 'Optimisation of reference signals for character recognition systems', IRE Trans Comput, 9 , pp 54—61 (March 1960).

BEYOND SPEECH RECOGNITION: LANGUAGE PROCESSING

R Linggard

ABSTRACT

It's conceivable that in the next few years, speech recognisers will be improved to the point where whole sentences, rather than isolated words, will be recognised with low error. It is at this point that machines will have to cope with the problems of language processing. This paper looks ahead to that happy time, and discusses the issues involved in 'understanding' language and in constructing appropriate linguistic responses. The division of language processing into syntax and semantics is explained by way of a computer analogy, and a simple hierarchy of problem complexity is given. The central difficulties in semantics are identified as those of database construction and access. Finally, the problems of semantic reference are discussed in relation to the functioning of human memory and sensory experience.

1. Introduction

For many years, a prime objective of speech recognition has been to design a system which would convert an acoustic speech signal into a typed version of its linguistic message. Though this task is easily accomplished by humans, it has proved impossible for machines to achieve it with anything like human competence. It has now become widely accepted that the acoustic signal of natural, conversational speech is inherently ambiguous, and that in order to resolve this ambiguity it is necessary to use informaton from 'higher' cognitive levels relating to the speaker, his emotional state, the language, the subject of conversation, and about the world in general. In other words, it is impossible to recognise natural, conversational speech without also understanding it.

Thus, the 'decoding' of the speech signal is not simply a set of one-way transformations, through ascending levels from the acoustic waveform via phonetic, phonemic, morphemic, lexical and syntactic forms to the semantic message. At each of these levels there is feedback to the level below as well as feed forward to the level above. Hence it is not possible to terminate the process at a particular level without impairing the efficiency of the levels below. Furthermore, it is by no means certain that these are the only levels that exist, or even that they exist at all. However, what is certain, is that the speech recognition process in humans is part of an integrated system which involves, at the highest levels, the whole intellectual apparatus of language, thought and understanding.

This paper attempts to look beyond the immediate problems of speech recognition to the task of speech understanding. As speech recognisers become more efficient, there is an increasing necessity to 'process', in some way, the linguistic message that the speech signal contains. This is partly to assist the recognition process itself, but mainly to facilitate more complex man/machine interactions, which is the original *raison d'etre* of speech recognition.

2. Problems of processing language

The 'linguistic message' in a speech utterance may be defined as the corresponding written transcription produced by a competent and literate speaker of the language. Such a transcription ignores information concerning the speaker's identity, his background, class and emotional state, and any emphasis that cannot be encoded in conventional punctuation marks. As yet, no machine exists which can perform this task automatically. However, nonwithstanding the difficulties of speech recognition, it is still possible to study the problems of speech understanding by simply typing the linguistic message into a computer. With the speech recognition problem effectively by-passed, the task of the machine is then to 'understand', in some sense, the linguistic message, and construct, in some way, an appropriate response. It is at this point that language processing begins.

In most languages, the linguistic message will consist of a sequence of symbols — letters and words. The study of processing such sequences, or strings, lies in the domain of linguistics, which has traditionally divided the problem into two sub-problems, syntax and semantics. Thus, there is a large body of literature on the problem of deciding whether or not sentences are syntactically correct. Likewise there is much interest in the task of assessing semantic validity, though this is not so well developed. From the viewpoint of designing an understanding system, knowing that a sentence is syntactically and semantically valid is not much help unless it can point the way to constructing an intelligent response. However, the idea of separating syntax from semantics is useful in isolating the purely formal part of language from the knowledge dependent aspect.

The syntax of a language, and more generally, the way in which words change in different situations, are all governed by the grammar of the language. Though it would appear that all human languages have grammatical rules, it is by no means clear that semantic influences can always be separated from syntactic constraints. Fortunately, in English the rules of word structure and sequence can, to a considerable extent, be divorced from the actual meaning of the words themselves. Consider the first verse from the nonsense poem 'Jabberwocky' by Lewis Carroll.

'Twas brillig, and the slithy toves
   Did gyre and gimble in the wabe;
All mimsy were the borogoves,
   And the mome raths outgrabe.'

This can be analysed syntactially even though many of the words are not to be found in any dictionary. Furthermore, these unknown words can readily be classified as nouns, verbs and adjectives.

A simple way of analysing English words is to divide them into two classes, content words and function words. The content words consist of all nouns, adjectives, verbs and adverbs. If these words are taken away, the few hundred words that are left, the pronouns, prepositions, conjunctions, auxiliary verbs, etc, are the function words of the language. Any valid sentence in English can, to a large extent, be 'semantically neutralised' if the content words are replaced by blanks. This process should not affect the syntactic structure of the sentence. For example, the above verse can be rewritten as

'Twas A, and the A N
   Did V and V in the N;
All A were the N,
   And the A N V.'

Here N stands for noun, V stands for verb, and A stands for adjective. The sentence is still syntactically valid if N, V and A are replaced by other nouns, verbs and adjectives. However, the actual meaning (if any) will depend on the particular choice of the replacements.

It is possible to take this analysis a stage further by using rules which govern the way in which word-forms can change. This involves the modificaton of verbs by case endings, and the transformation of verbs to produce nouns and adjectives, and of nouns to produce verbs and adverbs. Continuing the above example, the nouns 'toves', 'borogoves' and 'raths' are obviously plural forms of 'tove', 'borogove' and 'rath'. They could be denoted $N + s$. The adjective 'slithy' seems to derive from the noun 'slith', and could be denoted $N + y$. Similarly, the adjective 'mimsy' might be derived from the noun 'mim' and could be replaced by $N + s + y$. The tense of the verb 'outgrabe' is past so can be written $V + ed$. The neutralised text now reads

'Twas N, and the $N + y$ $N + s$
   Did V and V in the N;
All $N + s + y$ were the $N + s$,
   And the A $N + s$ $V + ed$.'

This makes the specification of the grammatical structure much more specific yet without involving the problems of semantics. These endings and modifications act like the function words, and are part of the syntax of the sentence. English (in constrast to German, say) has relatively few such modifications and relatively many function words. Note that the phrase 'Did gyre and gimble' is past tense. However, this is indicated by the function word 'Did' and not by the verb form which would have been 'gyred and gimbled'.

Systems of grammatical rules, or 'grammars' are the subject of intense research in the field of linguistics. The procedure which performs the analysis according to some defined grammar, is called a 'parser'. Generalised phrase structure grammars (GSPG), have been shown to be quite powerful in encapsulating the rules of English, and parsers based on them are quite successful in performing syntactic analysis. However, no grammar has yet been found which explains the whole of English. They usually fail at the syntactic/semantic borderline, which seems to indicate that syntax can never be completely separated from semantics.

3. Syntax versus semantics

An analogy which helps to explain the distinction between syntax and semantics, is to compare natural languages with high level computing languages. For example, sentences in English can be compared to program statements in Pascal. The function words of English are then like the reserved words in Pascal; they define the structure of the sentence (program statement) in which the content words (variables) are embedded. Thus, content words act as the semantic variables, and a complete sentence is a statement of the relationship between these variables.

An appropriate compiler can check a Pascal program for syntactic validity without being given specific values for the variables. Likewise, a GSPG parser can be used to check the syntactic structure of an English sentence without having to deal with the semantic values (meanings) of the words involved. A sophisticated compiler for Pascal will check the type compatibility of the variables before values are assigned. Similarly, a good GSPG parser can check the number (singular or plural) of nouns and the tenses of verbs, without recourse to their meaning.

The essential problem in the processing of natural language is not simply that of devising a comprehensive grammar and constructing an approprite parser. Even if this could be done perfectly, there still remains the difficulty of dealing with the semantic variables and of constructing an appropriate response. Continuing the computing analogy, even if the program compiles, it still has to run, and it is at this stage that the actual variables have to be processed. The problem is somewhat akin to programme validation in software engineering. Programs that compile do not necessarily run, and programs that run do not necessarily perform their intended task. Similarly, sentences that are grammatically valid are not always semantically correct, and even when they are, they do not necessarily convey the meaning the speaker intended.

However, assuming that people are able to say what they mean and mean what they say, it is now possible to examine the problems of semantic processing. Again, the computer science analogy is useful in obtaining insight.

4. Semantic processing

A statement in a computer program specifies an operation on the program variables. Likewise, in English, a sentence states a relationship between semantic variables. In a computer, the variables are stored in a 'data structure' and it is the job of the compiler to set up areas of temporary memory for this purpose. In addition, a program may require special files of data which are called into operation at run time, and whose structure and content are pre-defined.

A computer program will not run succesfully on another computer unless that computer has the same special files that the program needs to access at run time. Likewise, a sentence created by one human mind can not be correctly understood by another, unless they both have the same, or very similar, cultural background. (This includes the assumption that they both speak the same language.) 'Understanding' then, depends just as much on the characteristics of the human knowledge base as the formal mode of expression.

When English, or any other natural language, is processed by a human mind, it must use analogous, temporary and permanent 'data structures' in its memory. However, the human mind is not so clear cut in its division of memory into temporary 'scratch-pad' and permanent files. In the human case, the short-term memory fades relatively slowly, whereas long-term memory, which represents our accumulated experience of life and language, continually restructures itself.

Continuing with the analogy, the content words act as semantic variables which must be replaced by 'values' when the sentence (program statement) is processed (run). These 'semantic values' are the meanings of words and phrases, and are obtained from the human 'knowledge base'. It is the construction of such a knowledge base and semantic reference to it, that constitutes a central problem in natural language processing.

If the objective of such processing is to elicit an 'appropriate response', then the appropriateness of the response will depend on the nature of the sequence of sentences being processed. For example, questions ought to evoke answers and statements might necessitate up-dating of the recipient's knowledge base. But before questions and statements can be processed they must first be understood, that is, they must be checked for semantic compatibility against the knowledge base. The way that humans accomplish this seems to be more a function of human thought than a property of language. Essentially, the complete meaning of a sequence of sentences is built up in short-term memory using semantic values obtained from the knowledge base. This semantic entity may be new information, in which case it may need to be assimilated into the knowledge base. However, if it is a question, then the answer will be found by comparing this temporary knowledge structure with the corresponding part of the knowledge base.

To summarise, semantic processing can be viewed as similar to running a computer programme which operates on an extensive knowledge base. The action required by a collection of sentences (program), is either an updating of this knowledge base, or a retrieval of information from it. The task of syntactic decoding of sentences so that the semantic variables can be referred to the knowledge base, is intimately connected with the problem of constructing and accessing such a knowledge base.

5. Information structures

The central difficulty in constructing natural language understanding systems is in devising appropriate structures to contain the semantic information. The greater the richness of the semantic material, the greater the complexity of the syntax required to support it, and the more sophisticated the nature of the information structure necessary to contain it.

For example, a computer operating system which supports simple commands of the kind 'get file number 987', needs only a list of alternative commands as syntax, and a file index as data structure. In this simple case it is important to distinguish between the items of semantic information (file contents) and their names (file numbers). In a more complex case each semantic item might have a name, or identifier, consisting of more than one part. For example, in a file indexing system each file number may consist of a folder number and a document number. This is simple enough to appreciate, since the information is usually text and its address is usually numeric. However, in the more complex case of a relational database, each item of information may be referred to via several fields, both names and numbers.

The key concept which helps to explain the difference between indexed files and relational databases, is that of the dimensionality of the indexing, or addressing, system. A relational database is essentially multi-dimensional, and the items of information can be viewed as existing in a multi-dimensional space. Any particular item can be accessed via its 'co-ordinates', even though the co-ordinates themselves might be names rather than numbers.

For example, a database of people accessed via age, weight and height, could be considered as being three-dimensional. The co-ordinates of any point in the space would be numbers specifying age, weight and height, and the items of information would be names of individuals. An alternative structure would be to make the access via the individual's name so that the items of information are age, weight and height. In this case the database access is one-dimensional and the information is three-dimensional. Other arrangements are possible, depending on the way in which the database is to be used. It is at this point that the difference between the name of information and the information itself becomes blurred, because now the items of information can be used as address co-ordinates.

In order to obtain greater facility in accessing a multi-dimensional database, it would be convenient to be able to specify any parameters as indexing terms and thereby gain access to the others. This is called an associative database because the relationships between items are via association rather than indexing. This kind of structure is also known as 'content addressable' memory, however, it is perhaps wise to abandon the idea of addressing. Separate address parameters are no longer required, and the information items themselves act as indexing terms. Human memory is very much like an associative database, in that one memory leads naturally to another in an endless chain of recollection.

There is, however, one important difference between the human knowledge base and the simple associative database described above. In the human case the items of information are not just words. Language itself seems to be merely one means of accessing the knowledge base, essentially for the purposes of communication and contemplation. The essential information in the database consists of sensory memories, which embody our experiences of life. Thus access may also be gained associatively, via new sensory experiences. It is this sensory experience which represents the 'semantic value' of words, and gives language its basic meanings.

6. Machine understanding

The elegance and utility of separating syntactic and semantic aspects of language is that the task of understanding can then be represented in terms of two components, syntactic analysis and semantic reference. It is the complexity of these two dimensions which determines the complexity of the understanding task. Figure 1 shows a simple representation of language complexity in terms of the complexity of the syntactic and semantic processing tasks. Since syntactic analysis is essentially algorithmic, its complexity lies in its intricate processing. Whereas, the complexity of semantic reference lies in the sophisticated structure of the knowledge base.

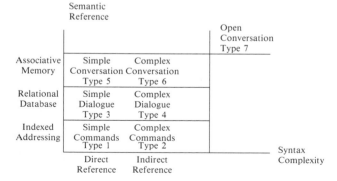

Figure 1   Language complexity.

The word 'understanding' implies a process, and, for the purpose of this discussion, can be defined as a desirable property of a language processing system. However, it is now necessary to qualify and quantify the exact nature of such a property. More specifically we ask, if a perfect speech understanding system existed, and even if it could type out whatever we said, how would we know that it really understood? Obviously it would not do to just ask the machine 'do you understand?' because it could easily be programmed to answer 'yes'. The only really practical way to validate understanding is to apply a functional test. The complexity of this test, or examination, will depend on the level of understanding that the machine is supposed to possess.

To assist insight into this problem it is worthwhile formalising the levels of understanding that might be required for useful speech understanding systems. The continuum from simple, one-word commands to open conversation, can be quantized to an arbitrary number of steps; however, for the purposes of this study, it is convenient to define seven levels of man/machine interaction, as follows.

- **Simple commands (level 1).** Here the machine is simply expected to obey the command, for example, 'get file number 987'. The command protocol 'get file number' is direct and the parameter '987' is completely unambiguous.

- **Complex commands (level 2).** These are of the form 'do X' where X is some kind of context variable task, for example 'get the next file'. The machine has to evaluate the unknown parameter 'next file' as a file number.

- **Simple dialogue (level 3).** This is essentially access to a database for the purpose of inputting and retrieving information. As with simple commands, the items of information and the names of their corresponding fields in the database are referred to directly. Statements of the form 'the weight is ten pounds' are decoded into commands to enter 'ten pounds' in the database field 'weight'. Similarly, questions are decoded into requests for information with the relevant data fields being referred to directly.

- **Complex dialogue (level 4).** This is like simple dialogue except that the items of information and their names may be referred to indirectly. For example, 'how long is it to lunch time' needs more than a clock and a data base of meal times. The machine must understand that the colloquialism 'how long' implies, in this case, that 'clock' must be subtracted from 'meal time' with the parameter 'lunch'. In this kind of dialogue pronouns and other references can be used.

- **Simple conversation (level 5).** Like simple dialogue items of information are referred to directly, but the machine now has an opinion of its own. It can check the 'truthfulness' of input statements and question their validity. Contradictory information can be held simultaneously, and incorrect data is not over-written. This implies a sense of time, it can reply 'now you say X, but before you said

Y'. The data structures required for this are necessarily more complicated, and an associative database of some kind is implied.

- **Complex conversation (level 6).** Like complex dialogue items of information may be referred to indirectly, but the machine has its own opinion and is unwilling to change its 'mind' without reasoned argument. It can use concepts which are not named explicitly and can add such concepts to its knowledge base. This level of understanding is equivalent to that of an intelligent adult with limited detailed knowledge and a tendency to take things literally. Also absent are emotions and a sense of humour. The data structures required for this kind of interaction will have to be very sophisticated indeed.

- **Open conversation (level 7).** This is the highest level of communication possible and represents conversation between intelligent, adult humans. The subject is open and any topic within the experience of the individuals may be addressed. Metaphor, allusion, irony and other devices may be used. It is unlikely, and perhaps unnecessary, that machines will ever achieve this level of interaction.

Clearly, the type of functional test required to evaluate understanding will depend on the understanding level. Simple and complex commands, levels 1 and 2, can be tested exhaustively, since there is a one-to-one relationship between command and response. Machines of this kind are at the lowest levels of the speech understanding hierarchy, and it is only by stretching the concept of understanding that they can be included at all. They are typical of computer operating systems.

For simple input and output of information via simple dialogue (level 3), the protocol may be more or less flexible and can be tested independently of the database access. The database is assumed to be of the conventional kind, with pre-defined fields and relations. The items of information which form the subject of the dialogue, must correspond with the data fields in the database, and must be referred to directly. Given this simplification, the sophistication of such systems resides entirely in the protocol. English allows a wide variety of ways in which statements can be made and questions can be posed, and the level of understanding is directly related to the generality of the input/output protocol translator which facilitates this.

It is at the level of complex statements and requests via complex dialogue (level 4), that tests of understanding become difficult. The assumption here is that the database is conventional but that the machine 'translates' complex statements and requests into conventional database protocol. It is important to distinguish between names of information types and the information itself. In the simple case the information and its type is named directly in terms similar to the database search parameters. In the complex case the information and its type may be referred to indirectly (for example by pronoun), so that some deduction or translation must be employed before it can be used to access the database. For example, the question 'what age is John?'

is a simple request if 'age' is a field in the database and 'John' is a parameter. However, 'how old is he?' requires some translation to equate 'he' with 'John' as the subject of the dialogue, and to deduce that 'how old' is equivalent to a request for the parameter 'age'.

At levels 1, 2, 3 and 4, the problem of semantic reference is dealt with, essentially, by the database which is assumed to be conventional. Since the content words of the dialogue are also fields in the database, or simple derivatives, the database protocol translator will detect any inconsistencies in the data types. For example, 'the weight is green' would be judged semantically incorrect because the expected data type for 'weight' is a number not a colour. Words not in the vocabulary of the translator would be treated as invalid, and would be the equivalent of nonsense words in English.

Conversation, at levels 5 and 6, would be very difficult to assess in terms of understanding. In simple conversation the concepts used are directly accessible in the data structure, even though the ways of expressing them might be quite complicated. Time sequence of events and 'truthfulness' will have to be included in the data structure. In complex conversation, the concepts used in the discussion may not exist in the database, and temporary equivalences may be set up. The use of abstractions considerably complicates the problem of semantic reference. Data structures to handle this kind of process would have to be very sophisticated, and have yet to be invented.

To summarise, in assessing the level of 'understanding' of a machine it is necessary to formulate a test of some kind. At the lowest levels an exhaustive test of the machine's repertoire is possible. At higher levels only sample tasks can be tested, and at the highest level an exam would be necessary, somewhat akin to an IQ test. It is only at levels 5 and 6 that the machine could be said to have any intelligence, and its level of understanding would be judged by the level of its intelligent response.

8. Semantic reference

In the discussion on levels of understanding, no attempt was made to distinguish between limited and unlimited subject domains. The reason for this is that the relationship between size and complexity is by no means simple. The essential problems are those of constructing and referencing an appropriate data structure (knowledge base). At the simple level, increase in size does not imply much increase in complexity. But at higher levels of sophistication, increase in size is achieved by merging domains, and the interaction of different domains leads to an increase in complexity.

However, it must be acknowledged that some limited domains are inherently more difficult to formalise than others. For example, arithmetic is a particularly easy subject for which to devise a data structure. The types of relationships between numbers are well categorised and the relationships themselves are explicit. These remarks hold true, to greater and lesser degrees, for sciences where the content words usually have firm definitions, and the relationships between them are fairly well defined. On the other hand, music, painting and literature, and the arts in general, are all so subjective that it is unlikely that any two humans would give identical judgements on a range of such topics.

It is this kind of 'subjectivity' that lies at the very heart of the semantic reference problem. In a subjective domain like music, for example, many of the content words used in discussion symbolize sensory experience. Other words would relate to ways in which a rational mind might organise such experiences during learning or contemplation. Thus a data structure appropriate for a conversation on music would consist of information derived from direct sensory experience, and other information relating to the way in which this experience had been organised under the influence of reason and education.

The essential problem of semantic reference is that it is difficult to build a data structure with the appropriate sensory information, even though the corresponding abstract, organisational terms can be input via language. For example, the word 'furniture' is the name of a class of terms, 'chairs', 'tables', etc which are themselves names of classes of objects. Any reference in conversation to 'furniture' can be decoded as referring to any, or all, of the objects 'chairs', 'tables', etc. However, there can be no further decoding of 'chairs' or 'tables' because the appropriate referents are collections of sensory experiences relating to these objects. Thus a remark concerning some particular object being used as a table or a chair, cannot be validated without reference to this experience of tables and chairs.

9. Conclusions

The problem of using language to communicate with machines is not new. Computer scientists, involved in the design of computer operating systems and databases, have long been familiar with these difficulties. In most cases, the sophistication of the data structures being used is limited to what can be achieved by conventional computer languages, hence communication tends to be via highly artificial, specialist language. Computer languages themselves are examples of special purpose communication systems in which the complexity of the syntactic processing may be quite high.

Specialised languages are helped by the facility of keyboard and screen. In general, people think as they type, pausing when necessary to remember; this and the visual feedback helps them to use formal protocols. Unfortunately, people do not always think as they speak, and they cannot spontaneously limit their vocabulary. Thus, even if speech recognition were to be perfected, the problems in accomplishing speech understanding are inherently more difficult than those of text understanding. A speech recogniser is not simply a replacement for a keyboard.

In terms of syntax, it seems that natural speech is somewhat more complicated than text. Since there are no punctuation marks, sentences are not delimited, so that, even with simple semantic structures, syntactic processing is likely to very difficult. In particular, the temptation to use pronouns and other reference terms, is almost impossible to overcome. One way to simplify speech recognition so as to facilitate communication with computers is to use isolated words. Though it is difficult to speak in this mode, its very unnaturalness does make it easier to use simplified syntax and limited vocabulary.

On the axis of semantic complexity, practical systems can use quite simple data structures. For example, directory enquiry service would require only an index of names, addresses and telephone numbers. More complicated services which could be envisaged, might require full relational databases. However, a more complex service requiring 'intelligent' response will await the advent of the more complex, associative knowledge structures.

The subjective impression of intelligence in a conversation is directly related to the sophistication of the knowledge base rather than the complexity of the syntax. (A conversation with an intelligent foreigner is none the less intelligent because he uses simplified grammar.) A major obstacle to the advent of intelligent man/machine interaction, therefore, is the design of associative memories with similar properties to that of the human brain. But even given this, it is unlikely such memories will be of much use unless they have the same, or similar, training to the humans with whom they will converse.

Perhaps the best hope for the future of natural language processing lies in research work currently being carried out into 'connectionist' methods of pattern recognition. Connectionist machines are based on the structure of neural networks and possess the inherent property of associative recall. Some of these devices are self-learning, so that it would be possible to use language to help them organise the patterns they are given to learn. In addition, they are being used for recognising visual and acoustic patterns, so that they have the ability to store 'sensory' information.

HIDDEN MARKOV MODELS FOR AUTOMATIC SPEECH RECOGNITION: THEORY AND APPLICATION

S J Cox

ABSTRACT

Hidden Markov modelling is currently the most widely used and successful method for automatic recognition of spoken utterances. This paper reviews the mathematical theory of hidden Markov models and describes how they are applied to automatic speech recognition.

1. Introduction

Machine transcription of fluent speech — the so-called 'phonetic typewriter' — remains a challenging research goal. A machine capable of performing this task would require an enormous amount of knowledge about the real world working in conjunction with a mechanism for decoding acoustic signals. However, automatic speech recognition (ASR) has reached the point where, given some restrictions on speakers, vocabulary and environmental noise, reliable recognition of isolated words or short phrases is possible.

A distinction is generally made in ASR between recognition of utterances from a speaker who has previously 'enrolled' his voice (speaker dependent recognition) and a speaker whose voice the recogniser has never 'heard' previously (speaker independent recognition). To some extent, it is possible to trade vocabulary size for speaker dependence, so that it is currently feasible to build either a speaker independent ASR device that recognises a small vocabulary (5-20 words or phrases), or a speaker dependent device that recognises a large vocabulary ($\approx 10\ 000$ words). For telephony applications, enrollment free ASR is clearly crucial and it turns out that many useful applications are possible with a small vocabulary.

Broadly speaking, attempts at ASR fall into two categories — a knowledge-based approach, in which knowledge about speech from the domains of linguistics and phonetics is used to construct a set of rules which is in turn used to interpret the acoustic input signal, and a 'pattern-matching' approach in which *a priori* knowledge about speech is largely ignored and techniques of pattern classification are applied

209

to the input signal. The knowledge-based approach is able to exploit a body of knowledge about speech and, in particular, the relationship between features extracted from the speech signal and higher level linguistic representations (e.g. phonemes, syllables). However, this relationship, which is very complex, is still far from being understood, largely because of the enormous variability of signals interpreted by the brain as representing the same linguistic units. Of the knowledge that is available, it is not yet clear how best to represent or use it in a computational framework.

The pattern-matching approach makes no attempt to use this kind of knowledge, but gathers its 'knowledge' of the speech signal in a statistical form by being shown examples of speech patterns. As such, it would work equally well on any acoustic patterns — birdsong, machinery noise, seismic signals etc. However, powerful mathematical techniques are available which are guaranteed to optimise the technique and these ensure that the approach is surprisingly successful, even though almost all knowledge of speech production, perception and the speech signal is ignored.* Furthermore, these techniques are applicable to patterns at any level and hence can be used to optimally decode other representations of speech signals (e.g. phonetic segments, words), thus providing a coherent framework for speech recognition and understanding.

This paper focuses exclusively on the pattern matching approach which is used by all commercial ASR devices. In particular, two techniques have been found to be especially appropriate to ASR — dynamic time warping (DTW) and hidden Markov modelling. DTW is a special case of hidden Markov modelling and is discussed in Appendix A. A third *connectionist* approach is now evolving, based on adaptive parallel distributed processing networks [1].

2. Pattern classification

Figure 1 shows a block diagram of a pattern classifier in training and recognition modes.

In training mode, many examples of each class are used to build a model for the class, and these models are subsequently stored. In recognition mode, a pattern of unknown class is compared with each model and classified according to the model to which it is 'closest'. When performing recognition of isolated words, each different word is regarded as a class.

The feature extraction shown in Fig 1 is necessary for two reasons. Firstly, it enables focusing on information within the signal which is important for discriminating between patterns of different classes; a good set of features '...enhances within-class

---

* The two approaches to ASR have been pithily summarised by one researcher as 'doing the right thing wrong or the wrong thing right'.

similarity and between-class dissimilarity' [2]. Secondly, it enables data reduction so that manipulation of patterns becomes computationally feasible. (A telephone speech signal has a typical data-rate of 64 000 bits/s, too high for practical computation.)

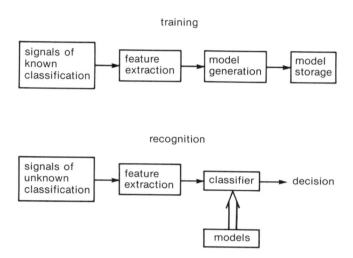

Fig 1   A pattern classification system in training and recognition modes.

Features for speech recognition are generally either related to the instantaneous spectrum of the speech signal or to the instantaneous shape of the vocal tract; clearly, there is a large overlap of information in these representations. Feature selection is of great importance in speech recognition, as accuracy is highly dependent on the type and number of features used [3]. Because of the sluggishness of the speech articulators, an adequate representation of the speech pattern can be made by measuring features at regular intervals of approximately 1/100 s. Each sample is a d dimensional vector of features, so that an utterance of length t seconds is reduced to a sequence of $T = 100 * t$ d-dimensional analysis vectors. In this paper, utterances are considered to be isolated words and so the approach to recognition is sometimes called whole word pattern matching [4].

3. Speech pattern classification using hidden Markov models

Speech differs from most signals dealt with by conventional pattern classifiers in that information is conveyed by the temporal order of speech sounds. A *stochastic* process provides a way of dealing with both this temporal structure and the variability within speech patterns representing the same perceived sounds. Stochastic processes '...develop in time or space in accordance with probabilistic laws' [5]; a stochastic process that has been found to be particularly useful in ASR is a hidden Markov model (HMM).

3.1 Description of a hidden Markov model

Figure 2 shows an example HMM.

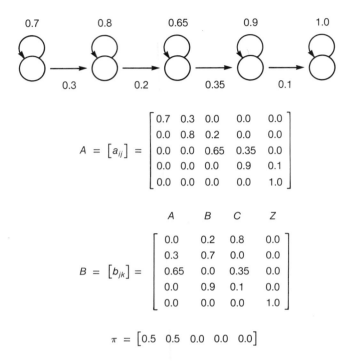

$$A = [a_{ij}] = \begin{bmatrix} 0.7 & 0.3 & 0.0 & 0.0 & 0.0 \\ 0.0 & 0.8 & 0.2 & 0.0 & 0.0 \\ 0.0 & 0.0 & 0.65 & 0.35 & 0.0 \\ 0.0 & 0.0 & 0.0 & 0.9 & 0.1 \\ 0.0 & 0.0 & 0.0 & 0.0 & 1.0 \end{bmatrix}$$

$$B = [b_{jk}] = \begin{array}{c} \begin{array}{cccc} A & B & C & Z \end{array} \\ \begin{bmatrix} 0.0 & 0.2 & 0.8 & 0.0 \\ 0.3 & 0.7 & 0.0 & 0.0 \\ 0.65 & 0.0 & 0.35 & 0.0 \\ 0.0 & 0.9 & 0.1 & 0.0 \\ 0.0 & 0.0 & 0.0 & 1.0 \end{bmatrix} \end{array}$$

$$\pi = \begin{bmatrix} 0.5 & 0.5 & 0.0 & 0.0 & 0.0 \end{bmatrix}$$

Fig 2   A 5-state left-right hidden Markov model with 4 output symbols.

The five circles represent the states of the model and, at a discrete time instant t, the model occupies one of the states and emits an observation. At instant $t+1$, the model either moves to a new state or stays in the same state and emits another observation, and so on. This continues until a final terminating state is reached at time T. An important characteristic of this process is that the state occupied at time instant $t+1$ is determined probabilistically and depends only on the state occupied time t — this is the Markov property. The probabilities of moving from state to state are tabulated in a $N \times N$ state transition matrix, $A = [a_{ij}]$ — an example A is shown in Fig 2. The i, jth entry of A is the probability of occupying state s_j at time $t+1$ given state s_i at time t. Since the total probability of making a transition from a state must be 1.0, each row of A sums to 1.0. Notice also that A is upper triangular, because this particular HMM is a left-to-right model in which no 'backwards' jumps are allowed and the model progresses through the states in a left-right manner. In a generalised HMM, a transition is possible from any state to any other state, but there is clearly no point in using anything but a left-to-right HMM for ASR as only left-to-right models will effectively model the temporal ordering of speech sounds. The topology of the model shown in Fig 2 is rather simple, and richer topologies in which states may be skipped are used to advantage in ASR.

An observation emitted at a time instant t by the HMM shown in Fig 2 can be one of only 4 symbols, A, B, C or Z. In general, a model can emit any of a finite alphabet of M symbols $(\nu_1, \nu_2, ..., \nu_M)$ from each state, and the probability of emitting symbol ν_k from state s_j is given by the j, kth entry of a $N \times M$ matrix $B = [b_{jk}]$ (an example B is shown in Fig 2). A final parameter needed to set the model in motion is a vector π whose ith component $\pi(i)$ is the probability of occupying state i at $t = 1$ — again, an example is given.

An observation sequence is produced by the model of Fig 2 as follows.

- Use the vector π and a random number generator (RNG) to determine which state the model starts in — assume this is state s_i. Set $t = 1$.

- Use the probabilities in row i of B and the RNG to select a symbol ν_k to output.

- Use the probabilities in row i of A and the RNG to determine which state s_i to occupy next. Set $t = t + 1$.

- Repeat the second and third steps until a terminating state is reached. (State 5 in the model of Fig 2 is such a state, because it has a self transition probability of 1.0 and only outputs the symbol Z. Hence the observation sequence would be an infinite succession of Zs once state 5 is reached.)

A typical observation sequence produced by this process acting on the model of Fig 2 might be: CCBCCBBBACAAACACBBBZ. Notice that the states that produced each symbol are hidden in the sense that, given an observation sequence, it is in general impossible to say what the state sequence that produced these observations was[§]. An algorithm which finds the most likely state sequence given an observation sequence and a model is introduced later.

3.2   Relationship of HMMs to speech production and recognition.

The above description of an HMM was deliberately kept abstract, but the reader may already have an inkling of how the process is related to speech production. Let us make the following premise about the production of an utterance of a particular word: *an utterance is produced by the articulators passing through an ordered sequence of 'stationary states' of different duration; the 'outputs' from each state (i.e. the observations) can be regarded as probabilistic functions of the state.* This is a crude

---

§ If a one-to-one correspondence between states and symbols exists, the process is known as a *Markov chain*.

and drastically simplified model of the complexities of speech; speech is a smooth and continuous process and does not jump from one articulatory position to another. However, the success of HMMs in speech recognition demonstrates that if the model is correctly optimised on speech data, it captures enough of the underlying mechanism to be powerful.

The observation sequence of the HMM is thus the sequence of analysis vectors described in section 2. The model described in section 3.1 can output only a finite alphabet of symbols but the analysis vectors are continuously valued — hence each analysis vector must be mapped to a symbol by the process of vector quantization [6]. This process causes an inevitable loss of accuracy and it will later be seen how HMMs can be extended to handle continuous distributions rather than discrete symbols.

The correspondence of HMM states to articulatory states is by no means clear cut because it is difficult to define what one means by a 'state' in a smoothly produced utterance. The closest physical correspondence to a state might be the articulatory position in a long vowel sound. Although this correspondence is of considerable theoretical interest for future work in modelling speech signals, it is not necessary to attempt to make it for the purposes of performing speech recognition, and it is not of present concern.

There are two problems in the application of HMMs to isolated word speech recognition.

- Given a set of utterances of a vocabulary of words (the training set), construct one or more HMMs for each word (training).

- Given a set of HMMs, one or more for each word in the vocabulary, classify an unknown utterance (recognition).

The recognition problem is solved by computing the likelihood of each model emitting the observation sequence corresponding to the unknown utterance and assigning the unknown utterance to the class of the model which produced the greatest likelihood. The training problem is more difficult, but a powerful algorithm exists (the Baum-Welch algorithm) which guarantees to find a locally optimal model. These two problems are considered in detail in sections 4.1 and 4.2.

4. The recognition problem

The recognition problem is tackled first because it is the more straightforward of the two and the training problem builds on some of the definitions it introduces. Firstly, a more formal definition of some of the notation already used is given below: +

+ The notation used here generally follows that of [7] and [8].

s_j = jth state of the HMM $j = 1,2,...,N$
v_k = kth output symbol in the
       alphabet $k = 1,2,...,M$
a_{ij} = Pr(state s_j @ $t+1$ | state
         s_i @ t) $i = 1,2,...,N$
                         $j = 1,2,...,N$
b_{jk} = Pr(outputting symbol v_k
         from state s_j) $j = 1,2,...,N$
                             $k = 1,2,...,M$
O_t = tth observation (analysis
       vector) $t = 1,2,...,T$
$b_j(O_t)$ = Pr (outputting observation
           O_t from state s_j)
         = b_{jk} when $O_t \rightarrow v_k$
w_i = the ith word in the
       recognition vocabulary $i = 1,2,...,W$

The hidden Markov model M is fully defined by the parameter set $[\pi, A, B)$. We are given W such models, $M_1, M_2,... M_w$, one for each word in the vocabulary, and an unknown utterance O, which consists of a sequence of T observations $O_1,O_2,...,O_T$; each O_i is one of the symbols $v_1,v_2,...,v_M$. Recognition is achieved by computing the likelihood of each model having produced O, i.e. by computing $Pr_i(O|M_i)$, $i=1,2,...,W$, and assigning O to class k where $P_k = \max_{i=1,2,...,W} Pr_i(O|M_i)$.

4.1   Baum-Welch recognition

The most obvious way of computing $Pr(O|M)$ is to consider every possible sequence of states that could have generated the observation sequence and find the one which produces the highest $Pr(O|M)$. However, it is easy to see that this is unrealistic, as in general there are N^T possible sequences. This number is considerably reduced if A is sparse, but it is still impossibly large for practical purposes ($N^T \cong 9 \times 10^{20}$ for $N=5$, $T=30$). Fortunately, a recursive algorithm exists to calculate $Pr(O|M)$. The algorithm depends upon calculating the so-called forward probabilities, which are the probabilities of the joint event of emitting the partial observation sequence $O_1,O_2,...,O_t$ and occupying state s_j at time t. These probabilities are later used in the Baum-Welch training algorithm and so the associated $Pr(O|M)$ is denoted by P^{BW}. Let the forward probabilities be denoted by $\alpha_t(j)$ i.e.

$$\alpha_t(j) = Pr(O_1,O_2,...,O_t, \text{ state } s_j \text{ @ time } t|M)$$
$$j = 1,2,...N$$

......(1)

It should then be clear that the required probability is:

$$P^{BW} = \sum_{j=1}^{N} \alpha_T(j) \qquad \qquad \ldots\ldots (2)$$

since $\alpha_T(j)$ is the probability of emitting O and ending in state s_j. The $\alpha_t s$ can be computed recursively, as follows. Suppose $\alpha_\tau(i), i = 1,2,...,N$, has been computed at some instant t, then

$$Pr(O_1, O_2,...,O_t,\ state\ s_j @ time\ t+1 | state\ s_i @ time\ t,\ M) = \alpha_t(i)a_{ij}$$

Hence the probability of occupying state s_j at time $t+1$ is:

$$Pr(O_1, O_2,...,O_t,\ state\ s_j @ time\ t+1 | M) = \sum_{i=1}^{N} \alpha_t(i)a_{ij}$$

Finally, accounting for observation O_{t+1} from state s_j gives:

$$\alpha_{t+1}(j) = [\sum_{i=1}^{N} \alpha_t(i)a_{ij}]\ b_j(O_{t+1}) \quad t=1,2,...T-1 \qquad \ldots\ldots(3)$$

Figure 3 illustrates these steps by showing the computation of α_{t+1} (4) for a six state HMM.

Since $\alpha_1(j) = Pr(O_1,\ state\ s_j @ t=1 | M)$, the recursion in equation (3) is initialised by setting $\alpha_1(j) = \pi(j)b_j(O_1)$.

4.2 Viterbi recognition

In the above calculation of P^{BW}, each α_{t+1} is calculated by summing contributions of α_t from all states and hence P^{BW} is the likelihood of emitting O, summed over *all* state sequences. The Viterbi algorithm computes the likelihood P^v of the most likely state sequence emitting O; by backtracking, this sequence can also be recovered.

This likelihood P^v, and the associated most likely state sequence S_T, are found by computing $\phi_t(j)$, where:

$$\phi_{t+1}(j) = \max_{i=1,2,..,N} [\phi_t(i)a_{ij}]\ b_j(O_{t+1}) \qquad t=1,2,\ ...\ T-1 \qquad \ldots\ldots(4)$$

216

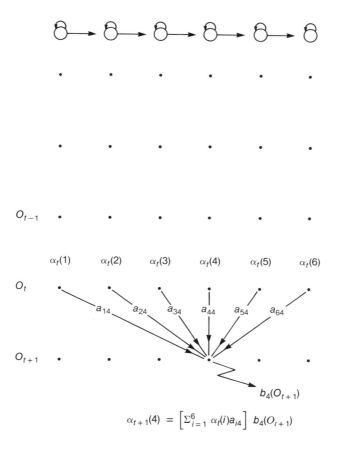

Fig 3   Computation of $\alpha_{t+1}(4)$ for a six state HMM.

Equation (4) is identical to equation (3) except the summation has been replaced by the max operator. The probability of outputting O is then given by:

$$P^v = \max_{j=1,2,..,N} \phi_T(j)$$

$$\dots(5)$$

Compare equation (5) with equation (2). If it is desired to recover the most likely state sequence, $\psi_t(j)$ is also recorded, where $\psi_t(j)$ is the most likely state at time $t-1$ given state s_j at time t. Hence $\psi_t(j) = i^*$, where i^* is the number of the state which maximises the RHS of equation (4).

Having calculated all the ϕs and ψs for $j = 1,2,\dots,N$ and $t = 1,2,\dots,T$, the backtracking proceeds as follows: the most likely state at time T is state s_k, where k maximises the RHS of equation (5); hence $\psi_T(k)$ gives the most likely state at time $T-1$, from which the most likely state at time $T-2$ is found and so on until the most likely state at $t=1$ is recovered. Figure 4 gives an example of the most likely state sequence for a 20 frame utterance and a six state HMM.

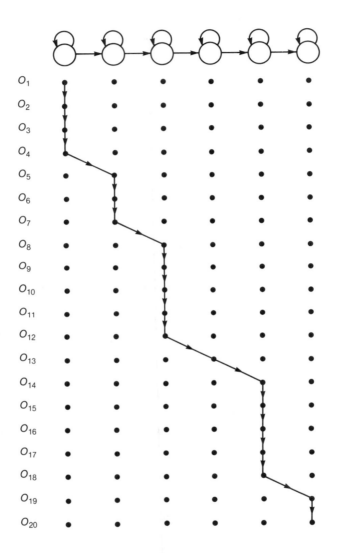

Fig 4   A Viterbi state sequence for an observation sequence of length 20 and a six state hidden Markov model.

Notice that $P^v \leq P^{BW}$, with the equality satisfied only when the state-sequence producing the observations is unique.

5. The training problem

The principal reason for using HMMs in isolated word recognition is to capture statistical information about the variability in patterns representing the same word, and so a training technique that optimises the model for a large number of utterances (observation sequences) is required. However, assume for the moment a single observation sequence O for each word; the extension to multiple observation sequences is straightforward (section 5.2). The essential steps in the training algorithm for a given word are as follows: an initial estimate of M is made; the re-estimation algorithm and O are used to generate a new model M', with the property that $Pr(O|(M')) \geq Pr(O|M)$; M' then plays the rôle of M' and a new estimate is determined. This process iterates until the inequality in the above expression is arbitarily small. Two re-estimation algorithms, the Baum-Welch and Viterbi algorithms, are discussed here.

5.1 The Baum-Welch (forward-backward) algorithm

The underlying idea behind this algorithm is that, given some estimate M of the model and an observation sequence O, the best estimates of the parameters of a new model M' are:

$$a'_{ij} = \frac{Pr(\text{transition from state } s_i \text{ to state } s_j | M)}{Pr(\text{transition from state } s_i \text{ to any state} | M)}$$

......(6)

$$b'_{jk} = \frac{Pr(\text{emitting symbol } \nu_k \text{ from state } s_j | M)}{Pr(\text{emitting any symbol from state } s_j | M)}$$

......(7)

$$\pi'_i = Pr(\text{observation sequence begins in state } s_i | M)$$

......(8)

The remarkable property of the Baum-Welch algorithm is that the above re-estimates of A, B and π are guaranteed to increase $Pr(O|M)$ until a critical point is reached, at which point the parameters do not change.

To compute these quantities, the forward probabilities $\alpha_t(j)$ are complemented, by defining backward probabilities $\beta_t(i)$ as follows:

$$\beta_t(i) = Pr(O_{t+1}, O_{t+2}, ..., O_T, \text{state } s_i \text{ @ time } t \mid M)$$

In other words, $\beta_t(i)$ is the probability of starting in state s_i at time t and then completing the observation-sequence (N.B. beginning with observation O_{t+1}, not O_t). The reader should have no difficulty in convincing himself that, using similar reasoning to the calculation of equation (3), $\beta_t(i)$ can be calculated by the following backward recursion:

$$\beta_t(i) = \sum_{j=1}^{N} a_{ij}b_j(O_{t+1})\beta_{t+1}(j) \qquad t = T-1,\ T-2,...1 \qquad \qquad ......(9)$$

with $\beta_T(i) = 1$, $i = 1,2,...,N$. The numerator of equation (6) is then given by:

P(transition from state s_i to state $s_j|M$) =

$$\sum_{t=1}^{T-1} \alpha_t(i)a_{ij}b_j(O_{t+1})\beta_{t+1}(j)$$

This is built up as follows: $\alpha_t(i)$ gives the probability of being in state s_i at time t; $a_{ij}b_j(O_{t+1})$ accounts for moving to another state s_j and outputting symbol O_{t+1} from this state; $\beta_{t+1}(j)$ accounts for occupying state s_j at time $t+1$ and then completing the sequence. This probability is summed over all times at which it is possible to make a transition i.e. from 1 to $T-1$ (N.B. not T). To calculate the denominator of equation (6) recall that:

$$\alpha_t(i) = Pr(O_1,O_2,...,O_t,\ state\ s_i@time\ t|M)$$
$$\beta_t(i) = Pr(O_{t+1},O_{t+2},...,O_T,\ state\ s_i@time\ t|M)$$

Hence $\alpha_t(i)\beta_t(i)$ is the probability of occupying state s_i at time t given M. So the denominator of equation (6) is:

$$Pr(\text{transition from state } s_i \text{ to any state}|M) = \sum_{t=1}^{T-1} \alpha_t(i)\beta_t(i)$$

and the complete equation is expressed in terms of the forward and backward probabilities as:

$$a'_{ij} = \frac{\displaystyle\sum_{t=1}^{T-1} \alpha_t(i)a_{ij}b_j(O_{t+1})\beta_{t+1}(j)}{\displaystyle\sum_{t=1}^{T-1} \alpha_t(i)\beta_t(i)} \qquad \qquad ......(10)$$

A similar reasoning leads to expressing equation (7) as:

$$b'_{jk} = \frac{\displaystyle\sum_{k \ni o k \quad vk} \alpha_k(j)B_k(j)}{\displaystyle\sum_{t=1}^{T} \alpha_t(j)\beta_t(j)} \qquad \qquad ......(11)$$

The summation of the numerator of the above equation is read: 'Sum over all ts at which O_t is symbol ν_k'. Finally, the re-estimation of π is shown to be:

$$\pi'(i) = \frac{1}{P^{\text{BW}}} \alpha_1(i)\beta_1(i) \qquad \qquad ......(12)$$

Although equations (6), (7) and (8) seem a plausible way of updating the model parameters, no proof has been given that they are guaranteed to increase $Pr(O|M)$. The reader interested in rigorous proofs will find them in Liporace (9).

5.2   Training on multiple observation sequences

Equations (10), (11) and (12) are extended to permit re-estimation on many observation sequences by simply considering the definitions in equations (6), (7) and (8) to act over all the observation sequences. However, given a certain model, each observation sequence will have a different P^{BW} and the probabilities from sequences having low P^{BW} will give a disproportionately low contribution in equations (6), (7) and (8) — the result is that the model is optimised only for utterances having high P^{BW}. The solution is to weight all probabilities by $1/P^{\text{BW}}$. Denoting equation (10) as $a'_{ij} = N/D$, the change is:

$$a'_{ij} = \frac{\sum_{l=1}^{U} \frac{1}{P_l^{\text{BW}}} N_l}{\sum_{l=1}^{U} \frac{1}{P_l^{\text{BW}}} D_l} \qquad \qquad ......(13)$$

N_l and D_l are the numerators and denominators formed when processing observation sequence (utterance) O^l, P_l^{BW} is $Pr(O^l|M)$ and U is the total number of utterances in the training set. Similar alterations apply to equations (11) and (12). When applied to multiple observation sequences, the Baum-Welch algorithm is guaranteed to increase $\sum_{l=1}^{U} P_l^{\text{BW}}$ at each iteration.

5.3   Viterbi training

The Viterbi algorithm can be used for model re-estimation as well as for recognition. In this case, the backward probabilities (βs) are not required and there is a significant computational saving. Conceptually, the Viterbi training procedure is simple: the Viterbi algorithm is used to segment each utterance according to the current model, as in Fig 4. The new values of $[\pi, A, B)$ are then derived directly by examining the numbers of transitions to and from each state and the symbols output by each state. The procedure is as follows.

●   Make an initial estimate of the model, $M = M^0$.

- Using model M, execute the Viterbi algorithm on each of the observations $O^1, O^2, ..., O^U$. Store the set of most likely state sequences produced, $S^1, S^2, ..., S^U$, and set

$$L = \sum_{1=1}^{U} P^v(O^1|M).$$

- Use the Viterbi re-estimation equations ((14,) (15) and (16) below) to generate a new M.

- Iterate the second and third steps until the increase in L upon each iteration is arbitarily small.

The re-estimates are given by considering all the sequences $S^1, S^2, ..., S^U$ and setting:

$$\overline{a_{ij}} = \frac{\text{(No of transitions from state } s_i \text{ to state } s_j | M)}{\text{(Total no of transitions out of state } s_i | M)} \quad \text{......(14)}$$

$$\overline{b_{jk}} = \frac{\text{(No of emissions of symbol } \nu_k \text{ from state } s_j | M)}{\text{(Total no of symbols emitted from state } s_j | M)} \quad \text{......(15)}$$

$$\overline{\pi_i} = \frac{\text{(no observation sequences beginning in state } s_i | M)}{U} \quad \text{......(16)}$$

Note that weighting by $1/P$ is not required here since numbers of transitions are considered rather than probabilities of transitions. As with the Baum-Welch algorithm, this procedure is guaranteed to increase $\Sigma_{1=1}^{U} P_1^V$ at each iteration.

6. Extension to continuous probability density functions

So far, it has been assumed that the HMM must output one of a finite alphabet of M symbols. This means that the observation vectors from the speech signal must be quantized, with an inherent loss of accuracy. If it is attempted to minimise this quantization distortion by using a large number of quantization symbols, a large number of probabilities in the matrix B must then be re-estimated (for instance, with 128 symbols and 10 states in the HMM, it is necessary to re-estimate 1280 probabilities on each iteration of the training algorithm). There is rarely enough training data available to estimate such a large number of parameters.

If it can be assumed that the observation vectors from a particular state are drawn from some underlying continuous probability distribution, the information in the corresponding row of B can be replaced by the parameters of this distribution. This is equivalent to making a Normal approximation to some histogram data and replacing the individual probabilities in the histogram by the mean and variance of the Normal distribution.

The question is then immediately raised of how well the observed data fits the parametric distribution. Experimentally, the analysis vectors in a particular state tend to cluster rather than produce a smooth distribution [8]. However, it has been shown that an arbitary multivariate continuous probability density function (PDF) can be approximated, to any desired accuracy, by mixtures (weighted sums) of multivariate Gaussian PDFs. It is therefore appropriate to model the probability distribution of each state as a Gaussian mixture (although the re-estimation formulae have been proved for any log-concave distribution [9]). The probability $b_j(O_t)$ of emitting an analysis vector O_t from state s_j is then:

$$b_j(O_t) = \sum_{m=1}^{X} c_{jm} N[O_t, \mu_{jm}, U_{jm}] \qquad j = 1, 2, \ldots N$$

$$\ldots\ldots(17)$$

where X is the number of mixtures, c_{jm} is the weight of mixture m in state s_j and $N[O_t, \mu_{jm}, U_{jm}]$ is the probability of drawing the vector O_t from a multivariate Normal distribution with mean-vector μ_{jm} and covariance matrix U_{jm}§. Clearly, $0 \le c_{jm} \le 1$ and $\sum_{m=1}^{X} c_{jm} = 1$.

6.1 Re-estimation with continuous mixture distributions

How does the change from discrete to continuous distributions affect the equations built up in the previous sections? The only change in the equations in sections 4.1-5.2 is that $b_j(O_t)$ is now defined as equation (17), so that once $b_j(O_t)$ has been calculated for each O_t, the recognition algorithms (Baum-Welch or Viterbi) are unaffected.

The re-estimation formulae (both Baum-Welch and Viterbi) for a'_{ij} and π'_i are similarly only affected by the change in the definition of $b_j(O_t)$. However, the training procedure must now re-estimate c_{jm}, μ_{jm}, U_{jm}, $m = 1, 2, \ldots, X$ for each state s_j.

To cope with a number of mixtures in each state, a third function augments the forward and backward probabilities:

$$p_t(j, m) = Pr(O_1, O_2, \ldots, O_t, \text{ state } s_j,$$
$$\text{mixture } m @ \text{ time } t | M) \qquad\qquad \ldots\ldots(18)$$

Comparing equations (1) and (18), it is clear that:

$$\sum_{m=1}^{X} p_t(j, m) = \alpha_t(j)$$

The mixture-weights for each state are then calculated as:

---

§ For readers unfamiliar with multivariate Normal distribution, a brief review is given in Appendix A.

$$c'_{mj} = \frac{Pr(\text{mixture } m, \text{ state } s_j | M)}{Pr(\text{state } s_j | M)}$$

$$= \frac{\sum_{t=1}^{T-1} \rho_t(j,m)\beta_t(j)}{\sum_{t=1}^{T-1} \alpha_t(j)\beta_t(j)}$$

The re-estimate of the mean vector of mixture m in state s_j is:

$$\mu'_{jm} = \frac{\sum_{t=1}^{T} \rho_t(j,m)\beta_t(j)O_t}{\sum_{t=1}^{T} \rho_t(j,m)\beta_t(j)}$$

......(19)

Notice that if $X = 1$ (i.e. a single Gaussian distribution per state), equation (19) becomes:

$$\mu'_j = \frac{\sum_{t=1}^{T} \alpha_t(j)\beta_t(j)O_t}{\sum_{t=1}^{T} \alpha_t(j)\beta_t(j)}$$

......(20)

$$= \frac{\sum_{t=1}^{T} Pr(\text{state } s_j @ t | M).O_t}{Pr(\text{state } s_j | M}$$

......(21)

The re-estimate of the mean vector of a state is thus an average of each of the T analysis vectors, weighted by the probability of occupying the state at time t. The elements of the covariance matrix are found in the usual way by considering the mean vector μ_{jm} and the T analysis vectors. In practice, a diagonal covariance matrix is usually used because of the difficulty in estimating $d(d+1)/2$ components for each mixture and state with limited training data. Proofs of all the re-estimation equations for the case of a single mixture density per state are given in Liporace [9]. The Viterbi algorithm can also be extended to re-estimate the parameters of continuous mixture distributions.

7. Some considerations of implementation

Sections 2—6 have presented the mathematical theory of HMMs. This section discusses some of the practical issues raised in using HMMs for automatic speech recognition.

7.1 Preventing underflow

It is apparent that many of the equations in sections 4 and 5 will underflow quite rapidly on real computers as they involve recursive products of small probabilities. One solution is to introduce scaling terms at certain points in the recursion [7]. A seemingly more direct method is simply to use logarithms thoughout. However, it is necessary to add terms in many of the equations, so a function returning $\log(a+b)$ given $\log a$ and $\log b$ is required. This function requires an exponentiation and a logarithm so that computationally, there is little to choose between these solutions.

7.2 Zero symbol probabilities

When using discrete HMMs with finite training data, it sometimes happens that the probability of observing a certain symbol v_k from state s_j is 0. If this occurs, any α, β or ϕ of an equation in section 5 will be 0, which will be fatal to both recognition and training algorithms. The obvious, although somewhat inelegant solution, is to set the offending probability to some small but non-zero value, ϵ. This situation has been analysed theoretically by Levinson et al ibid [7] who also ran some experiments on the effect on recognition accuracy of the value of ϵ ibid [10]. Their conclusions were that the performance was almost identical using values in the range $10^{-10} \le t \le 10^{-3}$, for $M = 128$.

7.3 Initial model estimate

The Baum-Welch re-estimation algorithm is a hill-climbing algorithm which converges to a locally optimal model; hence the final model will depend on the initial model. The question then arises of how to make a good initial estimate of A and the output parameters, B (in the discrete case) or c_{jm}, μ_{jm} U_{jm} (in the continuous case). The initial estimate of A is chiefly determined by the topology chosen for the model, but the initial estimate of the output parameters can be based upon the training data. Rabiner, Levinson et al have shown that continuous HMMs are very sensitive to poor initial estimates of means ibid [11]; it therefore seems wise to base the initial estimate of the output parameters on the available training data.

Two sensible methods of obtaining initial estimates of the output parameters are as follows.

- **Uniform segmentation:** each utterance in the training set is partitioned into N segments of equal length and the analysis vectors in each segment are pooled.

In the case of discrete distributions, they are then quantized and an estimate of b_{jk} is made:

$$b_{jk} = \frac{\text{No of vectors of symbol } \nu_k \text{ in segment } j}{\text{Total no of vectors in segment } j}$$

In the case of continuous mixture distributions, the initial estimates of means and covariance matrices are made by applying a clustering algorithm to the vectors of segment j(state s_j) to produce X clusters. μ_{jm} and U_{jm} are then respectively the mean vector and covariance matrix of cluster m in the state.

- **Optimal segmentation:** each utterance in the training set is partitioned into N segments according to the algorithm of Bridle and Sedgwick [12]. This algorithm finds the optimal segmentation of the utterance into N segments in the sense that, if the mean vector of each segment is computed, the sum of the intra-segment variances is minimised. The vectors in each segment are pooled and the estimates are made as described above.

All elements of A are set initially equal to $1/K_i$, where K_i is the number of allowed transitions (non-zero elements) in row i, and similarly, the first l elements of π may be set to $1/l$.

8. Summary

Hidden Markov models provide a coherent framework for dealing with variability in speech patterns. Although the assumptions about speech made by HMMs are crude, they are offset to a great extent by the availability of powerful optimisation techniques. An attractive feature of HMMs is that it is possible to extend and improve them whilst retaining their mathematical rigour. *Pace* section 1.2, this can be done in such a way as to utilise some knowledge about the speech signal (see, for instance, Russell and Cook [13]) and this offers promise for future speech recognition algorithms.

HMMs need large amounts of training data to work effectively on large speaker populations, leading to a considerable computational requirement for building the models. However, this is done 'off-line' and recognition of a small vocabulary using HMMs can be implemented to work in real time. Using some of the techniques described in this paper, a speaker independent recognition algorithm has achieved an accuracy of 98.1% on a vocabulary of the digits.

Acknowledgements

My thanks are due to Dr M J Russell of the Speech Research Unit, RSRE, for his helpful comments and discussions during the preparation of this paper, and to Dr R K Moore (also of the Speech Research Unit) for permission to reproduce Fig 5.

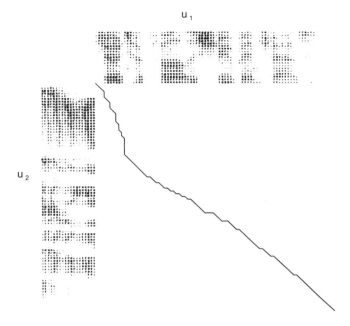

Fig 5   Dynamic time warping alignment of two utterances.

Appendix A

Dynamic time warping and hidden Markov models

An earlier and still much used pattern matching technique for ASR is dynamic time warping (DTW). It was the desire to extend and generalise DTW that lead to the use of HMMs for ASR and it was quickly realised that DTW is a special case of hidden Markov modelling [14,15].

The science fiction sound of the name of this technique refers to the way in which an utterance is non-linearly 'stretched' or 'compressed' in time to align it with another utterance. Figure 5 shows an example of this process.

The analysis vectors (frames) of the two utterances U_1 and U_2, of lengths T_1 and T_2 respectively, are positioned with their first frames in the top left corner of the figure and subsequent vectors following in a rightwards and downwards direction respectively. In this case, each frame is a spectrum of the instantaneous speech signal, formed by sampling the outputs of 19 bandpass filters along the audio spectrum. The partially enclosed rectangle can be thought of as a $T_2 \times T_1$ grid whose i,jth element, $M(i,j)$, is the distance between frame i of U_1 and frame j of U_2 . Commonly used distance metrics are the Euclidean and the City-Block (Manhattan) metric.

The zig-zag path through the grid is known as the optimal time registration path and maps every frame of U_2 to a frame of U_1. If a constraint is imposed on the mapping that the beginnings and the ends of the utterances must coincide, the optimal mapping is a path through the grid which starts in the top left square, ends in the bottom right square, and minimises the total cumulative 'distance' en route. This minimisation is performed by using the technique of Dynamic Programming. Imagine a second grid whose i, jth element $N(i,j)$ holds the lowest cumulative distance to that position. This element may be calculated as follows:

$$N(i,j) = M(i,j) + \min[N(i-1,j), N(i-1), N(i-1, j-2)] \qquad \ldots\ldots(22)$$

In other words, the cumulative distance to element i,j is found by minimising over three possible 'routes' to the element, as shown in Fig 6.

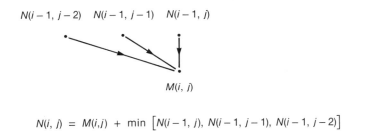

$$N(i, j) = M(i,j) + \min\left[N(i-1, j), N(i-1, j-1), N(i-1, j-2)\right]$$

Fig 6   Calculation of the cumulative distance to element (i,j).

The cumulative distance in the bottom right square, $N(T_2, T_1)$, is regarded as a measure of the dissimilarity of the two utterances.

The similarity to the calculation of the Viterbi coefficients (section 4.2) should be obvious. If each frame of U_1 is regarded as an HMM 'state', then the DTW 'path' is equivalent to the 'most likely state sequence' of Fig 4. Furthermore, if the Euclidean metric is used to measure the distance between two frames, this is equivalent in HMM terms to the assumptions of a multivariate Normal distribution with identity covariance matrix for each 'state' (see Appendix B). Notice that in the DTW algorithm, the 'state transition probabilities' are equal and in the algorithm of equation (22), a skip of only one state is allowed. Historically, attempts were made to refine the DTW algorithm by the addition of 'penalties' (which can be interpreted in terms of altering HMM state transition probabilities) and incorporating more complex 'routes' to an element (skipping states in HMM terms).

The chief drawback of DTW is that it has no mechanism for optimising models on large amounts of data, although the technique of 'clustering' [16] goes some   way in the direction of HMMs. However, DTW is espcially attractive in applications where only limited training data is available, because a single utterance can function as training data for a class.

Appendix B

The multivariate normal distribution

The equation of the PDF of the multivariate Normal distribution is:

$$f(x) = \frac{1}{(2\pi)^{d/2}|U|^{1/2}} \exp\left[-\frac{1}{2}(x-\mu)^{\mathrm{T}}U^{-1}(x-\mu)\right]$$

......(23)

Here, d is the dimensionality of the vectors x and μ, and the matrix U (the covariance matrix) is a $d \times d$ symmetrical matrix. The superscript T denotes vector transposition.

Notice that when $d = 1$, the equation collapses to the familiar univariate Normal probability density function:

$$f(x) = \frac{1}{\sqrt{2\pi}\sigma} \exp'\left[-\frac{(x-\mu)^2}{2\sigma^2}\right]$$

Notice also that the term $\left[-\frac{1}{2}(x-\mu)^{\mathrm{T}}U^{-1}(x-\mu)\right]$ in equation (23) is a scalar, since it is a $[1 \times d]$ vector $\times$ a $(d \times d)$ matrix $\times$ a $(d \times 1)$ vector. Computation of this term is particularly simplified if the covariance matrix U is diagonal, when it becomes:

$$-\frac{1}{2}\sum_{i=1}^{d}\frac{(x_i-\mu_i)^2}{\sigma_i^2}$$

......(24)

where σ_i^2 is the variance in dimension i. Furthermore, if $\sigma_i^2 = 1$, equation (24) reduces to (squared Euclidean distance between x and μ.

In Appendix A, it was stated that if the Euclidean distance was used as a metric between two vectors A and B, it was equivalent to calculating the probability of observing A from an HMM state with a multivariate Normal distribution, of mean vector B and identity covariance matrix. Because the term in equation (24) is exponentiated in the calculation of the probability, there is, in fact a non-linear relationship between the Euclidean distance and the probability. However, as the exponential is a monotonic function, this relationship is monotonic and hence classification is not affected.

References

1 Lippmann R P and Gold B: 'Neural net classifiers useful for speech recognition', In Proc 1st Int Conf on Neural Networks, San Diego (June 1987).

2   Devijver P and Kittler J: 'Pattern recognition — a statistical approach', Prentice-Hall International Inc (1982).

3   Dautrich B A, Rabiner L R and Martin T B: 'On the effects of varying filter bank parameters on isolated word recognition', IEEE Transactions on Acoustics, Speech and Signal Processing, 31 , pp 793—807 (August 1983).

4   Russell M J, Moore R K and Tomlinson M J: 'Dynamic programming and statistical modelling in automatic speech recognition', J Opl Res Soc 37(1) , pp 21—30 (1986).

5   Cox D R and Miller H D: 'The theory of stochastic processes', Meuthuen and Co Ltd (1965).

6   Makhoul J, Roucos S and Gish H: 'Vector quantization in speech coding', Proc of the IEEE, 73 , pp 1551—1588 (1985).

7   Levinson S E, Rabiner L R and Sondhi M M: 'An introduction to the application of the theory of probabilistic functions of a Markov process to automatic speech recognition', The Bell System Technical Journal, 62 , pp 1035—1074 (1983).

8   Rabiner L R and Juang B H: 'An introduction to hidden Markov models', IEEE ASSP Magazine (January 1986).

9   Liporace L A: 'Maximum likelihood estimation for multivariate observations of Markov sources', IEEE Transactions on Information Theory, 28 , pp 729—734 (1982).

10   Levinson S E, Rabiner L R and Sondhi M M: 'On the application of vector quantization and hidden Markov models to speaker-independent, isolated word recognition', The Bell System Technical Journal, 62 , pp 1075—1105 (1983).

11   Rabiner L R, Juang B H, Levinson S E and Sondhi M M: 'Some properties of continuous hidden Markov model representations', AT and T Technical Journal, 64 , pp 1251—1270 (1985).

12   Bridle J S and Sedgwick N S: 'A method for segmenting acoustic patterns, with applications to automatic speech recognition', In Proc IEEE Conf on Acoustics, Speech and Signal-processing, pp 656—659 (1977).

13   Russell M J and Cook A E: 'Experimental evaluation of durational modelling techniques for automatic speech recognition', In Proc IEEE Conf on Acoustics, Speech and Signal-processing, pp 2376—2379 (1987)

14   Bridle J S: 'Stochastic models and template matching: some important relationships between two apparently different techniques for automatic speech recognition', In Proc The Institute of Acoustics (1984).

15   Juang B H: 'On the hidden Markov model and dynamic time warping for speech recognition — a unified view', AT&T Bell Laboratories Technical Journal, 63 , pp 1213—1243 (1984).

16   Wilpon J G and Rabiner L R: 'A modified k-means clustering algorithm for use in isolated word recognition', IEEE Transactions on Acoustics, Speech and Signal Processing, 33 , pp 587—594 (June 1985).

FIXED DIMENSION CLASSIFIERS FOR SPEECH RECOGNITION

P Woodland and W Millar

ABSTRACT

This paper compares the performance of three different types of fixed dimensional pattern classifier on a speaker independent recognition task. The database used contains tokens of the words 'yes' and 'no' from more 700 talkers recorded over the public telephone network. A theoretical outline of each of each of the classifiers used (nearest heighbour, Gaussian mixtures and multi-layer perceptron) is given. The results of speaker independent recognition experiments are presented and the properties of each classification paradigm discussed in order to explain their relative performance. It is found that the multi-layer perceptron not only gives the best test set accuracy, but also results in the simplest classifier.

1. Introduction

Pattern recognition systems can be split into two parts — pattern feature extraction followed by pattern classification. In most speech recognition systems feature extraction is performed at fixed time intervals (e.g. 10 ms), and a n-dimensional vector is produced (n is of the order of 10) that usually contains spectral information. The pattern that represents a particular class of utterance varies in total length (overall dimension) and requires a suitable classifier. Further, utterances of a particular class vary not only in total length but contain non-linear time variations throughout a word — this is particularly true of utterances from different speakers. To tackle these time alignment problems, speech recognition systems typically use classifiers based on 'dynamic time warping' [5] or hidden Markov model [2] techniques.

An alternative approach for speech pattern classification is to segment the acoustic stream into variable length blocks so that an utterance (or part of an utterance such as a syllable) can be viewed as a fixed dimensional vector by extracting n-dimensional features in m segments. A classifier for fixed length patterns can then be used. If the incoming speech is segmented appropriately (so that each segment represents an acoustic event) time alignment can be avoided. This type of approach has two potential application areas — connected speech recognition and isolated word recognition for low cost hardware that uses simple features and a computationally efficient classifier.

A comparison of classifiers for the latter area is the subject of this paper. In particular we investigate the classifiers on a vocabulary of the words 'yes' and 'no' for speaker independent recognition over the public switched telephone network (PSTN). While this two class problem appears to be relatively simple, it is important for several reasons. There exist many applications in which the requirement is for simple processing to be added to an existing product to enhance functionality. Further, it is a constrained problem that demonstates the type of approach that may be viable for a larger vocabulary system. For instance, one of the classifiers investigated, the multi-layer perceptron (MLP), has recently aroused much interest in the field of speech recognition. By comparing the classification ability of the MLP with other classification paradigms on real speech data in a limited domain, its potential advantages can be assessed.

The following sections present a theoretical summary of the classifiers investigated including training and recognition techniques; details of the speech database used and the feature extraction methods; and results of classification experiments and the implications of these for the type of recognition system under study.

2 The classifiers

The section below gives a theoretical outline of three classifiers that are suitable for recognising fixed dimensional speech patterns — two of the classifiers explicitly model each class of data separately whilst the third essentially tries to separate the classes to model a class dependent function.

2.1 Nearest neighbour/K-means clustering

A nearest neighbour classifier requires a set of training data labelled with the corresponding class of each example. In the basic classifier, each example in the training set is used as a prototype vector for that class. A distance metric is defined, $\delta(x,y)$, that reflects the difference between two vectors x and y in the pattern space. Often, as is the case here, the Euclidean distance metric is used which reflects the geometrical distance from x to y. For d-dimensional vectors with components x_i, it is defined as

$$\delta(x,y) = \sqrt{\sum_{i=1}^{d} (x_i - y_i)^2} \qquad \ldots\ldots(1)$$

To classify an unknown vector y from a set of n training vectors x^i, the nearest neighbour vector x' is found such that

$$\delta(x',y) = \min_{i=1,n} \delta(x^i,y) \qquad \ldots\ldots(2)$$

The vector y is classified as belonging to the class of x'.

A nearest neighbour classifier of this type can be effective in modelling a large range of vector distributions in pattern space — however for a large amount of training data it can become impractical both in terms of the storage required for the x^i and the computational expense of calculating all the $\delta(x^i,y)$. The number of prototype vectors can be reduced by clustering techniques that aim to group similar vectors of the same class and use a single representative vector for each cluster. Many clustering algorithms have been developed — the one used here is the modified k-means algorithm of [7]. This algorithm strives to generate clusters whose mean vectors are far apart (large inter-cluster distance) whilst reducing the average distance within a cluster (intra-cluster distance). Further, it solves some practical difficulties encountered in clustering. The algorithm proceeds as follows to form C clusters from a training set.

1   Compute the matrix of distances for all n vectors in the training set $D(i,j) = \delta(x^i,x^j)$ for $1 \le i,j \le n$.

2   Initially, number of clusters, $c = 1$. Compute the cluster centre of the training set.

3   Classify each pattern in the training set as belonging to one of the c clusters by applying the nearest neighbour rule.

4   Recompute the cluster centres for each cluster.

5   Check to see if clustering changed — if yes go to 3.

6   Calculate the intra-cluster distance for each cluster.

7    $c \rightarrow c+1$. If $c > C$ then finish else split the cluster with the largest intra-cluster distance and go to 3.

If there are J patterns within a cluster denoted $\{x^1,x^2,...,x^J\}$, one of their number x^l is chosen to be the cluster centre such that

$$\max_{1 \le i \le J} \delta(x^l,x^i) = \min_{1 \le i \le J} \max_{1 \le j \le J} \delta(x^i,x^j) \qquad\qquad ......(3)$$

When the clustering procedure has terminated, the C cluster centre vectors are finally calculated as the mean of the vectors within each cluster. This clustering procedure is used to split each class into C clusters and the resulting averaged vectors used as the prototype vectors for the class. During recognition an unknown vector is classified using the nearest neighbour rule.

2.2   Gaussian mixture classifier

If a probabilistic model of the vectors of each class (the distribution of each class in pattern space) can be developed, then an unknown vector can be classified as belonging to the class whose model gives the vector the highest probability. This is a maximum likelihood classification given the class model. It can be shown [6] that any continuous probability distribution can be modelled arbitrarily closely by a sum of multivariate Gaussian distributions. For the Gaussian mixture classifier the probability density of a particular d-dimensional vector x from a m mixture distribution is given by

$$b(x) = \sum_{k=1}^{m} c_k N(x, \mu_k, U_k) \qquad \qquad \ldots\ldots(4)$$

where c_k is called a branch probability and $c_k \geq 0$ and $\sum_{k=1}^{m} c_k = 1$. Here, $N(x, \mu, U)$ denotes the d-dimensional multivariate Gaussian (normal) density function of mean μ and covariance U which is defined as

$$N(x, \mu, U) = \frac{1}{(2\pi)^{d/2}|U|^{1/2}} e^{-1/2(x-\mu)' U^{-1}(x-\mu)} \qquad \qquad \ldots\ldots(5)$$

where U^{-1} is the inverse of U
$|U|$ is the determinant of U
x' is the transpose of x.

For this type of distribution, surfaces of equal probability density form hyper-ellipsoids — the angles of the principal axes of which are related to the correlation between dimensions as expressed in the off-diagonal terms of the covariance matrix. The parameters of a Gaussian mixture classifier can be found from a series of training examples by noting that it is equivalent to a single state hidden Markov model (HMM) which has a Gaussian mixture output probability distribution associated with the state and a single transition probability (value unit) to the same state. For such a model a likelihood function can be defined for the series S of training vectors, $L_\lambda(S)$, which represents the probability that the model with parameter set λ generated the series. Here S is defined as $\{x^1, x^2, \ldots, x^n\}$ and since we are discussing a single state model the ordering independence of the x^i is retained. The likelihood function is defined as

$$L_\lambda(S) = \prod_{i=1}^{n} b(x^i) \qquad \qquad \ldots\ldots(6)$$

The training problem is to therefore to select λ such that the likelihood function is maximised. This maximisation can be performed using simplified versions of the re-estimation formulae developed for training HMMs that employ Gaussian mixture output distributions [1]. Starting with initial guesses of the parameters for a m mixture model, $\lambda = \{c_k, \mu_k, U_k, k = 1, \ldots, m\}$, re-estimates of the model $\bar{\lambda} = \{\bar{c}_k, \bar{\mu}_k, \bar{U}_k, k = 1, \ldots, m\}$ are obtained by applying the re-estimation formulae that have the property that $L_{\bar{\lambda}}(S) \geq L_\lambda(S)$. The inequality is strict unless λ is a critical point of the likelihood L. Models can therefore be trained by repeated application of the formulae — this iterative procedure is terminated when some criteria (e.g. the change in L over two iterations) indicates that a critical point has been reached. For the Gaussian mixture classifier the re-estimation formulae can be expressed as follows

$$\bar{c}_k = \frac{\sum_{i=1}^{n} q_k^i}{n} \qquad \qquad ......(7)$$

$$\bar{\mu}_k = \frac{\sum_{i=1}^{n} q_k^i x^i}{\sum_{i=1}^{n} q_k^i} \qquad \qquad ......(8)$$

$$\bar{U}_k = \frac{\sum_{i=1}^{n} q_k^i (x^i - \mu^i)(x^i - \mu^i)'}{\sum_{i=1}^{n} q_k^i} \qquad \qquad ......(9)$$

where

$$q_k^i = \frac{c_k N(x^i, \mu_k, U_k)}{b(x_i)} \qquad \qquad ......(10)$$

Initial estimates for the parameters can be found by partitioning the training into m parts — the initial values for mixture m are calculated as the mean and variance of the mth part of the training set. The training set partitions can be found either by dividing the training set into m equal parts or by using a k-means clustering technique — in the experiments described below the former technique was used.

2.3 Multi-layer perceptron

The Multi-Layer Perceptron (MLP) is a feed-forward network [4] with an input layer on which data is presented, an output data where results are obtained, and one or more intermediate layers of nodes (hidden layers). MLPs are trained to map sets of exemplar input vectors into corresponding sets of output vectors and in the process capture the underlying structure of the mapping. When used as a classifier, the input consists of the pattern feature vector and the output is the (usually binary) code that represents the pattern class. For instance, to classify a pattern into two classes either a single node output can be used with a value of 1 to represent class A and a value of 0 to represent class B — alternatively a two node output could be generated with each node representing a separate class. To recognise an unknown pattern, the feature vector is presented on the input nodes and the output vector is compared to the pre-determined class output vectors. The class that most nearly corresponds to the actual output is chosen as the classified class.

A processing node in a MLP performs only a simple function — it sums its weighted inputs; adds this value to a bias or offset and then forms the node output value by applying the node activation function. The input nodes simply copy the input value

235

to the output and perform no processing function — hidden layer and output nodes process their inputs as described below. The input to processing node j, x_j, is

$$x_j = \theta_j + \sum_i y_i w_{ji} \qquad \ldots\ldots(11)$$

where y_i is the output value of nodes in previous layers connected to node j; w_{ji} is the multiplicative weight on the link between nodes i and j and θ_j is the bias of node j. In this study, the output of node j, y_j is found by applying the 'sigmoid' activation function

$$y_j = \frac{1}{1 + e^{-x_j}} \qquad \ldots\ldots(12)$$

MLPs are typically trained to model the training data input/output relationship by minimising the sum squared error between the desired (training) output vector and the actual output vector. For n training patterns where D^i is the desired output vector and A^i is the actual output the total error E is defined as

$$E = \sum_{i=1}^{n} |D^i - A^i|^2 \qquad \ldots\ldots(13)$$

Since there is a known analytic functional relationship between the input and the output, and the activation function of each node is differentiable, the partial derivatives of the total error E can be found with respect to all weights and biases in the network. These derivatives can be used to calculate suitable weight changes for all the weights and biases so as to reduce E. In practice the partial derivatives are calculated by a method known as error back propagation [4]. The weight change for weight w_{ji} at iteration t, $\Delta w_{ji}(t)$ is typically calculated as

$$\Delta w_{ji}(t) = -\epsilon \frac{\delta E}{\delta w_{ji}} (t) + \alpha \Delta w_{ji}(t-1) \qquad \ldots\ldots(14)$$

where ϵ and α constants known as the learning rate and momentum respectively.

Whilst strictly this updating process should occur after all n patterns have been presented, in practice weights and biases are often updated after only a small fraction of the patterns have been seen by the network with the current weight values [4] — however this causes training to be dependent on the ordering of the training set and does not necessarily mean that the weight update will be in the correct direction (in a 'weight space') to reduce the value of E. In this study, to avoid these problems, weight updates are made after all the training input/output pairs have been presented.

3. The database

The speech data used was part of a large database collected by British Telecom from long distance calls over the public switched telephone network. It consisted of a single utterance of the words 'yes' and 'no' from more than 700 talkers. 798 of these utterances were used for training the classifiers and a further 620 were used for testing. The talkers in the test set were completely distinct from those in the training set.

The speech was band-pass filtered using a telephone codec type response, and digitally sampled at 8 kHz. Each utterance collected has been listened to, manually endpointed, and any incorrect or totally unintelligible utterances discarded, leaving a total of 1418 utterances. The resulting data set included speech samples containing impulsive switching noise, and very high background noise levels.

In order to reduce the data to a fixed dimensionality, a simple energy based segmentation scheme was used. Each utterance was segmented into five variable length portions using an algorithm suitable for monosyllabic utterances. The segmentation procedure starts by locating the vowel nucleus, and by fixing thresholds based on a smoothed pseudo-energy measure at this point selects the vowel region. This region is segmented into three parts to represent the transition into the vowel, the nucleus and a transition region from the vowel. The first and fifth segments represent the pre-vowel and post-vowel sections of the utterance. This procedure was found to be insensitive to both impulsive and background noise levels and performed well on the data used here.

Within each segment simple features inspired by [3] were extracted. This was done by using a segment length autocorrelation linear prediction analysis of low order and choosing as features two cepstral coefficients and the normalised prediction error. Although the segmentation boundary decisions cannot be made until the vowel nucleus is detected, the bulk of the computation required can be performed as the utterance is being said. This procedure is therefore suitable for real-time implementation using simple hardware.

4. Experiments and results

A range of classifiers of the generic types described above were trained using 381 'yes' tokens 417 'no' tokens. A test set using 301 'yes' tokens and 319 'no' tokens was also prepared. For the k-means classifier, a family of classifiers with the number of clusters ranging from 1 to 300 were trained along with a full nearest neighbour classifier. The results of testing these classifiers both on the training set and tet set are shown in Table 1.

Gaussian mixture classifiers were trained, using the same data, varying both the number of mixtures and covariance matrix type. When training classifiers of this type, restricting the form of the covariance matrix (forcing some elements to be zero) can give two advantages:

Table 1   Accuracy using k-means clustering

Number of Clusters	Training Set Accuracy %	Test Set Accuracy %
1	78.6	79.8
2	87.1	85.8
3	85.0	79.0
4	89.0	90.0
5	89.0	89.5
10	91.9	88.9
20	91.4	89.2
30	89.7	85.7
40	90.7	86.6
50	92.5	89.0
100	95.9	89.0
200	99.4	88.4
300	99.9	89.5
N.N.	100.0	91.3

- less parameters to estimate giving better estimates from the available training data,

- reduced computational burden during classification.

It should be noted that to gain a computational advantage a significant number of the terms of the *inverse* covariance matrix must be zero. It can be shown that for the covariance matrix types considered here, the inverse is of the same form as the covariance matrix itself. The matrix types considered were:

- full covariance,

- diagonal covariance — only the diagonal terms are non-zero,

- 'segment' covariance — only the variance terms and the covariance terms within a segment are non-zero,

- 'corresponding' covariance — only the diagonal terms and the covariance between corresponding features in different segments are non-zero.

The last two types of covariance matrix offer compromises between a full matrix and the diagonal matrix. Their relative effectiveness will depend on which covariance terms are most significant in accurately modelling the data. While training Gaussian classifiers with m mixtures it is possible that the covariance matrix for a particular mixture becomes singular. This happens, for full covariance matrices, if less than $d + 1$ d-dimensional vectors have a significant probability, given the limited accuracy of numerical representation, of being generated by each mixture. This effect limits the maximum number of mixtures that can be used. Training set and test set results for these classifiers are shown in Table 2.

MLPs using 15 input nodes, a number of hidden nodes (between 2 and 15), and a single output node, were trained using learning parameters of $\epsilon = 0.01$ and $\alpha = 0.9$. These values were found to be effective for this data by a process of trial and error. The class 'yes' was represented by an output value of 0.9 and the class 'no' by a value of 0.1, as suggested in [4]. A maximum of 5000 presentations of the complete training set (5000 epochs) was used — the weights were updated only after the completion of each epoch. During testing, an utterance that produced an output node value greater than 0.5 was classified as a 'yes', less than 0.5 as a 'no'. The classification accuracy results are given in Table 3.

Accuracy values for the MLP with 'yes' in the range (0.8, 1.0); 'no' in the range (0.0, 0.2) and other utterances rejected are listed in Table 4. The accuracy figures are given as a percentage of the utterances remaining after rejection. These values give an indication of the range of values produced for each class, and hence the accuracy of the desired input/output mapping.

In summary these results clearly show that, for the best classifier of each type, the MLP is the most effective, followed by the Gaussian mixture classifier with the k-means clustering classifier performing least well. The best test set results for each paradigm are repeated in Table 5.

Table 2   Accuracy using multiple mixture Gaussian classifiers.

Covariance Type	Number of Mixtures	Training Set Accuracy %	Test Set Accuracy %
Full	1	92.4	91.8
Full	2	93.5	92.7
Full	3	96.4	93.2
Full	5	97.0	93.1
Diagonal	1	79.2	78.4
Diagonal	2	88.5	85.0
Diagonal	3	92.9	91.0
Diagonal	5	93.6	92.4
Diagonal	10	95.0	91.0
Segment	1	86.2	87.6
Segment	2	90.7	89.5
Segment	3	93.8	91.8
Segment	5	94.4	92.4
Segment	10	95.7	92.4
Corresponding	1	89.7	86.9
Corresponding	2	91.5	88.1
Corresponding	3	92.0	87.3
Corresponding	5	94.4	89.5

Table 3   Multi-layer perceptron accuracy (no rejection).

Number of Hidden Nodes	Training Set Accuracy %	Test Set Accuracy %
2	97.0	95.2
3	97.9	93.7
4	98.6	95.0
5	98.9	94.5
7	99.3	94.5
10	99.8	94.0
15	99.8	94.0

Table 4   Multi-layer perceptron accuracy with rejection.

Number of Hidden Nodes	Training Set		Test Set	
	Accuracy %	Rejected %	Accuracy %	Rejected %
2	98.9	10.7	97.6	12.4
3	99.6	11.2	97.6	13.4
4	99.3	10.8	98.0	10.8
5	99.7	10.5	97.5	11.0
7	99.9	6.4	97.3	9.5
10	99.9	6.5	97.2	15.2
15	99.9	5.1	96.4	10.5

Table 5   Best test set results.

Classifier Type	Best Test Set Accuracy %
Nearest Neighbour	91.3
Gaussian Mixtures	93.2
MLP	95.2

5. Discussion

This section discusses the above results to provide some explanation of the relative effectiveness of the classifiers discussed. It also compares the relative complexity and computational load of the classifiers in both the training and recognition phases.

5.1   Performance and information sources

It is interesting to compare the types of information available when training the classifiers and how much of this is encapsulated by the different paradigms. For the nearest-neighbour classifier the training points (in 'feature space') for each class are labelled as belonging to that class. No information about points in the space that correspond to other classes is provided. Further to information about the likelihood that a point, or points close to the labelled point, correspond to part of the class is noted. Infrequently occuring, noisy points are just as 'valid' as the most frequent point. The clustering technique aims to generate vectors to represent *all* the points in the training set for a class and not just those that occur frequently. This is important because the similarity measure used during recognition gives all the clusters equal weight. The Euclidean distance metric used gives all features equal importance and does not use feature correlations.

The Gaussian mixture classifier also only has information about a single class when the model for that class is being formed. However, since an explicit probabilistic model is used, the classifier encapsulates the relative frequency of points in the training set. Different mixtures of the model can represent different parts of the space, and the relative likelihood of these regions is also stored. Further, by using a non-diagonal covariance matrix, correlations between features are detected. The particular correlations detected vary with the form of covariance matrix used — the diagonal matrix only includes feature variance terms. By comparing the result for a single mixture diagonal covariance Gaussian classifier with the single cluster classifier, it can be seen that just using feature inverse variance weighting has little influence. Using only the correlations within each 'segment' gives improved classification — although the resulting classifier is not as accurate as one using a full covariance matrix. The covariance matrix effectively allows the model to select features — however this feature selection is only based on within class modelling. It should be noted that this type of parametric model may poorly fit the data for some types of data (i.e. if the data exhibits a non-Gaussian mixture form). In such cases a non-parametric model (such as k-means clustering) may serve as a more effective classifier. Here, it is clear that superior modelling of relative class distribution is achieved by using a multiple mixture Gaussian classifer with either a full, diagonal or 'segment' based covariance matrix.

Whereas the k-means and mixture Gaussian techniques essentially classify vectors by using a similarity measure to a class model, the MLP maps input vectors from all classes to output vectors representing the classes. The MLP constructs decision surfaces between classes in the feature space based on *all* the training data. The MLP is, therefore, required to encapsulate the difference between the classes rather than the classes themselves. It can select features (and combinations of features) based on their discriminatory value rather than modelling feature variations within classes. This seems to be highly advantageous in this application and allows improved classification accuracy using a very simple classifier. The training set is modelled almost completely (0.2% error with 15 hidden nodes), the drop in accuracy to about 95% on the test set can be ascribed to under training. It is interesting to compare the rejection and no rejection results. These show that while the peak, test set, no rejection accuracy was obtained with only two hidden nodes, an increased number of hidden nodes improve the feature space mapping onto the original (0.1,0.9) targets. When testing with rejection, the maximum classification accuracy is obtained using a four hidden node classifier, and the rejection rate also falls below the two hidden node level.

5.2   Training set/test set trends

For all the classifiers, the training set accuracies show how well the training set is modelled, the performance degradation of test set results indicates the difference between the training and test samples when examined with a classifier of a certain complexity. As the classifier complexity increases it is therefore expected that training set accuracy will improve and the difference between test set and training set performance will increase. This increasing difference is caused by a combination of improved training set modelling and (for the Gaussian classifier and MLP) a degradation in test set performance after a certain peak value is reached. Degradation in performance is due to the classifier becoming too highly tuned to the training corpus and generalization to the test set suffers. These broad effects are illustrated by the results presented above.

5.3   Complexity

The classification complexity of each of the classifiers is roughly proportional to the number of parameters, P, in the classifier. These can approximately be expressed for 2 class, d-dimensional data as follows:

MLP $P = (d+2).H$,
   where H is the number of hidden nodes. This assumes the structure of MLP discussed.
Clustering $P = 2.d.C$,
   where C is the number of clusters.

Gaussian mixtures $P = 2.d.M.X$,
   where M is the number of mixtures and X is a constant that depends on the covariance matrix.
   For a full covariance matrix, $X = (d+3)/2$; a diagonal matrix, $X = 2$; the 'segment' matrix used here, $X = 3$; and the 'corresponding' matrix, $X = 4$.

The training burden is harder to quantify, but is, very roughly between one and two orders of magnitude greater for the MLP than for either the clustering classifier or the Gaussian mixture classifer.

It should be noted that complexity is linear in the number of classes for clustering and the Gaussian mixture classifiers since a model for each class is used. The rate of complexity increase is expected to be less for the MLP, and therefore may be more suitable for applications that require a larger number of classes (larger vocabulary).

6. Conclusion

The theory of three classifiers for fixed dimensional patterns has been described. Experiments applying these classifiers to a speaker independent speech recognition task of distinguishing 'yes' and 'no' using telephone speech have been presented. The multi-layer perceptron gives not only the simplest classifier, but is able to give the best classification results. The MLP shows promise for larger vocabulary isolated word problems and application to problems of connected speech.

References

1   Juang B H: 'Maximum likelihood estimation for mixture multivariate stochastic observations of Markov chains', AT&T Tech J, <u>64</u> , pp 1251—1270 (1985).

2 Levinson S E, Rabiner L R and Sondhi M M: 'An introduction to the application of the theory of probabilistic functions of a Markov process to automatic speech recognition', Bell System Tech J, 62 , pp 1075—1105 (1983).

3 Millar W: 'Time domain acoustic parameters for speech recognition:' Proc European Conference on Speech Technology, pp 136—139, Edinburgh, Scotland (1987).

4 Rumelhart D E, Hinton G E and Williams R J: 'Learning internal representations by error propagation', In D E Rumelhard and J L McClelland (eds), Parallel Distributed Processing: Explorations in the Microstructure of Cognition, Volume 1: Foundations, MIT Press, Cambridge, MA (1986).

5 Sakoe H and Chiba S: 'Dynamic programming optimization for spoken word recognition', IEEE Trans ASSP, 26 , pp 43—49 (1976).

6 Sorenson H W and Alspach D L: 'Recursive Bayesian estimatin using Gaussian sums', Automatica, 7 , pp 465—479 (1971).

7 Wilpon J G and Rabiner L R: 'A modified k-means clustering algorithm for use in isolated word recognition', IEEE Trans ASSP, 33 , pp 587—594 (1985).

NEURAL ARRAYS FOR SPEECH RECOGNITION

G D Tattersall, P W Linford and R Linggard

ABSTRACT

Certain types of neural array are capable of self learning to form topologically ordered maps of the data to which they are exposed. This paper describes how these arrays could be used in automatic speech recognition systems which are insensitive to time warp variability and are able to learn the primitive grammar of speech.

1. Introduction

In recent years interest in neural-like computation for processing patterns and obtaining machine intelligence has been re-kindled. This follows the general disillusionment in the 1960s with the perceptron and related machines precipitated by Minsky & Papert's [1] analysis which showed that simple processing tasks such as parity detection were impossible using simple neural systems.

These limitations have now been overcome by the multi-layer-perceptron [2] and Boltzmann machine [3]. However, an essential characteristic of these machines is that they are explicitly supervised during their training. In general, this means that a human supervisor must examine each training pattern before it is applied to the machine, and then signal to the machine what type of output should be produced by that class of input pattern.

Another type of neural system has recently been discovered [4]. This new system is self-organising and does not require explit supervision. In its most basic form the system consists of a rectangular array of neural elements which form a topologically ordered map of data to which it is exposed. This means that the relative physical positions of neurons fired by different stimulii mirrors some significant relationship between the stimulii. Neural maps of this type are useful when the perceptual relationship between stimulii is reflected in the pattern space from which they are drawn. Application of patterns with this type of structure to a neural map causes firings of neurons whose positions correspond to the perceptual distance between the patterns. For example, if the neural array is exposed to spectral vectors which represent the vowel sounds, different neural elements in the array become atuned to different vowels. The relative positions of neural elements which are excited by different sounds reflect the phonetic relationship between the sounds. This property, originally discovered by Kohonen [4], has been exploited to make speech recognition systems using neural maps. This paper describes an approach to speech recognition which is based on the use of several topologically ordered neural maps arranged in a stack as shown in Fig 1.

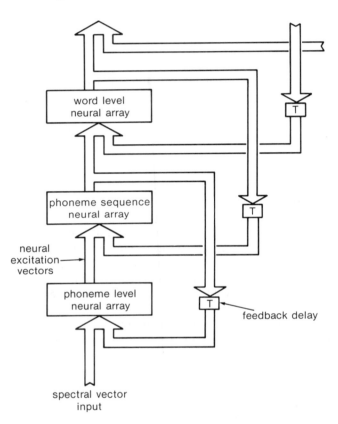

Fig 1   Neural array architecture for speech recognition.

Development of the system is not yet complete, but it is hoped that the chosen architecture will eventually be able to work with continuous speech and continuously improve its recognition performance by learning primitive and higher level grammars of speech to which it is exposed.

This paper starts by examining the nature of topologically ordered neural maps and then goes on to look at the main features of the speech recognition architecture. In particular, it will be shown that a speech recognition system based on neural arrays can be insensitive to the time registration and time warp of speech. Perhaps an even more important property that will be demonstrated is that neural arrays can learn the *phonetic grammar* of speech and use this knowledge to improve recognition.

2. The neural array

The basic self-organising neural array was discovered by Kohonen [4] and is based upon his interpretation of the group behaviour of biological neurons. It has long been assumed that a single neuron can be modelled as shown in Fig 2 by a node which sums weighted amounts of a set of input signals. The weighting factors are often called synaptic weights because they model the synapses of the biological neuron; it is generally believed that learning is associated with the modification of these weights. The weighted summation may also be subject to some non-linearity, such as a threshold or compression function before being output. Kohonen's contribution was to take this neuron model and postulate a way in which a group of neurons might interact and have their synaptic weight modified during unsupervised exposure to input stimulii.

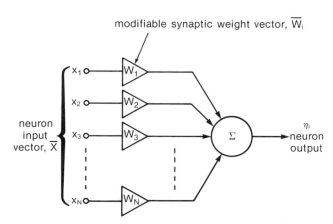

Fig 2   Model of a single neuron.

The model for synaptic weight modification and neuron interaction was prompted by the examination of the biological system which suggests that some cortical neurons are laid out in distinct strata with dense lateral interconnections within each stratum and rather fewer vertical connections between strata. Moreover, it has been shown that excitation of one neuron within a single layer of neurons, causes physically adjacent neurons to become excited or inhibited according to the function shown in Fig 3. A final clue in the search for an accurate model is that each neural element appears to have its synaptic weights modified by an amount which is a function of that element's output and the magnitude of signal applied to a particular synapse.

Gathering all these ideas together, Kohonen proposed the neural system shown in Fig 4 which models a single layer of neurons. The model consists of a rectangular array of neural elements, which are all supplied with the same N-dimensional input pattern vector $\overline{X} = [x_1 ... x_N]$. Each element contains storage for its own set of synaptic weights. Thus for the ith element in the array a weight vector, $\overline{W}_i$ can be defined, where $\overline{W}_i = [w_{i1}, w_{i2} ... w_{iN}]$.

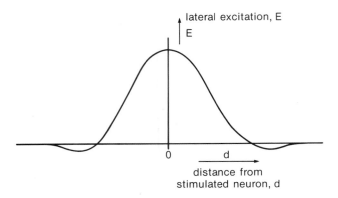

Fig 3   'Mexican hat' lateral excitation function.

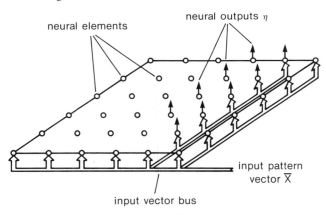

Fig 4   Model of single two-dimensional neural array.

Returning to the basic model of the neural element shown in Fig 2, it can be seen that the output of the ith element will be:

$$\eta_i = f \left\{ \sum_{j=1}^{N} x_j \, x_{ij} \right\}$$

or $\eta_i = f \{ \overline{X} . \overline{W}_i \}$

It has been found at the British Telecom Research Laboratories (BTRL) that defining the neural output as the scalar product of $\overline{X}$ and $\overline{W}_i$ gives very attractive properties in the context of speech recognition. However, in general the way in which the output, η_i i produced is not important to the basic operation of the maps and any function which gives a measure of similarity, S, between $\overline{X}$ and $\overline{W}_i$ may be used.

i.e. $\eta_i = f\{S(\overline{X}, \overline{W}_i)\}$

In Kohonen's original work, S, $(\overline{X}, \overline{W}_i)$ was defined by the Euclidean distance between $\overline{X}$ and $\overline{W}_i$, and this metric is used in this section to explain the operation of the array.

It will be noticed that there are no physical lateral connections between elements in the model of Fig 4, even though it has been stated that lateral interaction is an important facet of the neural system. In fact, the lateral interaction is modelled implicitly by the training algorithm.

The training of the array takes place as follows, a large representative set of pattern vectors, $\overline{X}$ are collected and are applied without supervision and in random order, to the neural array. Every time a vector is applied, the following algorithm is executed:

- The element with the largest output or greatest similarity between $\overline{X}$ and $\overline{W}$ is found.

- A spatial neighbourhood is defined around the most excited element.

- The synaptic weight vectors of all neural elements lying within the neighbourhood are updated such that:

$$\overline{W}_i^{n+1} = W_i^n + k.(\overline{X} - \overline{W}_i^n) \qquad\qquad ......(1)$$

It can be seen from this equation that the array's weight vector will tend to take on values which match the values of commonly occurring input vectors. Thus specific elements will become excited by particular patterns. However, the array has a more remarkable property, under certain conditions, the toplogical relationship between patterns can be mirrored by the spatial relationship of the neural elements excited by the patterns. This is demonstrated by the simulation result shown in Fig 5. The two-dimensional pattern space contains a large number of pattern vectors represented

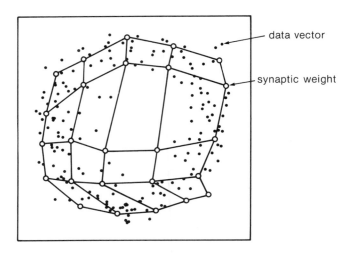

data vector

synaptic weight

Fig 5   2-D synaptic weight values of a 5×5 neural array.

by the dots. In this example, the patterns are arranged in a torroid with Gaussian distribution along a radius and uniform along a circumference. These patterns were presented to a neural array in random order, the synaptic weights adapted, and after completion of training, the value of each element's 2-D weight vector plotted back into the pattern space. In order to keep track of which weight vector belongs to which neural element, lines are drawn to connect the synaptic weight values of elements which are adjacent in the array. Figure 5 shows that the weight vectors have taken on positions that match patterns from different regions in a topologically ordered way (the grid is not folded). Since a particular element's excitation depends on the matching of its weight vector to the current input pattern, it is clear that the position of the peak of excitation in the array directly maps from the position of the input vector in its pattern space.

One difficulty with the self-organising algorithm is the definition of a spatial neighbourhood around the most excited element. If the neighbourhood is made large, global ordering is obtained, but the weight vectors do not expand to cover the data space. On the other hand, if the neighbourhood is made small, only local ordering is obtained even though the weight vectors spread all over the data space.

A solution to the problem is to start training with a large neighbourhood and gradually shrink its size as training progresses. This is the technique used in all the experiments using speech, although in a subsequent section it is shown that it is possible to use a fixed neighbourhood having both excitory and inhibitory regions. This latter method is more elegant because it does not need prior knowledge of the number of training patterns to be used. Unfortunately, it is not very robust and needs further work before it can be used with real speech data.

3. The inherent dimensionality of data

It would be impossible to obtain a globally ordered two-dimensional neural map of data that is truly 3-dimensional. If a 2-D neural array is trained on this type of data, the weight vectors of the neural elements tend to *fold* in waves in an attempt to fully cover the 3-D space, as shown in Fig 6. In this situation, a globally ordered mapping does not exist.

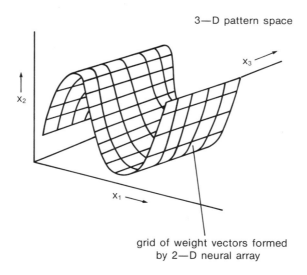

Fig 6   2-D neural array attempting to map inherently three-dimensional data.

However, quite often, real physical phenonomenon may be represented by N-dimensional vectors having an **inherent dimensionality** which is less than N. Sometimes this inherent dimensionality is only two in which case it may be mapped unambiguously by a 2-D neural array.

Figure 7a exemplifies the concept of inherent dimensionality. The dots in the 2-D pattern space represent the position of typical patterns in the space. It is evident to the eye that the positions of the pattern vectors lie approximately on a circle. Consequently, a single measurement around the circumference of the circle is sufficient to define the position of any of the pattern vectors in their two-dimensional space.

Thus, the data is **inherently one-dimensional.** Confirmation is given by the result shown in Fig 7b which depicts the weight vector values of a 1-D neural array after exposure to the data of Fig 7a.

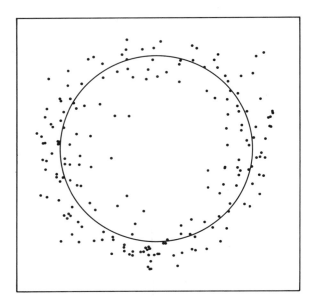

Fig 7a   Inherently one-dimensional data in 2-D space.

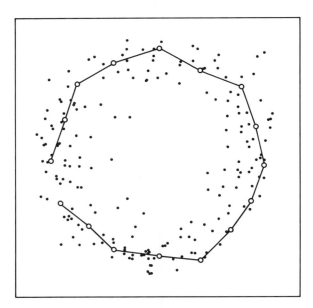

Fig 7b   Organisation of 1-D neural array on inherently 1-D data.

4. The inherent dimensionality of speech sounds

In machine speech recognition systems, speech is usually represented by sequences of short time spectra. This is normally provided by a bank of electrical or computational filters which provide time varying spectral vectors of typically 16-32 elements at about 10 ms intervals.

It has been found that exposure of a two-dimensional neuray array to the spectral vectors representing vowels, causes global ordering of the array, indicating that the inherent dimesionality of the sounds is only two. This result is consistent with the assessment made by phoneticians that the vowel sounds are representable in a **perceptual space** of only two dimensions as illustrated in the vowel trapezium of Fig 8. Thus, the starting point for the approach to speech recognition is that sounds can be represented in a self-consistent manner on two-dimensional neural arrays.

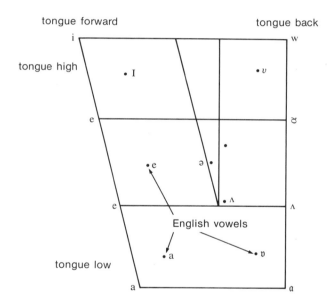

Fig 8   The vowel trapezium (cardinal vowels on perimeter of trapezium).

5. Neural arrays for speech recognition — the basic ideas

At this point the architecture and basic ideas underlying the proposed system using neural arrays are briefly described. A more detailed examination will appear later in the paper of three aspects of the system: arrays using the scalar product metric; time warp invariance; grammar learning.

The proposed speech recogniser consists of a stack of topologically ordered two-dimensional arrays as shown in Fig 1. The speech is coded as 16-dimensional spectral vectors which are sampled at least every 10 mS, and applied as input to the bottom array in the stack.

When a single vector is applied simultaneously to the inputs of all the neural elements in the bottom layer, all elements produce an output. However, only those neurons whose stored vectors closely match the input vector will give a large output and, because of the toplogical order, all these neurons will be physically co-located in the array. If the array could be viewed from above, application of the single speech vector would cause a peak of excitation in one part of the array whose position is characteristic of the type of sound.

The nature of the speech sounds produced during an utterance cannot change instantaneously because the vocal apparatus has mechanical inertia which smooths the phonological command signals to the system. Consequently, successive speech vectors taken at intervals of a few milliseconds will be very similar, and when applied to the neural array will tend to cause the position of the peak neural excitation to move by only a small amount. Again, this is only true because the array is topologically ordered. Extending this idea suggests that application of a series of vectors representing a complete utterance will cause the excitation peak to move along a characteristic trajectory in the array.

The idea behind the stack of neural arrays is that the trajectory produced on the bottom layer acts as input to the second layer where it produces a more compressed trajectory and, so on, up through the layers of the stack until a word, or even a sequence of words, generates a trajectory on a high layer, which is so short that it can be associated with just one or a very small group of neurons. This neuron can be labelled explicitly with the appropriate utterance name.

6. Compressing the trajectory using a soft window

How can a trajectory of neural firings on one layer of the stack cause a compressed trajectory on the next layer? The neural array described up till now, produces a sequence of instantaneous excitation patterns as each vector is applied, so that the excitations due to several consecutive input vectors do not co-exist. However, if the trajectory on one layer is to be used as an input to the next layer, it must be 'visible' as a single entity at some instant in time. On the other hand, if the system is to accept continuous speech, then the trajectory of excitations on the first layer must not be as long as the speech utterance itself, otherwise it would eventually become infinite in length. Since it is impractical to retain the entire trajectory for input to the second layer, the second layer must view the layer 1 trajectory through a window in time which only passes its most recent segment.

An appealing way of producing this window and at the same time making a complete section of the trajectory visible at a single instant, is to build persistence into each neural element. That is, once a neuron is stimulated by an input, it continues to produce an output of exponentially decaying magnitude even after the input has been removed. This type of soft window is illustrated in Fig 9. Excitation persistence is well known in real neurons and is atractive in this application because it gives most weight to the most recent part of the trajectory and diminishing weight with increasing time into the past. The choice of persistence time constant can only be determined by experiment, but it seems that a value a bit less than the length of the shortest word is appropriate. The consequence of this choice is that the trajectory produced by the shortest word will cause a trajectory on layer 2 which has near zero length, i.e. just one small group of neurons will fire.

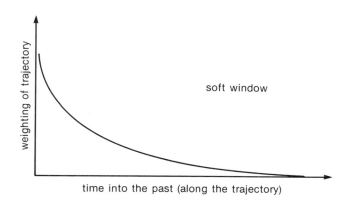

Fig 9   The soft window obtained by using exponential decay of neural excitation.

Consider now the original question of how the trajectory in one layer can give rise to a shortened trajectory in the next layer. Consider a segment of trajectory, extracted from layer n and used as input to layer $n + 1$. The input to layer $n + 1$ causes a single point to become excited, thus representing the line of points within the trajectory window of layer n. Moving the window along by one sample period does not greatly affect the form of the trajectory within the window because the window covers many previous samples. Thus the input $n + 1$ changes by a very small amount and only moves its point of maximum excitation by a correspondingly small distance, giving rise to a compressed trajectory.

7. Intra layer grammar

It is well known that speech contains much redundancy. This applies even at the lowest levels where only certain sequences of sounds occur, and at a higher level where only certain word sequences are allowed. At both these levels a form of *grammar* is at work, constraining the possible sequence of events. Knowledge of these grammars allows us to exploit this inherent redundancy to recognition of speech which is uttered in an unusual way, or corrupted by noise.

The inclusion of adaptive lateral weights between elements in an array leads to a method of making the arrays automatically learn the *grammar* of sequences of patterns which it receives as input. At the bottom layer of the stack, *grammar* relates to the constraints on the possible sequence of primitive speech sounds. At a higher level in the stack, the *grammar* could relate to the allowable sequence of words and has more in common with linguistic grammar. In either case, the way in which the grammar is learnt and exploited by the neural arrays is the same.

To understand how grammar can be encoded by lateral connection weights, consider the behaviour of the bottom layer in the stack when it is exposed to different examples of the same utterance. In the absence of any lateral interconnections, application of a particular example of the utterance will produce a natural trajectory T, which deviates from the archetypal or average trajectory shape for the utterance. However, if large positive lateral weights are now included between elements which lie on the path of the archetypal utterance, the trajectory will be *pulled* towards the archetypal shape as shown in Fig 10.

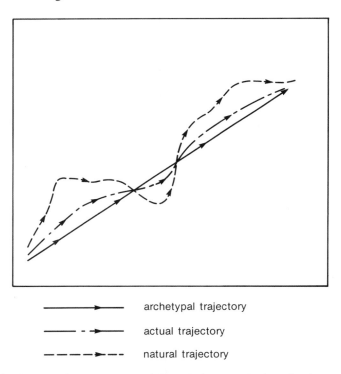

<pre>
————————▶   archetypal trajectory

———— · —▶—   actual trajectory

— — —▶— — —   natural trajectory
</pre>

Fig 10   Intra-layer grammar weights reducing perturbation of trajectory.

This happens even though the stimulation of the neural elements on the archetypal path is lower than those of neurons lying on the input trajectory. Just moderate stimulation of neurons on the archetypal path causes them to send large stimulating signals via the lateral interconnection to their neighbours along the path. These neighbours are already receiving some stimulation due to the input utterance, and when this is added to the stimulation derived via the lateral interconnection, the total may well exceed the input stimulation of neurons lying on the input trajectory. The overall result of the action is that the actual trajectory will lie somewhere between the paths of the archetypal and input trajectories.

This property of making any input utterance tend to produce a trajectory which follows one of a number of archetypal paths is very desirable because it means that the trajectory produced on the array will be less affected by noise and speaker variability. It may even provide some degree of speaker independence.

It should now be evident that the strong positive lateral weights along the archetypal path are effectively a representation of the *most likely* or *average* seqence of speech sounds and thereby encode the speech grammar. It is proposed that the lateral inter-connection weight be learnt during the application of many examples of utterances to the array. The learning algorithm basically makes the connection weight between a pair of neurons proportional to the time average of the product of their stimulations. A pair of neurons, lying on a frequent trajectory, will often be simultaneously stimulated, thus the connection weight between them will become large. Conversely, pairs of neurons which are rarely stimulated at the same time will only develop weak connections. In this way, the strongest connections will develop along the ridges of the frequency distribution of the trajectories. These ridges lie, by definition, along the spatial averages of each class of trajectory, and correspond to the archetypal trajectory mentioned earlier. Some experiment to demonstrate the intra layer grammar will be presented later in this paper.

8. Forward inter layer connection

It has been stated rather glibly in the previous sections that the neural firing pattern on one layer will be presented as an input to the subsequent layer. How this could be done in practice is now examined.

One obvious solution would be to form a very large vector from the outputs of every neuron in layer n and present it as input to every neuron in layer $n+1$. This arrangement is illustrated in Fig 11a.

For inter layer connections, this arrangement is unsuitable for two reasons. First, there may be several tens of thousands of neurons in layer n, giving rise to an input vector to the next layer whose dimensionality would also be tens of thousands — this would require around a billion inter layer connections — a nonsense both biologically and technologically. The second reason for avoiding this scheme is that the inherent dimensionality of firing patterns derived from the whole of a layer is almost certain to be much greater than two, and hence it would be impossible to map them in an ordered manner onto the next layer.

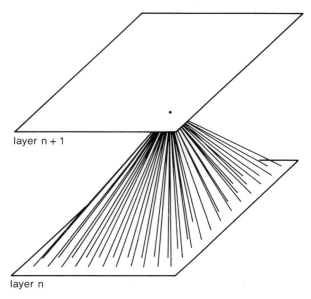

layer n + 1

layer n

Fig 11a   Possible interlayer connection scheme; all neural outputs in layer n connected to every neuron in layer $n+1$.

The number of interconnections can be reduced as illustrated in Fig 11b. Here the input vector to a neuron in layer $n + 1$ and having co-ordinates (x,y) is derived from the outputs of a fairly small number of neurons in layer n which lie within a small circle whose centre has the same co-ordinates (x,y). Notice that the circular regions in layer n overlap so that the inputs to neurons within a small locality in layer $n + 1$ will be very similar. This suggests that the array in layer $n + 1$ will become ordered in a similar way to an array which has a global input vector, except that the ordering will be local rather than global.

The second problem that this connection scheme may overcome is matching the inherent dimensionality of the pattern vectors derived from layer n to the two physical dimensions of layer $n + 1$. Fig 12a shows a continuous trajectory on layer n, passing through the circular regions from which connections are taken to layer $n + 1$ Fig 12a. If the circular regions are sufficiently small, the segment of trajectory within each region can be approximated by a straight line as shown in Fig 12b. A straight line drawn in any position across a circle only requires two parameters to be completely defined. This means that the inherent dimensionality of the vector representing the segment of trajectory is also only two, and consequently can be mapped onto layer $n + 1$.

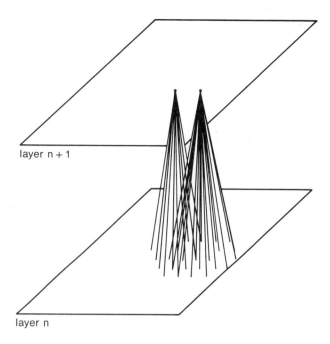

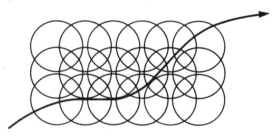

Fig 11b   Localised interconnection scheme; small groups of neural outputs in layer n connected to each neuron in layer $n+1$.

Fig 12a   Trajectory passing through the regions in layer n which are connected up to layer $n+1$.

9. Inter layer grammar

The intra layer grammar weights sould improve recognition of continuous trajectories within a layer. However, some trajectories will consist of a series of separate short segments. This might occur, for example in the bottom layer, as it receives a vowel — stop consonant — vowel (V_1-C-V_2) utterance.

The allowable V_1-C-V_2 sequences in a particular language are limited and it is desirable to exploit this constraint such that the occurence of a trajectory associated with (V_1-C) is used to prime the neurons which lie on the trajectory for (C-V_2) and make them more likely to be excited than other groups of neurons. In principle, this could be achieved using intra-layer connections between the separate areas of the array in which the $(V_1\text{-}C)$ and $(C\text{-}V_2)$ trajectories might occur. In the extreme, this could necessitate inter neural connections right across the array, and to cater for this situation, each neuron would need a connection from every other neuron in the array, leading to an impractically complex system.

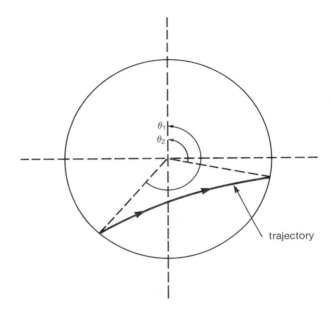

Fig 12b   Exploded view of trajectory passing through one region and demonstrating that it is characterised by two angular co-ordinates.

The alternative approach is to use feedback between arrays as shown in Fig 1. The global firing pattern in layer $n+1$ is fed back and presented as an input vector to layer n along with the ordinary input vector. The scheme would operate on the $(V_1\text{-}C)$ and $(C\text{-}V_2)$ trajectories in the following way. The occurence of the $V_1\text{-}C$ trajectory on layer n, causes a compressed trajectory to occur on layer $n+1$ due to the forward inter-layer connection. This compressed trajectory is encoded in the vector, $\overline{F}$ which is fed back, with delay to the input of layer n where it is appended to the ordinary input vector, $\overline{X}$, to form an overall input to layer n or $(\overline{X}:\overline{F}) = \overline{Q}$. In Fig 1 the delay is shown as a separate element in the system but in reality it is implicit in the neural arrays. If the feedback delay is similar to the time of the stop between V_1 and V_2, then $\overline{F}$ actually gets to the input of layer n at the same time as the vector $\overline{X}$ representing the start of V_2. Assuming that the self organisation of layer n takes place with the feedback path active, its presence should become a necessary input component to cause the trajectory of $(C-V_2)$ trajectory. However, the joint occurrence of an active feedback, $\overline{F}$, and input $\overline{X}$ should cause high excitation of the $C-V_2$ trajectory, since this is the input of which the system has been trained.

The problem with this idea is once again the number of interconnections. The global firing pattern on layer $n+1$ needs to be coded as vector, $\overline{F}$, whose dimensionality is equal to the number of neurons in layer $n+1$.

10. The Kohonen array problem

The type of neural array proposed by Kohonen suffers from a severe problem if it is used for speech recognition as described in the previous section. The problem arises because the array is ordered using the Euclidean distance to control the synaptic weight modification. The result is that different neural elements in the array are adapted to match different amplitudes of the same sound. Consequently a variation in amplitude of a single sound type causes movement of the excitation peak on the array. This is clearly undesirable in this system because the shape of trajectories on the array is intended to characterise the sequence of sound types within an utterance, but not the sequence of sound amplitudes.

A possible solution to the problem is to normalise the magnitudes of all the spectral vectors before they are input to the array. However, this means that the short term energy envelope of the function is lost for recognition purposes.

A more satisfactory approach is to use the scalar product metric during training and recognition. It will be shown that this causes the array to order solely in terms of the input vector's direction, while the intensity of the excitation peak in the array encodes the magnitude of the vector. This gives an encoding of an utterance as shown in Fig 13.

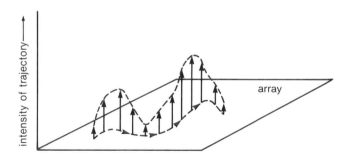

Fig 13   Trajectory with characteristic shape and intensity profile.

11. The scalar product array

The output of the neuron model in Fig 2 is:

$$\eta_{ij} = \sum_{q=1}^{N} x_q . w_{i,j,q} \qquad \qquad ......(1)$$

261

where x_q is the qth element of the input vector and w_{ijq} is the qth element of the synaptic weight vector of a neuron having co-ordinates i, j.

i.e. $\eta_{ij} \, X \cdot W_{i,j}$ ......(2)

But of course the value of a scalar product is proportional to the cosine of the angle, θ, between the two vectors.

So, $\eta_{i,j} = |\overline{X}| * |\overline{W}_{i,j}| * \cos\theta$ ......(3)

At first sight it appears that the scalar product metric is inappropriate because its value depends on the magnitudes of both $\overline{X}$ and $\overline{W}_{i,j}$ as well as the $\cos\theta$ term which measures the similarity of the direction of $\overline{X}$ measures the similarity of the direction of $\overline{X}$ and $\overline{W}_{ij}$. The array should be ordered just in terms of vector direction because this corresponds to a particular spectral profile and hence sound type.

However, for the purposes of self ordering it is only necessary to locate the neuron which matches most closely the input vector $\overline{X}$, and since $\overline{X}$ is applied to all neurons in the array, variations in the magnitude of $\overline{X}$ do not alter the ranking of the output value from each neuron.

Thus the neuron output can be redefined for the purposes of self ordering as:

$\eta'_{ij} = /\overline{W}_{ij}/.\cos\theta$ ......(4)

$\eta'_{i,j}$ is still unsuitable as a measure of similarity because it depends on the magnitude of the synaptic weight vector, $\overline{W}$. This problem is avoided if its magnitude is kept constant during the modification process. In effect this means that the synaptic weight vectors are constrained to lie on the surface of a unit sphere as shown in Fig 14a.

If $|\overline{W}_i| = 1$ ......(5)

Then $\eta'_{ij} = \cos\theta$ ......(6)

Under these conditions the neuron output can be considered a direct measure of the similarity in direction between the input pattern, $\overline{X}$, and the synaptic weight vectors, $\overline{W}_i$

The problem of how to update the synaptic weight vectors while keeping their magnitudes constant must now be tackled. Physiologically it appears that the synapses of real neurons are strengthened by frequent firing. This corresponds to the application of large input values, x, to the synapse. At first sight a reasonable model for this process is to increment a particular synapse's weight by a small amount proportional to the amplitude to the input being applied:

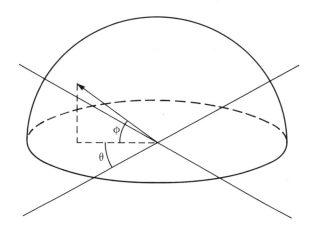

Fig 14a   Volume containing synaptic weight vectors obtained using city block normalisation.

$$\overline{W}_{i,j}^{n+1} = W_{i,j}^{n} + k(i\text{-}r, j\text{-}s)*\overline{X}$$

where $k(i\text{-}r, j\text{-}s)$ is a lateral interaction function which defines a spatial neighbourhood around the most excited neuron in the array at co-ordinate (r,s).

Clearly, this approach cannot be completely correct because eventually all the synaptic weights would attain very large values regardless of the values of inputs which had been applied. The problem is readily solved by using the weight vector normalisation that was also found necessary to make the neuron output a true similarity measure (equation 7).

Let $\overline{W}_{i,j}{}'$ be an intermediate term in the computation of $\overline{W}_{i,j}$. Then:

$$\overline{W}'_{i,j} = \overline{W}_{i,j}^{n} + k(i\text{-}r, j\text{-}s)* \overline{X} \qquad \qquad ......(7)$$

and

$$\overline{W}_{i,j}^{n+1} = \overline{W}_{ij}' / |\overline{W}'_{i,j}| \qquad \qquad ......(8)$$

This normalisation process allows the direction of the weight vector to vary while keeping its magnitude constant.

It seems very unlikely that information is available within the biological neuron about the weight vector's magnitude in an Euclidean sense. However, an alternative normalisation which approximately retains the similarity measure of equation (8), is to define the magnitude of the weight vector in a City Block sense.

$$\text{Magnitude } (\overline{W}_{i,j}) = \sum_{q=1}^{N} |\omega_{i,j,q}| \qquad\qquad \ldots\ldots(9)$$

This means that the total weight power of a neuron is constant and that synaptic modification involves a redistribution of this power around its synapses. A pattern space interpretation of this normalisation is shown in Fig 14b, in which all the weight vectors are constrained to lie on the surface of the unit height pyramid. This type of normalisation is much more attractive as a model of the biological mechanism because, speculatively, it is possible that the amount of neurotransmitting substances available within a single neuron is constant. Synaptic modification would correspond to a gradual redistribution of the chemical around the synapses.

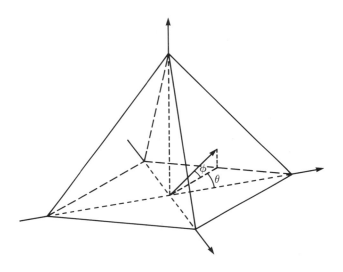

Fig 14b   Volume containing synaptic weight vectors obtained using City Block normalisation.

It is interesting to note that the form of synaptic modification defined by equation (9) causes the amount of modification to be larger for larger magnitude input patterns and will cause more weight vectors to congregate around those directions in which large input patterns frequently occur. High magnitude inputs cause rapid learning and cause more neurons to be devoted to matching that type of pattern.

12.   Computer based demonstration of the scalar product array

The normalisation and vector updating techniques described in the previous section were simulated on a computer to see if the topological ordering properties of the array were retained. An artificial set of input patterns consisting of 3-dimensional vectors with uniformly distributed polar co-ordinates were generated and were used in four separate simulations to test the various ideas proposed for the new model.

These simulations will be described shortly; however, first, the spatial neighbourhood function, another important parameter affecting the simulation, is discussed.

To obtain global ordering with a function which has no inhibitory region requires that the excitory region of the neighbourhood extend over a large portion of the whole array. Unfortunately, although ordering is obtained under this condition, the neural values do not expand to fill the space from which the input patterns have been drawn. The problem arises because virtually all the neural vectors are pulled towards the current input vector. Thus, as a sequence of input patterns, occupying uncorrelated positions in pattern space are applied, each neuron is subject to a series of random movements around the mean of the input patterns. Consequently, the synaptic weight vectors tend to gravitate to the mean position of the input pattern vectors instead of moving outwards.

At first sight this can be overcome by reducing the width of $K(r,s)$. However, this causes complete breakdown of the ordering process because the system is no longer being provided with any means of correlating the relative movements of weight vectors across the whole array.

It is now evident why Kohonen used the shrink trick: an initially wide function allows global ordering to be established. Subsequent slow reduction in its width allows the vectors to expand to cover the pattern space.

An alternative approach is to use a fixed width neighbourhood containing an inhibitory region as well as an excitory region. If the excitory lobe of the function is made fairly wide, global ordering will be achieved. However, the addition of an inhibitory lobe will tend to make the synaptic weight vectors expand outward through the pattern space away from the mean position of the input pattern vectors, in opposition to the gravitational tendency cause by the excitory part of the function. Clearly, instability will result if the expansion force exceeds the gravitational force and so in a stable system the weight vectors can never perfectly cover the pattern space. In the simulations described here, the neighbourhood function was derived by trial and error and is defined by:

$$E = 0.1*(\exp - (r^2 + s^2)/V1 - 0.4*\exp - (r^2 + s^2)/V2) \qquad \ldots\ldots(10)$$

where: $V1$ = (array dimension/2) and $V2$ = (array dimension).

Simulation 1 (Unity magnitude input vectors: Euclidean normalisation):

In this experiment the magnitudes of the input pattern vectors were made constant so that the effect of the Euclidean normalisation and vector updating described by equations (9) and (10) could be studied in isolation. The lateral interaction function of equation (12) was used while a sequence of 200 input patterns was applied to a 6*6 array.

The topological ordering of the array was tested in two ways. If ordering had occurred, the synaptic weights should lie on the surface of a unit radius hemisphere in a grid-like array. It is difficult to plot this kind of 3—D picture so the projections of the weight vectors onto the base of the hemisphere have been plotted as shown in Fig 15, in which ordering is evident. A test of the mapping property of the array was made by calculating the polar co-ordinates associated with each neuron in the array and using linear interpolation between neurons to superimpose upon the array contours of equal elevation and azimuth angle. This is shown in Fig 16, which vividly demonstrates the topologically ordered map of the surface of the hemisphere from which the input patterns were taken. The only defect is that the array has not fully enveloped the hemisphere. As discussed earlier this could be due to an inappropriate lateral interaction function, or perhaps an edge effect due to the smallness of the array.

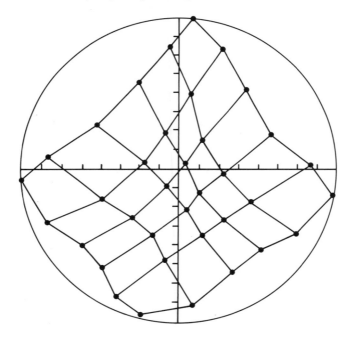

Fig 15   Projection of a synaptic weight vector onto base of hemisphere (Euclidean normalisation).

Simulation 2 (Unity magnitude input vectors, City Block normalisation):

In this experiment the idea of re-distributing the neuron's weight power is tested. The same test conditions were used as a simulation 1 and the results are presented in Figs 17 and 18. In this case the synaptic weight vectors should all lie on the surface of a pyramid shape and their projections should lie within a square in the x-y plane.

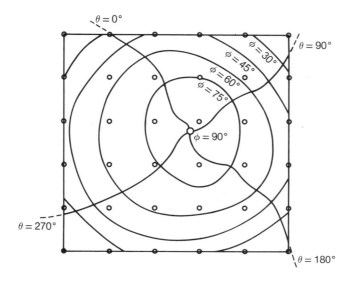

Fig 16   Polar contours superimposed on organised array (Euclidean normalisation).

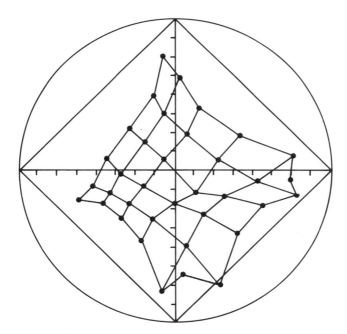

Fig 17   Project of synaptic weight vectors onto base of hemisphere (city block normalisation).

This is demonstrated to be the case in Fig 17, although again, the weight vectors have clearly not completely enveloped the space. Correct topological mapping is also evidenced by the contour plot of azimuth and elevation angle in Fig 18.

Simulation 3 (Variable magnitude input vectors, Euclidean normalisation):

One of the attractive properties of the new neural array model is that the neurons become sensitised to the directions of the input vectors, not to their amplitudes. Thus, the third experiment was intended to verify that the array will still form a topologically ordered map even if the magnitudes of the input pattern vectors are variable. The array was exposed to 200 input patterns whose directions were uniformly distributed as before. However, in this case, the vector magnitudes were also uniformly distributed between 0 and 5 units. The results are shown in Figs 19 and 20 and confirm that magnitude variability does not greatly effect the ordering process.

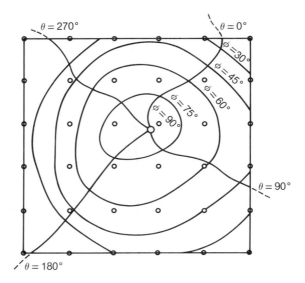

Fig 18   Polar contours superimposed on organised array (city block normalisation).

Simulation 4 (Variable magnitude input vectors, City Block normalisation):

The same conditions were used as in Simulation 3 but City Block normalisation was used rather than Euclidean normalisation. The ordering results are shown in Figs 21 and 22 and again confirm that ordering is not degraded by variable input vector magnitudes.

13.   A scalar product array organised on real speech

Many experiments have been performed on the organisation or scalar product arrays using 16-D spectral vectors at 10 mS intervals from a set of analogue bandpass filters whose centre frequencies are arranged at roughly equal intervals on a logarithmic frequency scale between 250 Hz and 4.5 kHz. The short term output energy of each filter is raised to a power of 0.4 to give some dynamic range compression before the vectors are used by the neural array.

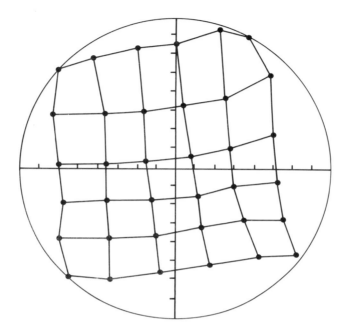

Fig 19   Projection of weight vectors onto base of hemipshere after training with variable magnitude
inputs (Euclidean normalisation).

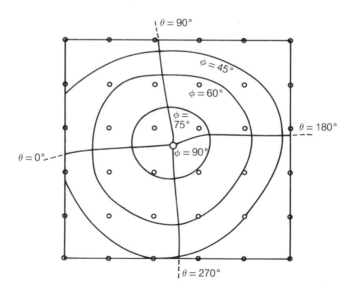

Fig 20   Polar contours superimposed on organised array after training with variable magnitude inputs
(Euclidean normalisation).

The first experiment attempts to show that a scalar product array can form an ordered map of speech data. The training data was produced by one person reading text from a newspaper for about 40 seconds. This produced 4000 spectral vectors which were applied to a 29 × 29 array of neural elements in the order in which they were produced. The self-organisation algorithm employed a shrinking update neighbourhood which started with a width of 28 elements and reduced linearly to one element after 3000 training passes.

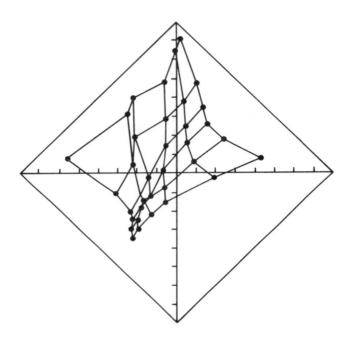

Fig 21   Projection of weight vector onto base of hemisphere after training with variable magnitude input vectors (city block normalisation).

On completion of training the synaptic weight vectors were examined. It was interesting to see if these vectors form an ordered grid, as was done earlier in the elementary simulation using 2-D data. Unfortunately, this is impossible because the speech vectors are 16-dimensional; however, they can be projected onto planes formed by pairs of axes within the 16-dimentional space. If the place projections form ordered grids then it indicates that the array itself is ordered. This turns out to be the case as shown by the example plotted in Fig 23, although some crumpling at the edges is evident. This is almost certainly due to insufficient training and in general, large arrays using high dimensional data require many tens of thousand of training patterns to produce full convergence.

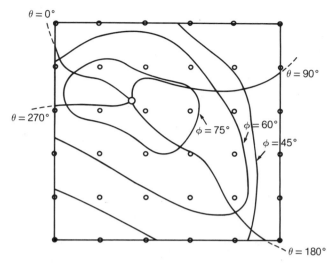

Fig 22   Polar contours on organised array after training with variable magnitude inputs (City Block normalisation).

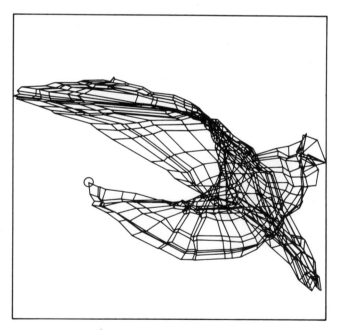

Fig 23   Projection of 16-D weight vectors onto dimensions 5 and 10. Array trained on natural speech.

14.   Testing the array with real speech vowels

The most important property of the array, if it is to be used for speech recognition, is that it responds to real speech sounds in a way which reflects the perceptual relationship between those sounds. To test this property hardware has been developed which makes it possible to display the instantaneous excitation of each neuron as a point of variable intensity on an oscilloscope screen. This system is able to work in near real time as speech is uttered into a microphone driving the filter bank and array.

Figure 24 shows the excitation produced by a speaker voicing each of the principal vowel sounds, and Fig 24 shows the position of the excitation peaks produced by

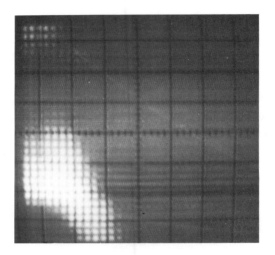

Fig 24a   Neural excitation caused by the sound 'EE'.

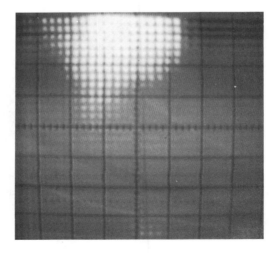

Fig 24b   Neural excitation caused by the sound 'E'.

each of the vowels in one diagram so that their relative positions can be studied. It is interesting to compare Fig 25 with Fig 8 which shows the vowel trapezium traditionally used by phoneticians to depict the perceptual relationship between the vowels. Evidently the neural array and vowel trapezium are ordered in an approximately similar manner.

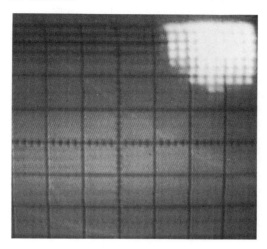

Fig 24c   Neural excitation caused by the sound 'AR'.

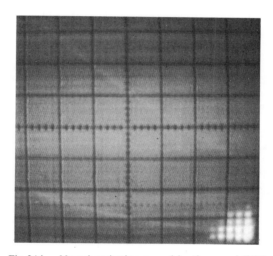

Fig 24d   Neural excitation caused by the sound 'UU'.

15.   Testing the array with non-stationary speech sounds

One of the most basic ideas behind this approach to speech recognition can be demonstrated at this point. Uttering a changing speech sound should cause the position

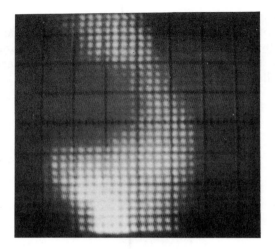

Fig 24e   Neural excitation caused by the sound 'AA'.

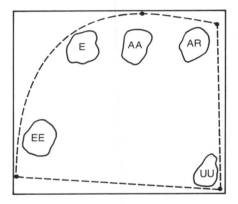

Fig 25   Excitation peak positions caused by vowel sounds applied to ordered arrays.

of the peak of excitation to move in a continuous trajectory over the array, the shape of the trajectory being characteristic of the non-stationary sound.

During this experiment, the array elements were given persistence with a time constant of about 200 mS, as described earlier in the paper.

As an example of the types of results obtained, the trajectories produced by the vowel transitions 'AA→EE', 'EE→AA', and 'EE→AA→OO' are shown in Figs 26a, 26b and 26c. These results demonstrate that trajectories are produced but also show a problem: The trajectories are very broad and tend to overlap one another. This problem has not yet been solved satisfactorily, but it is anticipated that some form of adaptive threshold may be useful to narrow the trajectories.

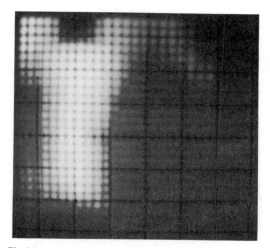

Fig 26a   Excitation caused by transition 'AA→EE.

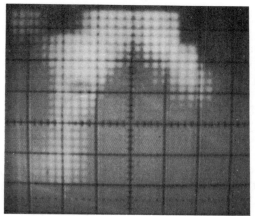

Fig 26b   Excitation caused by transition 'EE→AA'.

16. Time registration and time warp invariance in neural arrays

The paper now returns to the proposition made earlier that the shape of the trajectory produced on the array by a particular utterance is insensitive to its time warp function or its precise time registration. These properties are obtained by using neural excitation persistence together with over sampling of the speech spectrum.

The following section attempts to show that the phonetic description of an utterance is encoded by the trajectory shape and that the time warp is encoded by the excitation intensity profile along the trajectory. These two components of the excitation patterns can be weighted as desired before processing by the second layer array to give a controlled amount of time warp invariance.

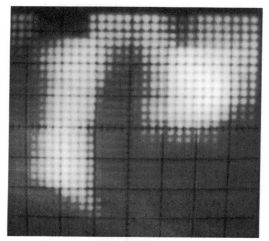

Fig 26c   Excitation caused by transition 'EE→AA→OO'.

17. Utterance trajectories

The vectors applied to the first array in the system are obtained by sampling the time varying spectrum, $Q(t)$, of utterance Q at intervals of T seconds to produce the vector sequence, $Q[n.T]$.

$$Q[n.T] = \overline{q_1}, \overline{q_2}, \overline{q_3} \ldots\ldots \overline{q_N} \qquad\qquad \ldots\ldots(11)$$

where $\overline{q_n}$ is the nth spectral vector.

If the array has previously been trained to form an ordered map, the sequence, $Q[n.T]$ causes a series of array excitations whose peak positions are in a sequence $P(nT)$.

$$P[n.T] = \overline{p_1}, \overline{p_2}, \overline{p_3} \ldots\ldots \overline{p_N} \qquad\qquad \ldots\ldots(12)$$

where $\overline{p_n}$ is a two-dimensional vector whose elements are the co-ordinates μ_{1n} and μ_{2n} of the nth excitation peak caused by the input sequence.

$$\overline{p}_n = [\mu_{1n}\ \mu_{2n}] \qquad\qquad \ldots\ldots(13)$$

Now consider the effect of increasing the sampling rate of the spectrum of the utterance, Q, by a factor, a, such that the new sample rate is T'.

$$T' = T/a$$

The new sequence of spectral vectors is $Q'[n.T']$, where:

$$Q'[n.T'] = \overline{q_1}', \overline{q_2}', \ldots\ldots \overline{q_p}' \qquad\qquad \ldots\ldots(14)$$

Notice that some of the new sequence's vectors will be the same as the vectors in $Q[n.T]$.

Specifically:

$$\overline{q}(n) = \overline{q}'(n.a) \qquad \qquad ......(15)$$

However, although the spectrum of Q is being sampled at above the Nyquist Rate, no extra information has been obtained by the increase in sampling rate. Therefore, in principle, it would be possible to obtain values for the extra vector samples in $Q'[n.T']$ from the values of the vectors in the original sequence $Q[n.T]$. This idea can be used to gain an insight into the nature of the new vectors which occur in the sequence $Q'[n.T']$.

Conceptually, one way to derive the new intermediate vectors of $Q'[n.T']$ would be to pass $Q[n.T]$ through a multi-dimensional interpolation filter. In the simplest case such an interpolation filter would place the additional vectors of the oversampled sequence $Q'[n.T']$ at equal intervals on a straight line between successive vectors in the sequence, $Q[n.T]$. Thus, in the spectral vector space, the extra vectors are bound to lie at intermediate positions between vectors in the original sequence $Q[n.T]$ as illustrated in Fig 27a.

Now consider what happens if the sequence, $Q'[n.T']$ is applied to the first neural array. Because the array is topologically ordered, vectors which have a particular spatial relationship in their vector space, will fire neurons which have a similar spatial relationship in the array. Thus the extra vectors obtained by oversampling will fire neurons which lie at intermediate positions between the neurons which were fired by the original sequence, $Q[n.T]$. This situation is shown in Fig 27b for the case where the sequence is oversampled by a factor of two. If the oversampling factor is increased further, the number of intermediate neural firings will increase until a continuous trajectory of fired neurons is formed as shown in Fig 27c. Increasing the oversampling factor beyond this point may cause multiple firings of the neurons along the trajectory, but will not change its shape.

18. Time registration invariance

It was previously demonstrated that the application of an oversampled sequence of vectors $Q'[n.T']$ to the array causes a continuous trajectory of neural firings. Consider now the effect of mis-registering the sampling points by a time Δt such that a new sequence of spectral vectors is applied to the array. The new sequence is $R[n.T']$ and:

$$R[n.T'] = Q'[n.T' + \Delta t] \qquad \qquad ......(16)$$

277

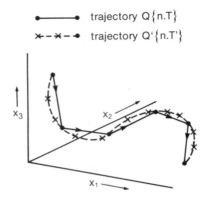

Fig 27a   Sequence of vectors $Q[nT]$ and $Q'[nT']$ in a 3-D vector space.

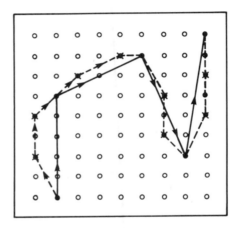

Fig 27b   Neurons fired by the vector sequence of $Q[nT]$ and $Q'[nT']$.

The values of the vectors in $R'[n.T']$ could in principle have been obtained by linear interpolation from the vectors in $Q'[nT']$ and must lie on a line through the vector space joining successive vectors in the sequence $Q'[n.T']$. Once again, because of the topological ordering of the array, the members of $R[n.T']$ will also fire neurons which lie on a line joining the successive positions of neurons which would have been fired by the sequence $Q'[n.T']$. Since the sampling rate is so high that a continuous trajectory is formed by the sequence $Q'[n.T']$, no additional intermediately positioned neurons exist and so $R[n.T']$ will fire exactly the same set of neurons as $Q'[n.T']$. Time mis-registration is therefore immaterial to recognition which is based upon the shape of the trajectory on the first array.

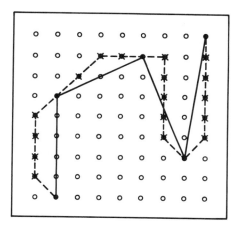

Fig 27c   Generation of a continuous trajectory by $Q'[nT']$ as T' is made very small.

19. Time warp invariance

One major source of variability in the sequence of spectral vectors produced by a particular utterance is time warp, i.e. the rate at which the utterance is articulated varies non-linearly. The variable time warp makes direct comparison of an incoming sequence of spectral vectors and a single stored reference difficult and for this reason dynamic time warping is commonly used in practical recognisers.

The arguments used in the previous section to show that the neural array trajectory is unaffected by time mis-registration can be extended to show that it is also unaffected by variable time warp in the utterance. Assume that an archetypal version of the utterance Q produces a short time spectrum, $Q(t)$. This function is sampled at uniform intervals, T', to produce a sequence of spectral vectors, $Q[n.T']$. Now compare this sequence with the sequence of vectors produced by a time warped version of utterance Q which has a time varying spectrum, $S(t)$. The sequence in this case is $S[n.T']$, and if the warp function is $w(t)$, as shown in Fig 28, the two sequences are related by:

$$S[n.T'] = Q[w(n.T')] \qquad\qquad ......(17)$$

Equation (17) indicates that $S[n.T']$ could have been obtained from the archetypal version of Q by sampling $Q(t)$ at times t_n:

$$t_n = w(n.T') \qquad\qquad ......(18)$$

Thus, the effect of time warp is equivalent to sampling an unwarped utterance at a rate which varies with time. However, it was argued earlier that if the time varying spectrum was sufficiently oversampled, the shape of the trajectory on the array would be unchanged, regardless of the actual value of the sampling rate. In consequence, it is evident that the trajectory shape will not be changed by a time warp as long as the spectrum remains oversampled, whatever the severity of the time warp.

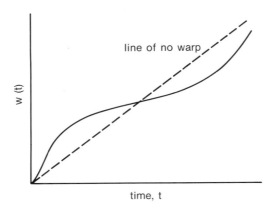

Fig 28   Time warp function.

20.   The soft window

As suggested earlier, the trajectory can be made visible for recognition by allowing the neuron excitation to decay slowly after the stimulus is removed. This closely resembles the biological system and its effect is to put a soft window over the most recent portion of the trajectory produced by a continuous stream of speech and so prevents the accumulation of unwanted trajectories of past utterances on the array. It also allows information about the time direction of the trajectory to be retained: the most excited neurons are at the most recent end of the trajectory.

Another effect of using a soft window is that different time warps for the same utterance will produce trajectories whose shapes are identical but whose excitation profiles along the length of the trajectory vary depending on the time warp function. This is because the amount of time a particular neuron on a trajectory is stimulated depends on the time warp at that point. If an element is stimulated for a long time, its excitation will build up due to the accumulation effect of persistence.

The pattern passed onto the second layer of the system is not just the trajectory shape but also the excitation profile, and therefore, time warps will modify the pattern seen by the second layer. The relationship between the degree of time warp, soft window width and pattern perturbation is explored in the following section.

21.   Time warp invariance and the soft window

It has been shown earlier that a particular class of utterance will produce the same trajectory shape regardless of its time warp, however, the intensity profile is affected, and this section investigates this effect, assuming a soft window defined by:

$$E(t) = E_0*\exp(-t/b) \qquad\qquad ......(19)$$

Where $E(t)$, is the excitation of the neural element after initial excitation of E_0. Let the sequence of fired neurons be $P[n]$.

Where $P[n] = \overline{P_1}, \overline{P_2}, ..., \overline{P_N}$

This sequence of neural firings is characteristic of a particular utterance and is not effected by the time warp. To deduce the degree of pattern perturbation it is necessary to derive an expression for the excitation profile of the trajectory as a function of the time warp. The excitation of a particular neuron depends on how much time has elapsed since it was fired, and so the first step is to find when each neuron in the sequence is fired.

The inverse of the time warp function gives the time at which the ith neuron in the sequence is fired:

$$t_i = w^{-1}(iT') \qquad\qquad ......(20)$$

Thus the excitation of the ith neuron at a time, t, is:

$$E_i(t) = E_{io}*\exp\left(-(t - w^{-1}(i.T'))/b\right) \qquad\qquad ......(21)$$

The excitation values define a vector $\overline{T}(t)$, representing the intensity profile of the trajectory for a particular inverse time warp function $w_1^{-1}(iT')$.

$$\overline{T_1}(t) = [E_1,(t), E_2(t), ..., E_N(t)] \qquad\qquad ......(22)$$

$$\overline{T_1}(t) = \exp(-t/b)*[E_{10}*\exp(w_1^{-1}(T')/b),$$

$$+ E_{20}*\exp(w_1^{-1}(2T')/b)$$

$$+ ......] \qquad\qquad ......(23)$$

Similarly if the inverse time warp function for a second example of the utterance is $w_2^{-1}(i)$, a vector, $\overline{T_2}(t)$ represents the excitation profile of the utterance.

$$\overline{T_2}(t) = \exp(-t/b), [E_{10}\exp(w_2^{-1}(T')/b) +$$

$$E_{20}*\exp(w_2^{-1}(2T')/b) +$$

$$......] \qquad\qquad ......(24)$$

The perturbation of the intensity profile for the utterance with the two different time warp functions can now be obtained by taking the vector difference between $\overline{T_1}(t)$ and $\overline{T_2}(t)$:

$$D = \exp(-t/b)*\{\sum_{i=2}^{N}[\exp(w_1^{-1}(iT')/b) -$$

$$\exp(w_2^{-1}(iT')/b)]^2\}^{1/2} \qquad \qquad \ldots\ldots(25)$$

Checking the properties of this function by substituting boundary values of b shows that if b is infinite, then the variation in time warp has no effect on the excitation profile. The soft window is infinitely wide and once fired, a neuron remains excited. Conversely, if b is zero, any time warp variation causes a massive change in profile.

Equation (28) can be simplified if the soft window is significantly longer than the utterance:

i.e. if $w^{-1}(iT^1)/b << 1$, then

$$D = \exp(-t/b)*\{\sum_{i=1}^{N} E_{io}*(w_1^{-1}(iT^1) - w_2^{-1}(iT^1))/b^2\}^{1/2} \qquad \ldots\ldots(26)$$

This shows that the perturbation of the excitation profile by different time warps is proportional to:

$$\sum_{i=1}^{N}(w_1^{-1}(iT^1) - w_2^{-1}(iT^1))/b$$

22. Experimental results on time warp invariance

It is believed that the time varying spectrum of speech should be sampled at about 5 ms intervals to avoid aliasing of the articulation frequencies. Thus, an oversampled time varying spectrum of the type required to produce continuous trajectories on the neural array should probably be sampled at 2 mS intervals. Unfortunately, such a high sample rate was not obtainable at the time of these experiments and so the full effect of oversampling cannot be seen.

Figure 29 shows three trajectories for the utterance 'Mike' spoken normally, quickly and slowly. The three utterances have very different time warps but according to the previous arguments should produce similar trajectory shapes. In this experiment, the spectral vectors were only taken at 32 mS intervals and it is no surprise that the trajectories are non-continuous. However, it is apparent that the interpolated trajectory shapes are similar, which supports the idea that the shape is a time warp invariant feature of speech.

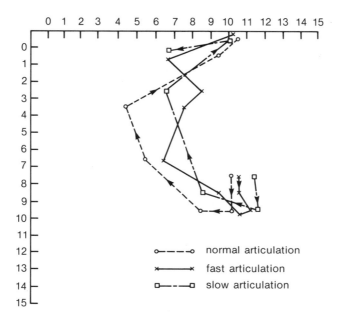

Fig 29   Trajectories produced by the utterance 'Mike' spoken normally and quickly.

23.   Intra layer grammar experiments

Two basic types of intra layer grammar systems have been considered for use in the neural array. The first is a multiplicative grammar system (MGS) in which the excitation of a particular neuron is given by the product of its inherent stimulation due to the input vector and stimulations received via the lateral connections due to the excitation of adjacent neurons. The excitation of the ith neuron at the nth sample instant is given by:

$$E_i^n = (E_i^{n-1} * \beta + \eta_i^n) * \sum_{j=0}^{7} E_{i,j}^{n-1} * \alpha_{i,j}$$

Where η_i^n is the stimulation of the neuron due to the input $\overline{X}$; $E_{i,j}^{n-1}$ are the excitations of the eight neurons surrounding the ith neuron, and $\alpha_{i,j}$ is the connection weight leading into the ith neuron from the jth neighbouring neuron. The MGS is very similar to a hidden Markov model scheme in which the lateral weights correspond to the state transitional probabilities and the inherent stimulation is related to a particular state probability given the current input vector. This is the best way of exploiting all the redundancy in the input speech in an information theoretic sense. However, experiments using artifical data demonstrated that it is impossible to obtain stability in such a system, the excitations in the array collapsing to zero if η is less than unity or growing without bound if η exceeds unity.

The MGS was consequently abandoned in favour of an additive grammar system, AGS, whose operation has already been briefly described. In effect it works by producing the spatial and intensity average of two trajectories. The first trajectory is the one which would be produced on an array without grammar, and the second is the nearest archeteypal trajectory. The excitation of the ith neuron is given in this case by:

$$E_i^n = \eta_i^n + \beta_s * E_i^{n-1} + \sum_{j=0}^{7} E_{i,j}^{n-1} * \alpha_{i,j} \qquad \ldots\ldots(27)$$

24. Simulations of the additive grammar system

The effect of additive grammar was initially investigated by simulation of an array which was artifically ordered on uniformly distributed data. A test set of four artificial utterances was prepared. The trajectories that these four utterances would produce on the array in the absence of any grammar weights are shown in Fig 30. The test utterance set actually consists of an archetypal version of each utterance and a noisy version of the same utterance. Thus AU4 is the trajectory of a perfect straight line and AU1 is its corrupted version. Similarly AU2 is a perfect L-shaped trajectory and AU5 is its corrupted form.

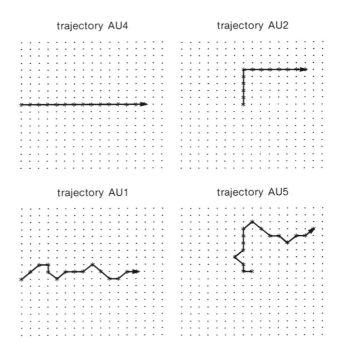

trajectory AU4   trajectory AU2

trajectory AU1   trajectory AU5

Fig 30   Trajectories used in intra-layer grammar simulations.

Examples of the simulation results are presented in Fig 31 and 32 as a series of snapshots of the array excitation as the particular trajectory progresses. Two types of additive grammar were tried, inhibitory and excitory. An excitory grammar is one in which the connection weights are allowed to be positive with the most positive weight lying along the line of the archetypal trajectory. An inhibitory grammar uses all negative weights, with the least negative lying along the line of the trajectory.

The results are self explanatory, but the important point to notice is that a corrupted version of an archetypal input is made to look more like the archetype by the grammar embedded in the array, confirming the predicted property of intra layer grammar.

A particularly interesting result is recorded in Fig 32 which shows the series of excitation patterns created by a corrupt version of utterance AU4 (AU1) applied to an array which has been programmed with the grammar weight for two different archetypes, AU4 and AU2. The resulting excitation clearly shows that the corrupt input excites neurons on its related archetypal trajectory and also slightly excites the second AU2 trajectory whose grammar is embedded in the array. It is believed that this low level excitation of other trajectories is desirable because they are thereby retained as low probability candidates for recognition. Less corruption of the input causes less excitation of these alternatives and more excitation of the input's archetypal trajectory.

25. Learning the grammar weights

The simulations of intra layer grammar used interconnective weights that were set manually and programmed into the array. In the experiments with real speech, the weights need to be learnt automatically from the input data.

The first form of learning algorithm tried, used leaky accumulation of the product of adjacent neurons' excitations to produce values used as the grammar weights $\alpha_{i,j}$:

$$\alpha_{i,j}^{n+1} = \alpha_{i,j}^{n} * \lambda + k_2 * E_i^n * E_{i,j}^{n-1} \qquad \ldots\ldots(28)$$

Where $\alpha_{i,j}$ is the value of the grammar weight directed into the ith neuron from the jth neighbour, λ is a forgetting factor for the old weight, k_2 is a learning gain factor and $E_{i,j}^{n-1}$ is the previous excitation of the jth neighbour of the ith neuron.

The preliminary experiments on this system soon revealed a problem: the rate at which the grammar weights grow is proportional to the excitation of the neurons and the neurons' excitations are in turn proportional to the grammar weights. This positive feedback causes the grammar weights to grow uncontrollably.

To break the feedback loop, the learning of the lateral weights was made proportional to the product of adjacent elements excitation e_i, in the absence of lateral connection.

$$e_i^n = \eta_i^n + \beta_s . e_i^{n-1}$$

$$\alpha_{i,j}^{n+1} = \alpha_{i,j}^n * \lambda + k_2 * e_i^n * e_{i,j}^{n-1}$$

The lateral weights learnt in this manner were then used to compute the total excitation of each elements.

$$E_i^n = e_i^n + \sum_{j=0}^{N} E_{i,j}^{n-1} * \alpha_{i,j} \qquad\qquad ......(28)$$

26. Intra-layer grammar experiments using real speech

The results obtained using real speech with intra-layer grammar have only recently been obtained and although promising, it is clear that more work needs to be done in this area before satisfactory results are obtained. As an example of the type of result obtained when grammar weights are learnt by exposure to speech, examine Fig 33, which shows the changing excitation pattern of the array as the utterance 'one' is repeatedly applied to the array. In the first snapshot, before the grammar weights have developed, the trajectory consists of isolated points of high excitation. Succeeding frames, after more training, show the trajectory filling out as the grammar weights develop.

The grammar weights developed by the system after repeated exposure to 'one' are shown in the photograph of Fig 34. The value of the weight between two adjacent neurons is represented by the intensity of a line drawn between two points corresponding to the positions of the neurons. Unfortunately it is not possible to represent the different weights in each direction between pairs of neurons and so in the figure the average value is shown.

These results shown a filling out of sparse trajectories. This is predictable and desirable. However, the broadening of the trajectory is most undesirable. Another undesirable property is a 'clumping' action in which the largest grammar weights develop in regions of high excitation along the trajectory and this in turn exaggerates the variation in intensity profile along its trajectory.

27. Conclusions

In this paper a possible approach to continuous speech recognition has been presented based upon the use of topologically ordered neural arrays which are obtained by unsupervised exposure to natural speech.

The basic architectural features of the system are a stack of ordered arrays in which the neural excitation of one array is presented as an input to the subsequent array and also back to the input of the previuos array. Moreover, each neural array his internal feedback in the form of lateral neural interconnections.

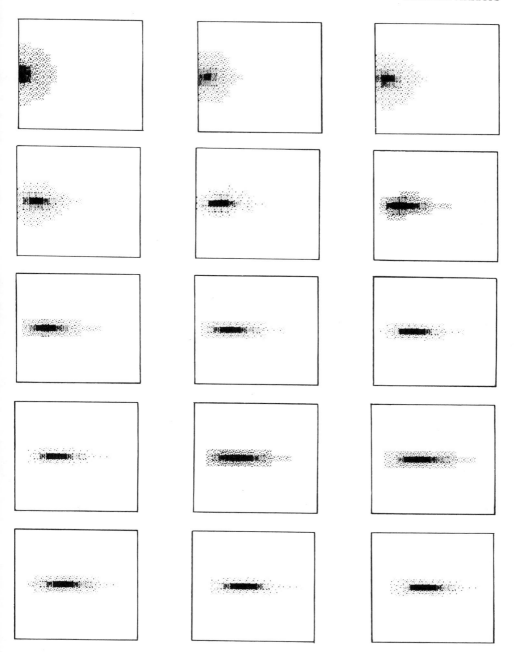

Fig 31   Simulation of array with excitory grammar weights. Grammar weights follow AU4. Input follows a noisy version of AU4 called AU1.

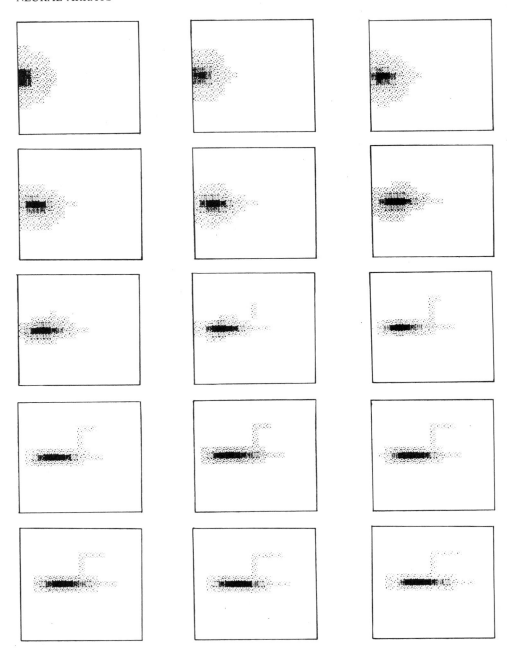

Fig 32   Simulation of array with excitory weights. Grammar weights for AU2 and AU4 are embedded in array and the input is a noisy version of AU4 called AU1.

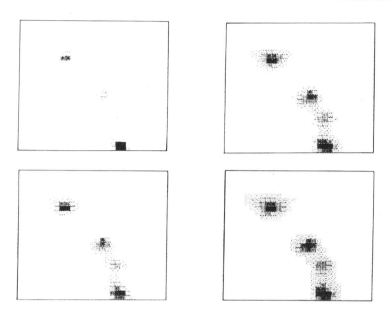

Fig 33   Series of excitation maps obtained as the utterance "one" is repeatedly applied to the neural array with adaptive grammar weights.

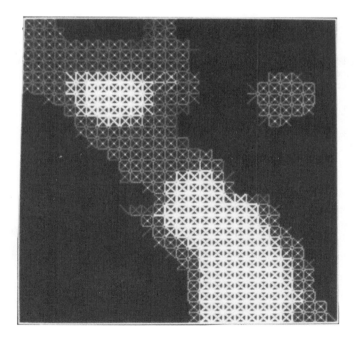

Fig 34   Distribution of grammar weights developed during the training run shown in Fig 32.

The purpose of these architectural features is primarily to enable the system to map relatively long segments of speech, say of word length, to localised neural elements at some level in the system. Another function of the chosen architecture is to enable the system to learn and exploit the grammar of speech from the phonetic level, through to the linguistic grammar and possibly beyond to semantic grammar, although of course this goal is beyond reach at the moment.

Preliminary experiments are already being performed on elements of the system and in particular it has been shown that trajectories can be produced which are characteristic of particular utterances and which are insensitive to time warp variation within the utterance.

The basic ideas behind intra-layer grammar learning have been confirmed, but more work is required to obtain a satisfactory performance when phonetic grammar is learnt from real speech.

References

1   Minsky M and Papert S: 'Perceptrons: an introduction to computational geometry', MIT Press, Cambridge Mass (1969).

2   Rumelhard D E and Hinton G E: 'Learing internal representations by error propagation, ICS Report 8506, University of California (September 1985).

3   Rumelhart and MacClelland: 'Parallel distributed processing — exploration in the microstructure of cognition', MIT Press (1986).

4   Kohonen T: 'Clustering, taxonomy and toplogical maps of patterns', Proc Int Conf on Pattern Recognition (October 1982).

MULTI-LAYER PERCEPTRONS APPLIED
TO SPEECH TECHNOLOGY

N McCulloch, W A Ainsworth and R Linggard

ABSTRACT

The original perceptron of the 1960s has been given new life in the 1980s by two innovations, a non-linear component and a new learning rule. This means that multi-layer perceptrons (MLPs) can be built which are capable of learning quite complicated non-linear mappings, and hence performing very difficult pattern classification tasks. This paper describes the MLP, contrasts it with the original perceptron, and discusses its application in two important areas of speech technology — speech synthesis and vowel recognition.

1. Introduction

The idea of constructing machines based on the structure of the human brain has fascinated scientists for most of this century. A central motivaton being to emulate the brain's amazing pattern processing capability, particularly in vision and hearing. In the 1950s, a device called the perceptron, [1], based on the layout of the retina and its neural connections, was the centre of much attention. This machine, illustrated in Fig 1, consists of simple processing units (neurons) arranged in layers connected together via 'weights' (synapses). The output of each unit in a layer, is the weighted sum of the outputs from the previous layer. During training, these weights are adjusted so that a pattern on the input layer is 'recognised' by a particular set of output units being activated above a threshold.

It was soon realised that the mapping between layers was a simple linear transformation, which could be represented by a matrix equation. It was also apparent that there was no point in having more than one layer, because the total transformation was simply the matrix product of the transformations for each layer. Thus, if each layer was a linear transformation then the whole perceptron could only be a linear transformation. There was also some difficulty with strategies for adjusting the weights to learn particular patterns.

Interest in perceptrons faded in the 1960s, and did not revive again until the mid 1980s, when two innovations [2] gave perceptrons an exciting new potential. The first discovery was that if each unit was followed by a non-linear compression, then the transformation between layers would also be non-linear. This meant that, in theory at least, such a machine was capable of performing complex, non-linear mappings. The second innovation was the invention of a weight-adjustment algorithm known as the 'generalised delta rule'.

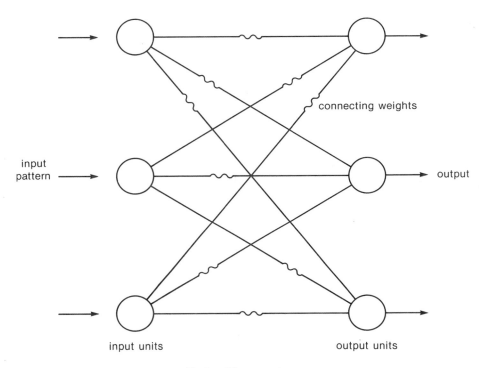

Fig 1   The perceptron.

Since a sequence of non-linear transformations is not, generally, equivalent to a single, non-linear transformation, the new perceptron could have as many layers as necessary to perform its complicated mappings. In fact, it can be shown that for any real-real mapping, only two hidden layers are necessary, and that for a binary mapping, only one hidden layer is needed [3]. Thus the new device came to be known as the multi-layer perceptron (MLP). The generalised delta rule enabled it to learn patterns by a simple training process. A pattern to be learned is 'clamped' to the input units of the machine, and the corresponding required output is presented to the output units. The weights, which connect input to output via the multiple layers, are adjusted so that the error between the actual and required output is reduced. This process is repeated many times for all the patterns in the training set. After an appropriate number of iterations, the MLP will recognise the patterns in the training set. If the data is structured, and if the training set is representative, then the MLP will also recognise patterns not in the training set.

The MLP is inherently an analogue machine. However, by limiting input variables to zero and one, and thresholding the output variables, it can be made to learn mappings between sets of digital patterns.

2. The perceptron

In a mapping process, a set of inputs activate a set of outputs as shown in Fig 1. If every input is connected to every output the result is a network known as a single layer perceptron. The mapping between the inputs, Xi, and the outputs, Oj, can be altered by varying the weight values, Wji, of the connections.

The input pattern is represented by the state of the input units, i. These send signals which are modified by the weights to the output units, j. The weighted sum of the X inputs which form the input to an output unit is given by

$$Yj = \sum_{i} Wji.Xi + Bj$$

where Bj is a bias to the value of the summed inputs. The value of Oj, the output of the output unit, is a function of Yj.

$$Oj = F(Yj)$$

In many perceptrons the signal values are restricted to 0 and 1, so that the function $F(.)$ is simply a threshold given by

$$Oj = 1 \text{ if } Yj > 0, \text{ otherwise } Oj = 0.$$

One of the advantages of using a network to perform a mapping is that the network can be trained by presenting pairs of required input/output patterns and adjusting the weights Wji. It can be shown that, provided the patterns are linearly separable, the desired mapping can be obtained by iterative adjustment of the weights, [1]. The incremental adjustment of weight Wji is given by

$$\Delta Wji = r.(Tj - Oj) X_i$$

where Tj is the required target output value. This weight adjustment strategy is known as the 'delta rule'. In the original perceptrons [1], monitor-driven potentiometers were used as the adjustable weights. These were eminently impractical and subsequently a number of alternatives were tried, these included the 'memistor' [4] and devices based on the growth of silver dendrites [5].

The great disadvantage of single-layer perceptrons is that the mapping can only be performed if the input patterns are linearly separable. That is, if the input patterns are to be mapped into two classes, their vectors (represented by points in n-dimensional space) must be separable by a hyperplane. In general, patterns are not so easily separated, and interest in perceptrons faded until the invention of the multi-layer device [2].

3. MLP Theory

In formal terms, an MLP consists of an array of processing units such as that shown in Fig 2. There is an input layer, an output layer, and any number of 'hidden' layers in between. The weights connect adjacent layers, but there is no connection within a layer, and normally no connections bridging layers. The functional equation of each unit is given by

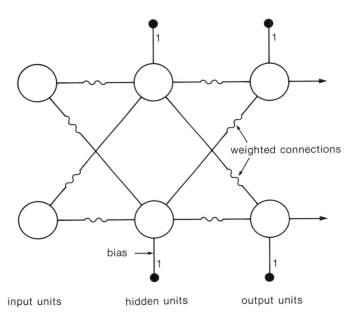

weighted connections

bias

input units   hidden units   output units

Fig 2   3 Layer MLP

$$O = C(Y)$$

Here O is the output value of the unit, Y is the weighted sum of the output units in the previous layer plus a bias term. $C(Y)$ is a compression function, which for mathematical convenience may be given by

$$C(Y) = \frac{1}{1 + \exp(-Y)}$$

Figure 3 shows the shape of this non-linear compression function.

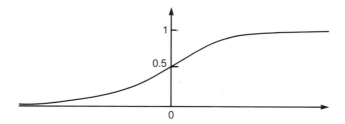

Fig 3   The compression function.

In order to train the MLP to classify any particular set of patterns, it is necessary to have available corresponding pairs of desired inputs and outputs. Starting with a set of randomly chosen weights, the outputs are calculated for a particular input pattern. These are compared with the required outputs and the resulting errors are used to adjust the weights so as to reduce the total sum-squared error. This is repeated many times for all input/output pairs in the training material, until the sum-squared error is minimised. If the set of training patterns is representative of the whole class then the device, when trained, may recognise not only the training set but all the patterns of that class.

The 'generalised delta rule' seeks to minimise a total error, Ep, by incremental adjustment of the weight values. Now Ep, the total error due to pattern p, is defined as

$$Ep = \frac{1}{2} \sum_j (Tpj - Opj)^2$$

where Tpj is the required output of unit j for pattern p, and Opj is the actual output of unit j for pattern p. The value of each weight is to be adjusted, iteratively, so that the total error Ep is reduced. Hence the change in weight Wji must be proportional to the derivative of Ep with respect to Wji, that is

$$\Delta Wji = -r.dEp/\delta Wji$$

The negative sign is to ensure that Ep decreases, and r is a scaling factor called the 'learning rate'.

Now $\delta Ep/\delta Wji$ can be written as

$$\delta Ep/\delta Wji = (\delta Ep/\delta Ypj).(\delta Ypj/\delta Wji)$$

where Ypj is the sum of $Wji.Opi$ (the weighted outputs of the layer preceeding unit j). Thus

$$\delta Ypj/\delta Wji = \frac{\delta}{\delta Wji} (Wji.Opi) = Opi$$

If the other term $\delta Ep/\delta Ypj$ is defined as $-\Delta pj$,

then $\Delta Wji = r.Dpj.Opi$

The derivative involving the awkward compression function $C(.)$ is now concentrated in the term Dpj. This can be expanded as

$$Dpj = -\delta Ep/\delta Ypj = -(\delta Ep/\delta Opj).(\delta Opj/\delta Ypj)$$

But since $Opj = C(Ypj)$,
and $C(Ypj) = \dfrac{1}{1 + \exp(-Ypj)}$

the derivative $\delta Opj/\delta Ypj = Opj(1 - Opj)$

This just leaves the term $\delta Ep/\delta Opj$ which can be evaluated from the expression for total error. If j is an output unit then $\delta Ep/\delta Opj = -(Tpj - Opj)$ which can be found since the target output, Tpj, is given. Therefore the term δpj is simply

$$\delta pj = (Tpj - Opj).Opj.(1 - Opj)$$

If j is not an output unit then Opj is the output of a unit in a hidden layer. This will contribute to the total error via the following layers. The adjustments to the weights Wji can thus be calculated from the error in the output layer propagated back to the layer containing j. The derivative

$$\delta Ep/\delta Opj = \sum_{k} (\delta Ep/\delta Ypk).(\delta Ypk/\delta Opj)$$

where the Ypk are the summed weighted inputs to the layer after j and to which it is connected. The term $\delta Ep/\delta Ypk$ has been defined as

$$\delta Ep/\delta Ypk = -\delta pk$$

and since $Ypk = \sum_{j} (Wkj.Opj)$,

$$\delta Ypk/\delta Opj = Wkj$$

and
$$\delta Ep/\delta Opj = -\sum_{k} Dpk.Wkj$$

the value of δpj for non-output units is given by

$$\delta pj = \sum_{k} \{\delta pk . Wkj . C'(Ypj)\}$$

The error back-propagation algorithm proceeds by calculating the values of Dpj for the output layer and using these values to calculate those for the preceding layer, and so on, back to the layer connected to the input. Once all the Dpj for each layer have been calculated, the adjustments to the weights can be made using the formula

$$\Delta Wji = r . Dpj . Opi$$

This is done many times, using all the patterns in the training material. The learning rate, r, is a factor which scales the adjustment to the weights so that a locally optimal set of values can be approached more or less quickly. To allow rapid learning without the problem of overshoot, a 'momentum' term, scaled by m, may be included, so that

$$\Delta Wji(t) = r . Dpj . Opi + m . \Delta Wji(t-1)$$

where the term $\Delta Wji(t)$ is the weight change at the t iteration. The speed of learning is very much dependent on the values of r and m. In general different values are required for different problems.

4. NETspeak — a re-implementation of NETtalk

Most modern text-to-speech (TTS) systems use a large set of letter-to-sound rules in conjunction with an exceptions dictionary to generate a phonemic transcription of the text. Further rules are then used to derive stress and pitch contours for the utterance. Finally, a set of phonetic realisation rules and tables are used to construct dynamic patterns of excitation, formant frequencies and amplitudes which then drive a formant speech synthesiser. Fig 4 shows a block diagram of a standard text-to-speech system.

The NETtalk system devised by Sejnowski and Rosenberg [6], replaced the letter-to-sound rules and the exceptions dictionary with an MLP. The input to the MLP was a binary coding of a context window of seven letters. The objective was to code the phoneme corresponding to the central letter in the window. To obtain training data, this text window was passed over a large body of text, with the phoneme corresponding to the central character being presented at the output. In this way, the MLP was made to learn the mapping between text and pronunciation. The phonemic and prosodic representation produced by NETtalk was fed into the second half of a text-to-speech system to produce synthetic speech.

As an initial experiment in the use of MLPs, it was decided to re-implement NETtalk. But because a different synthesis system had to be used, and due to other constraints, this re-implementation of NETtalk is somewhat different from the original.

297

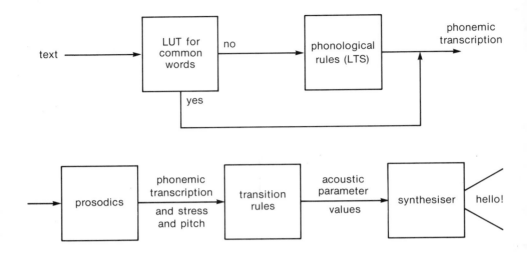

Fig 4   A standard text-to-speech system.

Consequently, the system is called NETspeak [7]; the description below notes the differences between the two systems.

Like the original NETtalk, NETspeak uses a text-window of seven characters which is stepped across the training data one character at a time. The seven character window was found to contain sufficient context to produce a reasonably accurate transcription, whilst avoiding the high computational expense of larger windows. However, the input coding which NETspeak uses for these letters is somewhat different. The original NETtalk system used a very simple but highly redundant 29 bit code for each letter. One bit was used for each letter and three extra bits for punctuation symbols to make up the 29. This required 7 x 29 = 203 input units and consequently a very large number of connections between the input layer and the hidden layer. Computationally, this was very costly. In the re-implementation, therefore, it was decided to use a more concise 11 bit coding, both to reduce the computation and to see if the network could learn to use this more compact input. The letters are grouped into five very rough phonological sets. The first 5 bits of each character code indicate to which set the letter belongs. The remaining 6 bits denote the character number within the group. The groups contain letters which are usually pronounced as ...

vowels	{I E A O U}
unvoiced plosives	{P T Q K C}
voiced plosives and miscellaneous punctuation	{B D J G __}
fricatives	{F V S Z X H}
miscellaneous liquids, glides and nasals	{M W L N Y R}

Other experiments indicate that the input/output coding method used for MLPs is very important, and that an appropriate coding can greatly assist learning whilst an inappropriate one can hinder or even prevent it. In particular, it seems that MLP networks have great difficulty if two items, which are close together in output space, are coded far apart from one another in input space. Thus it makes the training task a lot easier if input codings are chosen which reflect the distance relationships between the outputs. This is exactly what the 11 bit input coding is achieving, since it is reducing the Hamming distance between letters which tend to have similar phonemic realisations (and so are close together in output space). Or course, it is necessary to have some sort of measure of the 'true' distance relationships between the outputs, which in this case is the perceptual similarity of the most common pronunciations of the letters.

The output coding used by NETspeak is also slightly different from that used in the original NETtalk which used a distributed representation for the phoneme targets, consisting of 17 articulatory features, 4 punctuation features and 5 stress and syllable boundary features, for each phoneme. NETspeak uses only 2 punctuation features and 4 stress features, but includes 2 word type features, giving a total of 25 features. Each feature is represented by 1 unit in the output, indicating the presence or absence of that particular feature. NETspeak also uses a slightly different phoneme set so as to permit speech output via an existing RP English text-to-speech system.

A continuation symbol is used to pad out the phonemic transcription when it has fewer symbols than the English text-to-speech system. Similarly, in a few instances in which the phonemic transcription is longer than the text word (for example in the pronunciation of the word 'six'), compound phonemes are created to ensure that the one-to-one correspondence between character and phoneme is maintained.

5. Learning parameters

There are a number of small differences between the learning parameters being used in Netspeak and those used in the original NETtalk. NETspeak uses the back-propagation weight update formula [2] namely.

$$\Delta Wji(t) = r.Dpj.Opi + m.\Delta Wji(t-1)$$

where $\Delta Wji(t)$ is the weight change at iteration t to the weight joining units i and j when pattern p is being presented at the input. Opi is the output of the unit i, Dpj is the derivative of the error with respect to the input of unit j. The factor r is the learning rate and m is the momentum term. In NETspeak the weights are updated by simply adding $\Delta Wji(t)$ to $Wji(t)$, that is

$$Wji(t+1) = Wji(t) + \Delta Wji(t)$$

NETtalk used an exactly equivalent scheme. However, Sejnowski and Rosenburg [6] use different definitions of the learning parameters. Hence the values quoted in their paper have been converted to their equivalent values of r and m as defined above. NETtalk used a value of 0.1 for r, whereas a value of 0.05 was used here. The momentum terms were quite similar; NETtalk used 0.9 to NETspeak's value of 0.95.

It is also of passing interest that the range of magnitude of the starting weights used in NETspeak is ± 0.05, much smaller than the ± 0.3 used previously in NETtalk. The reason for this smaller value is to avoid having large values of input to the hidden units which occurs when the fan-in is large. There are other ways of dealing with this problem [8].

Perhaps the most important difference in the training procedures is that NETspeak updates its weights after each character, whereas the original NETtalk only updates after each word. There is no reason to believe that updating per word should be better than per character. The incremental changes in the weights required to improve the pronunciation of one letter in a word, should be independent of the increments needed for another letter in the same word. Experience with MLPs suggests that updating after every backward pass does tend to produce better results than after a set of forward and backward passes, although it is somewhat slower.

6. Training material

The original NETtalk system used two different training sets. The first was a transcription of the informal, continuous speech of a child. The second was the 1000 most common words in English, extracted from a 20,012 word dictionary. In the case of the continuous speech, the words were passed through the text window, one after another, with only a word boundary symbol between them. For the dictionary, the words were placed in random order and passed through the window individually. NETspeak, however, was trained on a phonemic transcription of the 16,280 word 'Teachers Word Book' dictionary, to which stress and word function information have been added. Unlike the transcription of informal, continuous speech used by NETtalk, the NETspeak transcription of a word was the same in all contexts. Thus the network did not have to learn the way in which a word's pronunciation varies with its context in the sentence.

7. Results for dictionary-based training

The results are very similar to those produced by original NETtalk system. Several different values for the learning parameters were tried and it was found that $r = 0.05$ and $m = 0.9$ give good results. The MLP network learned to place lexical stress first, along with the vowel/consonant distinction. It then began to distinguish between different vowels and consonants with the phonologically 'easy' distinctions being made before the more subtle ones. The network was tested on the training set using sets of weights learned after increasing amounts of training. It was also tested on a section of the dictionary which was not used in the training procedure. The results for both cases are shown in Tables 1 and 2.

Table 1   NETspeak performance on dictionary training set.

Number of characters used to train the MLP	% O/P Bits correct	% Best Guess O/P Vectors	% Perfect O/P Match
10,000	85.8	—	16.3
50,000	92.1	—	33.3
120,000	94.1	86.5	46.0
240,000	94.9	87.8	51.5
360,000	95.2	87.9	53.6

Three measures of accuracy have been used. The most obvious is the percentage of perfect output vector matches. This somewhat understates NETspeak's accuracy and a more favourable metric is the percentage number of output bits that are correct. However, the figures for this are rather high. Perhaps the fairest indicator is the percentage of the output vectors which are nearest to the correct phoneme. As can be seen, the MLP consistently performed better as training increased. The fact that the results on the test set were only slightly worse than those for the training set, indicates that the data is quite well structured and that the network has generalised successfully.

Table 2   NETspeak performance on dictionary test set.

Number of characters used to train the MLP	% O/P Bits correct	% Best Guess O/P Vectors	% Perfect O/P Match
10,000	85.4	—	16.0
50,000	92.9	—	32.4
120,000	93.8	84.2	44.9
240,000	94.7	85.5	49.7
360,000	94.9	86.0	52.3

The MLP network, using the most accurate set of weights, was also tested on sentences typed in by the authors. The phonemic output from these sentences was fed into the second half of the JSRU synthesis-by-rule program [9]. This produced reasonably intelligible speech. The majority of the errors made by the network arose from the fact that it had only seen one instance of each word, and so had not learned how to cope with all of the irregularities of the commonest words. It is interesting to note that most of the erroneous phonemes were close, in a perceptual sense, to the correct ones.

8. Summary of NETspeak

NETspeak is a re-implementaton of the original NET-talk system. When trained on a 16,280 word pronunciation dictionary, its performance is only slightly worse than of NETtalk trained on phonetically transcribed speech. Yet despite the remarkable results achieved by both NETtalk and NETspeak, the synthetic speech is still not as good as that of the best rule-based systems. However when the amount of time which the MLP network took to learn its internal representation of pronunciation is compared to the amount of time which it takes to construct a set of rules to perform that same task, it is clear that the MLP method has great promise.

There is no reason to believe that NETspeak cannot be further improved, perhaps even to the point at which it does as well as, or even better than, a rule-based system. Certainly, the experience of re-implementing NETtalk has shown that it is well worth considering the ways in which connectionist networks can be applied to the problems of speech technology.

9. An MLP vowel recogniser

A second experiment was devised to investigate the potential of MLPs in speech recognition applications. One of the most difficult problems in speech technology is speaker independent recognition of vowel sounds. This particular subset of sounds was chosen because it incorporates sufficient variability to be a good test of the MLP as a classification technique whilst avoiding the complications associated with time-varying data. This experiment, therefore, tests the ability of a MLP to extract invariant features from highly variable data.

The training and test data was obtained from the Oxford Alvey speech database [10]. The material used consisted of 30 adult speakers (15 male, 15 female) of the Received Pronunciation (RP) dialect of English, saying the words:

heed, hid, head, had, hard, hod, hoard, hood, who'd, Hudd, heard.

These 11 words contain the 11 steady-state vowels in RP English. A 54 channel filter bank analysis was performed on each of the utterances. The steady-state portion of the vowel in the spectral pattern of each utterance was extracted and averaged over the number of frames it covered to give a single 54-element vector, representing the spectral cross-section of each vowel. The component values of the vector were normalised to have a mean value of zero and a variance of one. Three sets of input and target files were constructed from the 330 vowel spectra. The spectra of all the vowels of 8 males and 8 females were randomly ordered to form one training set. The (randomly ordered) vowels of the remaining 14 speakers formed the corresponding test set. The second data set was created from just the female speakers, 8 speakers in the training set and 7 in the test set. The third data set was created from just the male speakers, again, 8 in the training set and 7 in the test set.

The networks consisted of 54 input units, one for each channel, 50 hidden units and 11 output units. Each target output consisted of a one at the output corresponding to the vowel which was being presented at the input, and zeros at all the other outputs. Thus the intention was that the MLPs would learn the mapping between the spectral cross-section of a vowel and its classification, regardless of speaker. To try and avoid the spurious effects of any particular training and test set, five rotations of the three data sets were used (i.e. each rotation used a different subset of the data in its training and test sets). Separate networks with the above configuration were trained and tested for all five rotations of the three data sets. Six random weight starts were used for each rotation giving a total of 30 runs per data set. The gradient descent with momentum optimisation technique [2] was used — a smaller set of exploratory runs gave rise to the choise of 0.05 for the learning rate and 0.9 for the momentum.

Each MLP correctly recognised all of the vowels in its training set. The test set results averaged over all 30 runs are shown in the first column of Table 3 (the standard deviations are in brackets below). The results indicate that the MLPs have successfully generalised from their training sets to achieve reasonable performance on the test set.

Table 3   Results for the MLP, Gaussian and K-nearest-neighbour classifiers

Classifier Data	MLP 1 out of 11 Gradient Descent and Momentum	Gaussian Identity Covariance Matrix	Gaussian Diagonal Covariance Matrix	K Nearest Neighbour
Trained on 8 Male 8 Female Tested on 7 male 7 female	81.67 (2.03)	80	83	83 (K = 6)
Trained on 8 Male Tested on 7 Male	83.55 (4.21)	81	81	84 (K = 7)
Trained on 8 Female Tested on 7 Female	84.89 (4.44)	83	81	82 (K = 6)

The performance of the MLP was compared with that of other classifiers such as Gaussian and K nearest-neighbour classifiers in order to find out whether the MLP was learning a mapping which was already easily determinable by conventional methods. The mean vectors and covariance matrices for each vowel class were calculated from the vowels in the training set. The Mahalanobis distance, defined in equation 1, was calculated between each of the vowel spectra in the test set and all of the vowel classes and the test vowel was classified as belonging to the nearest class.

$$D = (\underline{x} - \underline{\mu}_j)' \Sigma_i^{-1} (\underline{x} - \underline{\mu}_j)$$

......(1)

where $\underline{x}$ is the vector to be classified, $\underline{\mu}_i$ is the mean of class i and Σ_i^{-1} is the inverse of the covariance matrix for class i.

Two types of Gaussian classifier were tried: the first used an identity covariance matrix for each class (in which case the Mahalanobis distance simply becomes the Euclidean distance); the second used a separate diagonal covariance matrix for each class.

A K-nearest-neighbour classifier was also used to classify the test vowels, with the value of K varying from 1 to 10. Table 1 shows the test set performance averaged over the five rotations on each of the three data sets for both the Gaussian and K-nearest-neighbour classifiers. The KNN results shown are for the value of K which produced the best performance on the test set.

10. Vowel experiment conclusions

There is practically no difference between the Gaussian and K-nearest-neighbour results and those obtained with the MLP. This would seem to indicate that the data is sufficiently well clustered not to benefit from the sophisticated partitioning of the pattern space provided by a MLP. This raises the question of when to use a MLP rather than a simpler conventional technique. Current research [11] is exploring the relationship between MLPs and conventional classifiers with a view to answering this question.

11. General conclusions

This paper has described two experiments which were designed to access the potential of multi-layer perceptrons in solving problems in speech technology. In both cases, a MLP solution was implemented rapidly and easily. Furthermore, in neither case was it necessary to have specialist knowledge of the field. Though the results are not as good as state-of-the-art technology, they were sufficiently impressive to give hope that, with more development, the MLP will become a standard pattern classification technique. However, further research is necessary into the relationship between MLPs and traditional classifiers in order to be able to determine the size and type of network required for any specific task.

Acknowledgements

The authors would like to thank all those who assisted in these experiments. In particular, Paul Lloyd for the Gaussian and K-nearest-neighbour programs, Mark Bedworth, Stephen Cox, and John Bridle for numerous useful discussions and, David Bounds for support and encouragement.

References

1   Rosenblatt F: 'Principles of neurodynamics', Spartan Books, New York (1962).

2   Rumelhart D E and McClelland J L: 'Parallel distributed processing: explorations in the microstructures of cognition', 1, pp 318—362, Foundations, MIT Press (1986).

3   Longstaff I D and Cross J F: 'A pattern recognition approach to understanding the multi-layer perception', Patt, Recog Lett 5, pp 315—319 (1987).

4   Widrow B: 'An adaptive 'Adaline' neuron using chemical 'Memistors', TR No. 1557—2, Stanford Electronics Labs (1960).

5   Ainsworth A A: 'Electrolytic growth of silver dendrites', Science, 146, pp 1294—1295 (1964).

6   Sejnowski T J and Rosenberg C R: 'Parallel networks that learn to pronounce English text', Complex Systems, 1(1):145—168 (1987).

7   McCulloch N, Bedworth M and Bridle J: 'NETspeak — A re-implementation of NETtalk', Computer Speech and Language, 2, pp 289—301 (1987).

8   Plaut D C, Nowland S J and Hinton G E: 'Experiments on learning by back propagation', Technical Report CMU-CS-86-126, Carnegie-Mellon University (1986).

9   Stephens A P: 'The JSRU synthesis-by-rule system: installation and users guide', Technical Report, Speech Research Unit, RSRE, St Andress Rd, Malvern, England (May 1985).

10 The Oxford Alvey Speech Database, Phonetics Laboratory, 37/41 Wellington Square, Oxford, OX1 2JF.

11 Webb A R and LoweD: 'A theorem connecting adaptive feed-forward layered networks and nonlinear discriminant analysis', RSRE Memorandum 4209, Speech Research Unit, Royal Signals and Radar Establishment, St. Andrews Rd, Malvern, England (1988).

Single Layer Look Up Perceptrons (SLLUPS)

G D Tattersall, R D Johnston and S Foster

ABSTRACT

Multilayer perceptrons (MLP) have caused much excitement because of their ability to perform non-linear pattern classification. However, MLP learning times are often long and convergence is not guaranteed. This paper describes a new type of single layer perceptron which has similar properties to the MLP but learns much faster and will always converge.

1. Introduction

For many years it has been known that the simple single layer perceptron (SLP) is incapable of performing non-linear mappings from its input space to output space. This has meant that it cannot learn such apparently simple functions as EXOR. The solution to this defficiency has also been known for many years: use a multi-layer perceptron (MLP). However, it is only recently that a suitable MLP weight learning algorithm was discovered. This learning scheme, called the *backward error propogation algorithm,* has caused considerable excitement. Unfortunately, massive amounts of training are required in order to learn quite simple non-linear mappings and this has made the application of MLPs to real problems such as speech recognition and synthesis very difficult.

In this paper a new type of single layer perceptron is reported which incorporates n-tuple pattern recognition techniques in an SLP architecture to produce a *single layer look up perceptron* (SLLUP) which can learn the same types of non-linear mappings as an MLP but with a fraction of the training and computation.

2. SLLUP architecture and operation

All neural networks can be thought of as vector transformers in which the transformation is learnt. The learning is normally supervised as depicted in Fig 1. A training example of an input vector is applied to the system and a target output vector is shown to the system by the supervisor. The difference between the actual output and the target is used to modify the internal parameters of the system so that the actual becomes more like the target.

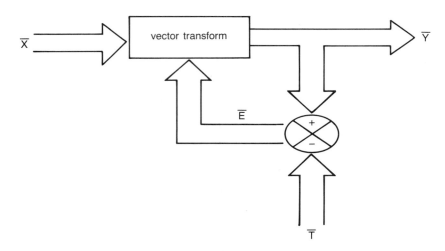

Fig 1   Supervised learning vector transformer.

In the case of the SLLUP, the vector transformer has the form shown in Fig 2. The input vector X is encoded as an image of black and white pixels formed by bits of the code representing the scalar elements of X. The code may be bar chart, gray code, binary code or some other code.

Random connections are made onto the pixels in the image and groups of n connections are formed into n-tuples which are used to address a large number of RAMs. The RAMs themselves are grouped into 'neuron' blocks and the outputs of all the RAMs in the ith block are added to form, y_i, the value of the ith element of the output vector Y.

The system is trained by applying a vector X to its input. This causes a specific set of n-tuple addresses to be generated, which access corresponding contents in each of the RAMs. The summation of the output of each group of RAMs produces the elements of the output vector Y. This vector is compared with the desired output T and the error vector, E, is used to modify the values of the currently addressed RAM locations so that next time the same input vector is applied, the output, Y, is nearer to the desired output T.

Repeated application of different training vectors allows the system to learn the required input-output mapping $Y=f(X)$. It is important to notice that with appropriate choice of n-tuple order and number of RAMs in each neuron block, the system can estimate the best function $f(X)$ to fit a rather sparse training set. That is, it is not necessary to expose the machine to all possible input-output vector pairs because it is able to interpolate the required function between training points. This property will be analysed in more detail later in the paper.

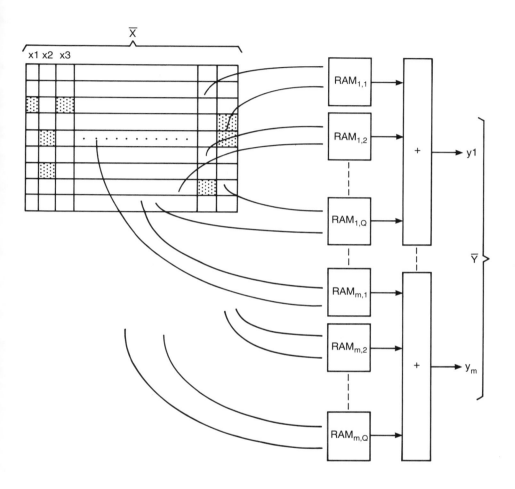

Fig 2   Schematic of single layer look up perceptron (SLLUP)

3. Analysis of the SLLUP learning procedure

The adaption of the RAM contents to develop the required mapping function is done using a gradient descent procedure. It will be shown that the gradient is very easily calculated and that the error surface for the system is quadratic thereby guaranteeing convergence.

Each RAM in the system is addressed by an n-tuple whose value depends on the vector X contained in the input image. Thus, the output of each RAM in the system depends in some complex way on X, and in general the output of the jth RAM in the ith 'neuron' block can be expressed as $C_{ij}(X)$.

The output of the ith neuron is then:

$$y_i = \sum_{j=1}^{Q} C_{ij} (\overline{X}) \qquad \qquad \dots\dots(1)$$

Where Q is the number of RAMs per neuron.

Let the target output vector when X is input be $T = [t_1 \dots t_N]$. The mean square output error of the system can then be expressed as:

$$\overline{E^2} = \frac{1}{N} \sum_{i=1}^{N} (y_i - t_i)^2 \qquad \qquad \dots\dots(2)$$

Substituting (1) into (2) gives an expression for the mean square error in terms of the contents of the RAMs:

$$\overline{E^2} = \frac{1}{N} \sum_{i=1}^{N} \left\{ \sum_{j=1}^{Q} C_{ij} (\overline{X}) - t_i \right\}^2 \qquad \qquad \dots\dots(3)$$

Equation 3 shows that the highest power team involving $C_{ij}(X)$ in the expression for mean square error is two. This indicates a single minima, quadratic surface, and so convergence to a global optimum is guaranteed using a gradient algorithm.

The gradient descent algorithm operates on the currently addressed RAM contents such that:

$$C_{ij}^{n+1} (X) = C_{ij}^{n} (X) + k. \frac{\partial \overline{E^2}}{\partial C_{ij}{}^{n}(X)} \qquad \qquad \dots\dots(4)$$

The gradient term required in (4) is simply calculated from (3) as:

$$\frac{\partial \overline{E^2}}{\partial C_{ij}{}^{n}(X)} = 2.(y_i - t_i) = 2\, e_i$$

Where e_i is the difference between the output of the ith neuron and its neuron and its target value. So, the algorithm for modifying the RAM contents becomes:

$$C_{ij}^{n+1} (X) = C_{ij}^{n} (X) + k.(y_i - t_i) \qquad \qquad \dots\dots(5)$$

4. Learning a mapping function and interpolation

It has already been noted that supervised learning machines are required to learn a mapping function $Y = f(X)$ without exposure to all possible input/output pairs of Y and X values. This is only possible if the system can *interpolate* between sample values of the function which are given during training. Later, the paper will attempt to show how this interpolation property is produced in a SLLUP, but first it looks generally at the relationship between supervised training and interpolation and examines the properties that are required of the interpolation.

The process is illustrated in Fig 3 for a simple one-dimensional case in which the required mappings is given by $y = g(x)$. During training, discrete input/output value pairs of the function are specified, as depicted by the arrows in Fig 3. This is done by applying a value of x to the machine, and specifying what value of y the machine should produce. The internal parameters of the machine are then modified to make the actual output the same as the specified output. Normally the internal parameter modification is done in small increments so that the target output is not attained until many examples of virtually the same input have been applied. However, after many training iterations, each training example constitutes a sample of the function which is to be learnt by the machine.

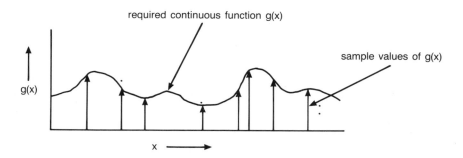

Fig 3   Sampled values of the required mapping function.

This view of the training process as a way of generating a sampled version of the required mapping functions, immediately suggests that the wanted continuous function could be obtained by passing the sample values through a suitable low-pass interpolation filter. That is, convolve the samples with an impulse response or kernel function as shown in Fig 4.

Three important points are raised by this view of the process:

4.1 Nyquist sampling criteria

Sufficient training examples must be given such that there is an average of two samples per cycle of the highest frequency in the mapping function. This suggests that the complexity of a mapping function be specified in terms of its bandwidth, B, and that the average interval between training examples be $\frac{1}{2}\beta$

sampled function interpolation kernel continuous function

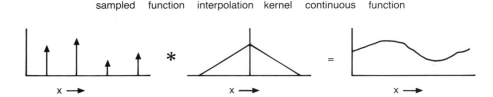

Fig 4   Convolution of sampled function with interpolation kernel.

4.2 Bandwidth of interpolation filters

To obtain a perfect, continuous function from the training examples, the interpolation filter should have a rectangular frequency response, cutting off at B Hz. This would require an infinite length sinc (x) impulse response which is obviously impossible. Practical interpolation filters should have a bandwidth of as near as possible B Hz, but it must be recognised that finite impulse response filters will always produce an error in the estimate of the continuous function.

4.3 Uniformity of function sampling interval

It is very unlikely that the training examples supplied to a supervised learning machine will be uniformly distributed across the pattern space. This means that the distances between samples of the required mapping function are non uniform. The nyquist sampling therorem requires at least two samples per cycle of the function if it is to be recovered without loss of information. However, a uniform sample interval is not specified and so the irregularity of the training points does not necessarily mean that the continuous mapping function cannot be recovered. Unfortunately, a simple interpolation filter is unable to recover a continuous function from a set of irregular samples because the function will be non-uniformly scaled in proportion to the density of the samples. However this is not a problem, if the learning is done iteratively, because incorrect scaling of the function will be corrected by the negative feedback action of the adaption algorithm.

5. The SLLUP interpolation kernel

The form of interpolation kernel produced by the SLLUP depends strongly on the way in which the input vector X is encoded. Analytically, bar chart coding is the simplest way of encoding X in 'image' form which can be sampled by the random n-tuple connections. Unfortunately, this technique makes inefficient use of memory because one pixel must be provided for every increment along every dimension of X. However, the analysis of this system will be pursued because of its simplicity and then go onto consider other input vector encoding techniques using binary and gray codes as well as other codes with controlled redundancy.

6. Bar chart coding

A bar chart encoding of a two-dimensional pattern $[x_1 \ x_2]$ is shown in Fig 5. In this example each vector element has been quantised to one of 8 values. The vector value shown in the example is $[5,3]$.

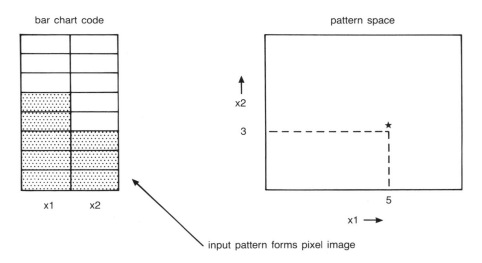

Fig 5   Bar chart encoding of a two-dimensional pattern.

Consider a single 1-tuple connection made onto the qth pixel of the x_1 bar. If $x_1 < q$ the 1-tuple value will be one, whereas if $x_1 > q$ then its value is zero. In the pattern space this connection effectively creates a threshold line at $x_1 = \mathbf{q}$. This idea can be extended to n connections forming an n-tuple. Each connection generates a threshold line in the pattern space and the intersections of the lines delineate particular regions of pattern space which are associated with particular n-tuple values as shown in Fig 6 for the case of a 4-tuple. If many n-tuples are connected onto the input 'image', the combination of n-tuple values delineate smaller and smaller regions of pattern space, with each region becoming a regular square as the number of n-tuples becomes very high.

The idea of a pattern space dissected by threshold lines can be used to predict the form of the interpolation kernel produced by a SLLUP. Qualitatively, the generation of the kernel can be understood in the following way. Assume that the RAMS have initially zero contents. A single training pattern, X_1, is applied to the system and the contents of the locations in the RAMS addressed by the n-tuples are iteratively modified until they produce the specified target output vector, T_1. Imagine now that other input patterns are applied, without further training, starting at value X_1 and gradually moving away from X_1 in pattern space. Each time a threshold line is crossed, a complete n-tuple value changes value and one of the RAMS which was contributing to the output value, T_1, switches to another location and produces zero output. Thus the vector output from the SLLUP slowly drops towards zero as the input pattern is progressively displaced from the training pattern. The shape of this fall in output value effectively defines the interpolation kernel of the system as shown in Fig 7 for a one-dimensional case.

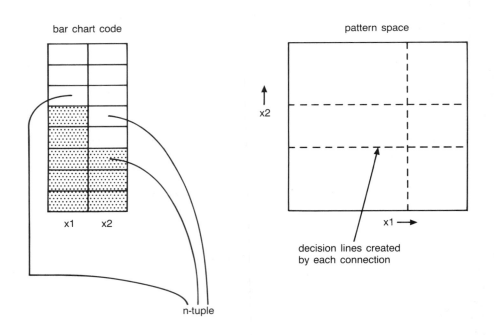

Fig 6   N-tuple sampling and resultant decision lines.

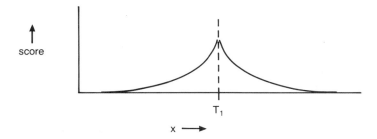

Fig 7   General form of interpolation kernel from SLLUP.

The shape of the interpolation kernel can be derived analytically if it is assumed that large numbers of n-tuples are connected to the 'image'. Let there be Q n-tuples per neuron block, D dimensions in the pattern space and W length to each dimension.

The output from each 'neuron' caused by an input pattern which is displaced by distance x from a training point, is given by $s(x)$.

$$s(x) = t - r(x).C_{av} \qquad \qquad \ldots\ldots(6)$$

Where t is the output from the neuron when the input is the training pattern, $r(x)$ is the number of RAMs whose addresses change when the input pattern is moved x units away in pattern space, and C_{av} is the average contribution of each RAM to the output value at the training point.

But,

$$r(x) = \int_{0}^{x} p(x).dx \qquad \qquad \ldots\ldots(7)$$

Where $p(x)$ is the probability density of crossing a threshold line at position x in the pattern space. Assuming large numbers of randomly connected n-tuples, this density is just the number of active threshold lines, $q(x)$, cutting any axis of the pattern space divided by the pattern space width over which the lines are distributed.

i.e. $p(x) = \dfrac{q(x)}{W}$ \qquad \qquad \ldots\ldots(8)

To solve for $p(x), r(x)$ and $s(x)$ investigate the variation of $q(x)$ as x increases by δx.

$$q(x + \delta x) = q(x) - \frac{n}{D}.p(x).\delta x \qquad \qquad \ldots\ldots(9)$$

The n/D term in the equation arises because crossing a single threshold line renders the other $n-1$ lines within the n-tuple ineffective, i.e. subsequent crossing any one of these other lines cannot effect the output from the RAM anymore because it is already switched to produce zero output. The n lines which are effectively removed

315

from play are spread over D dimensions and so the average number of lines along a particular axis, which are deactivated by crossing just one threshold line is n/D.

Rearranging (9) gives:

$$\frac{\delta q(x)}{\delta x} = -\frac{n}{D} \cdot p(x) \qquad \qquad ......(10)$$

But,

$$p(x) = \frac{q(x)}{W}$$

So,

$$\frac{\delta q(x)}{\delta x} = -\frac{n}{WD} \cdot q(x) \qquad \qquad ......(11)$$

This first order differential equation has a solution of:

$$q(x) = \frac{Q.n}{D} \cdot e^{\frac{n.x}{WD}} \qquad \qquad ......(12)$$

Substituting (12) into (8) gives $p(x)$

$$p(x) = \frac{Q.n}{W.D} \cdot e^{\frac{n.x}{WD}} \qquad \qquad ......(13)$$

And substituting (13) into (7) gives the required expression for $r(x)$.

$$r(x) = Q.e^{-n.x/W.D} \qquad \qquad ......(14)$$

Further substitution of (14) into (6) gives the expression for the interpolation kernel.

$$s(x) = t.(1 - e^{\frac{-n.|x|}{W.D}}) \qquad \qquad ......(15)$$

The approximate validity of this expression has been confirmed by a computer simulation whose results are shown in Fig 8. In the simulation a SLLUP has been trained on a single input pattern and the output caused by other patterns covering a 2—D input space recorded. The system used 24 quantization levels for each dimension and 124 tuples were connected onto the input image.

The expression for the kernel function of the SLLUP with bar chart coding reveals a severe limitation. The width of the kernel is large for practical values of n and D and so the complexity of mapping function which can be learnt is quite low. For example, if n is 8 and the input space has 8 dimensions, the $1/e$ width of the kernel is 2W. It is not practical to increase n much above 8 because the RAM size increases exponentially. Bar chart coding is therefore limited to problems in which the input space dimensionality is low or in which the mapping function is very simple.

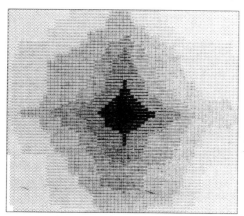

Fig 8   Computer simulation of SLLUP kernel obtained with bar chart coding.

7. Simple binary coding

A pattern may be presented to a SLLUP as image pixels whose values correspond to simple binary encoding of the pattern elements. Random n-tuple connections are made onto the pixels of this 'image' in the normal way. However, the interpolation kernel produced is poorly defined and irregular for the following reasons.

The output from the SLLUP is determined by the number of RAMS in each neuron which are addressed with the n-tuple on which they were trained. Loosely speaking, the probability of an n-tuple changing value is proportional to the Hamming distance, D_h, between the current input pattern and the training input pattern. Consequently the output of the SLLUP is a measure of the Hamming distance.

In a bar chart coded system the relationship Hamming distance and signal space distance is linear as shown in Fig 8a. However, for a binary coded system, the relationship is non-monotonic as shown in Fig 8b and this causes the SLLUP output to follow an irregular function as the input pattern is moved away from the training point in the linear pattern space.

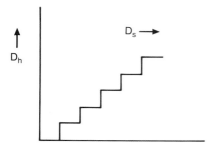

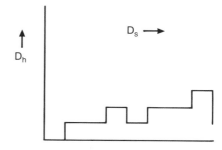

Fig 8a   Hamming vs signal distance for bar chart

Fig 8b   Hamming vs signal distance for simple binary code

Figure 9 shows an example of the type of kernel function produced by a single training point in 2—D space when the input pattern is binary coded. In this experiment, simple 5 bit binary coding with 32 4-tuples were used. The irregularity of the interpolation kernel is evident, but it should also be noted that the kernel is very much narrower than in the bar chart system. This is a possible advantage since it means that complex mapping functions can be synthesised if sufficient training data is available.

8. Gray coding

Some improvement in the regularity of the interpolation kernel can be obtained by using a gray code instead of simple binary code. Although the gray code Hamming distance versus signal space distance function is not monotonic, it is better than the binary code because the Hamming distance only changes by 1 for every 1 unit change in signal. Again, this type of encoding has been tested by simulation and the kernel function obtained using a gray code is shown in Fig 10.

9. Redundant gray coding

Perfect monoticity in the relationship between Hamming and signal space distance can only be obtained when the code has 1 bit for every signal level. However, it is possible to introduce redundancy into binary coding to improve the monoticity. A simple way of doing this is to represent each signal value by the concatonation of several shifted versions of an R-bit gray code for the value as shown in Fig 11. Connecting n-tuples onto all the bits in the new code causes the bumps in the relationship between D_h and D_s to be averaged resulting in a more regular kernel as shown by the simulation results in Fig 12.

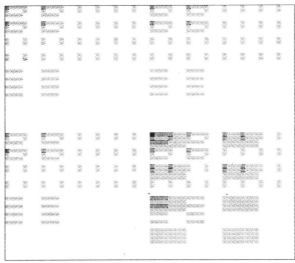

Fig 9   Computer simulation showing the kernel obtained with simple binary encoding of the input pattern.

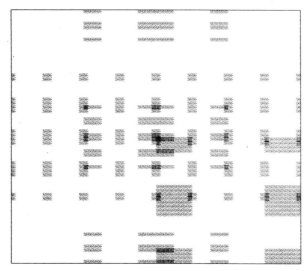

Fig 10   Computer simulation showing kernel obtained using gray coding of input pattern.

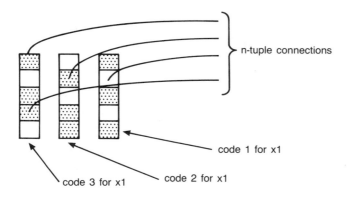

Fig 11   Introducing redundancy to improve moniticity of D_h vs D_s function.

10.Added offsets binary coding

An alternative method of controlling the regularity and width of the kernel function is by combining binary coding with added offsets to the input pattern. The samples x1 and x2 are stored in the image in binary code and n-tuple connections are made with n/2 connections to x1 and n/2 to x2. The connections always start on the most significant bits of the samples as shown in Fig 13. The n-tuple is connected to a RAM in the normal way. Patterns lying in different regions of the space will give rise to n-tuple addresses in accordance with a uniform grid of 2^n square elements covering the entire space. The dimension of each element being P.

319

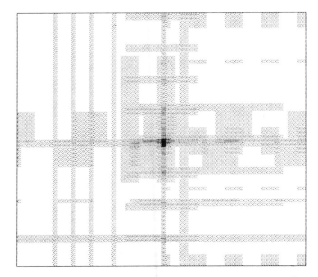

Fig 12   Kernel function obtained using redundant gray coding.

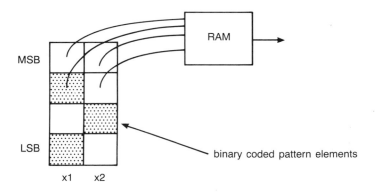

Fig 13   N-tuple sampling of most significant bits of binary coded pattern elements.

Where: $P = $ Pattern Space width $/2^{(n/2)}$

Ideally, many n-tuples are required producing grids with uniformly distributed positions over the length (P) of one element of the grid. This is shown in Fig 14 for a system using 4-tuples. In such a system, the maximum possible score is obtained when an input pattern coincides with a training point. As the input pattern is moved, the probability of changing the address of any one n-tuple is uniform within a range of P, of the training point. Beyond distance P from the training point the score will be zero. This imples that a triangular kernel function will be obtained around each training point, whose base width will be equal to $2P$. Since $P = 2^{-(n/2)}$, the kernel width can be controlled by choosing the order n of the n-tuple.

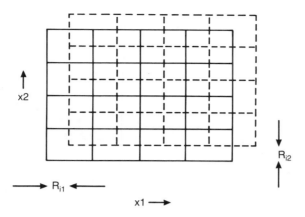

Fig 14   Effective position of binary n-tuple grid shifted by added offsets.

In reality there is no way of making n-tuple connections which result in distributed grid positions. However the same effect can be achieved by the following device: random variables, R_{i1}, R_{i2}, of peak value P are added to x1 and x2 respectively and each perturbed pattern xi1, xi2 is stored in a separate array connected to its own RAM by identical n-tuple connections. This has the same effect as perturbing the grid positions as shown in Fig 14. An outline of the complete system is shown in Fig 15.

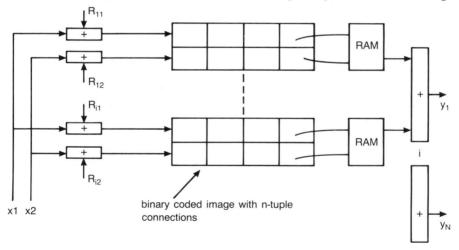

binary coded image with n-tuple connections

Fig 15   Added offsets N-tuple system.

11. LLUP experimental results — testing the interpolation property

A series of experiments have been done on a SLLUP to test its ability to synthesize simple mapping functions and to see how much training is required. However, before testing the system's ability to deal with these functions, a simple experiment was done to demonstrate the interpolation property. A SLLUP was trained on two input patterns at [24, 24] and [48, 30] to produce the same scalar output. The output from the SLLUP was measured when each of all the possible input pattern was applied. The result is shown in Fig 16 in which interpolation between the two training points is clearly visible.

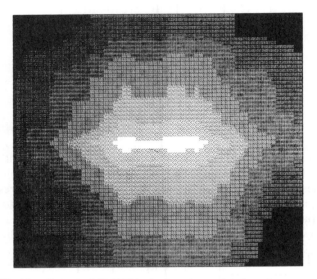

Fig 16   Output of SLLUP trained on two points in pattern space.

12.   Learning a function — the fuzzy EXOR problem

The first type of function investigated is a fuzzy exclusive OR as shown in Fig 17. The SLLUP is required to map any patterns lying within the two rectangles, marked C_1 in the input space, to the single point marked C_1 is in the output space. Similarly any pattern in the C_2 region of the input space should map through to the point C_2 in the output space.

It is apparent that the bandwidth of the specified mapping function is quite high because there are rapid transitions between the C_1 and C_2 regions in the input space. Consequently, it is to be expected that a fairly high training/sampling density be required in order that the SLLUP accurately learn the function.

To test the accuracy of the mapping learnt by the SLLUP, an error function has been defined where $e(x_1, x_2)$ is the Euclidean distance between the target output and actual output when an input pattern $[x_1\ x_2]$ is applied to the machine.

The error functions obtained with different numbers of distinct training points are shown in Figs 18a and 18b. These results have been collected after many incremental learning interations and tests have been done to check that the synthesised mapping function had completely stabilised.

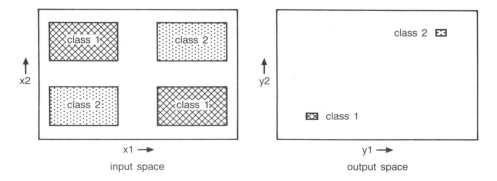

Fig 17   Fuzzy EXOR mapping function.

Figures 18a and 18b show the error function for C_1 and C_2 after the machine had been trained on just one example of C_1 and C_2 in the centres of the four class regions. As expected, the error function becomes zero in the vicinity of each training point and then increases with increasing distance.

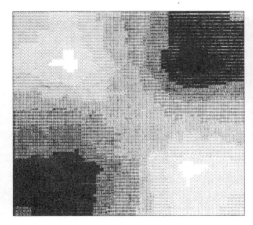
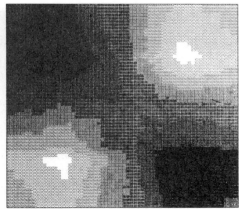

Fig 18a   Error Function for Class 1 in EXOR problem — 4 training examples.

Fig 18b   Error Function for Class 2 in EXOR problem — 4 training examples.

Figures 19a and 19b show similar results, but in this experiment a total of 16 training points have been used. The four points in each region are spaced 16 units apart around the centre of the region. In this case the synthesised mapping function is much nearer the specified function even though the system has only been trained on a very small subset of possible input patterns.

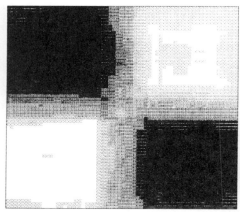

Fig 19a   Error function for class 1 in EXOR problem — 16 training examples.

Fig 19b   Error function for class 2 in EXOR problem — 16 training examples.

13. More complicated functions — three class bimodal problem

A more complex problem was given to the SLLUP. The required mapping function is shown in Fig 20 and consists of three classes each occupying two regions in the input space. The SLLUP is required to map these regions to one of three points in the two dimensional output space. In the experiment, nine of the possible eighty one patterns lying within each class region in the input space were used as training points and the resultant error functions are shown in Figs 21a, b and c.

14. SLLUP learning times

All adaptive vector transformers are trained incrementally by iteratively applying sampled values of the required mapping function. Although the number of distinct function samples may be quite small, the number of iterations may need to be very high in order that the synthesised function converge to the required form. This arises because the transform parameters of the system can only be adapted by a very small amount at each iteration. If large adaption steps are made, the system may not converge.

In the case of the MLP, the learning time can be very long because information about the error gradients in all layers, except the top layer, can only be obtained indirectly. The single layer perceptron can converge quite quickly but can not deal with non-linear mappings. The SLLUP is a single layer adaptive system and consequently can converge quickly like the single layer perceptron. However, unlike the SLP, the SLLUP can deal with non-linear mappings.

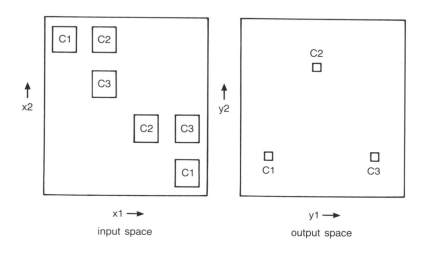

Fig 20   Mapping function for three class bimodal data.

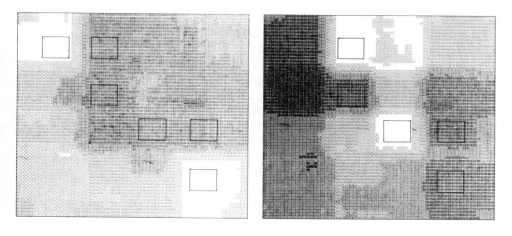

Fig 21a   Class 1 error function

Fig 21b   Class 2 error function.

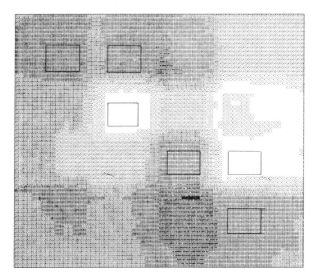

Fig 21c   Class 3 error function.

Figure 22 shows the time variation of the RMS error between the output of a SLLUP and the target values given during training on the fuzzy EXOR problem described earlier in the paper. In this experiment only four distinct input patterns have been used for training and each pattern lies the centre of one of the class regions shown in Fig 17. The SLLUP converges to an extremely low error value *at the training points* after only 100 iterations. The value of error with inputs other than those used during training is of course much higher, as shown by the error function plotted for the converged system in Fig 18a and 18b.

Figure 23 shows the convergence plot for the same system, but this time, a greater number of distinct training examples are used, with four training patterns within each class region shown in Fig 17. In this situation there is more competition between different input training patterns to adjust the contents of the RAMs in the SLLUP to their own particular optimal value. The result is a lengthened convergence time and a poorer RMS error after convergence.

The idea that different training input patterns are competing to optimise the RAM contents to improve their individual performance is further supported by the results shown in Fig 24. This is the convergence plot for the 3 class bi-modal system as specified in Fig 20, in which nine training examples are taken from each class region. In this case the system still has not fully converged at *the training points* after 1000 iterations, even though the error is very small. However, this is rather misleading and Fig 25 shows another way of indicating the convergence of the system which reflects the performance for any possible input patterna and *not just the training patterns*. The error value has been defined as the RMS value of the difference between the target function and the actual SLLUP output averaged over all of the possible patterns in the input pattern space. It can be seen that in this case the error does not drop to a very low value but that the system has converged in the global sense after only 10 iterations and that further training does not much improve the overall performance, even though the errors at the training points may continue to decrease for several thusand more iterations as shown in Fig 24.

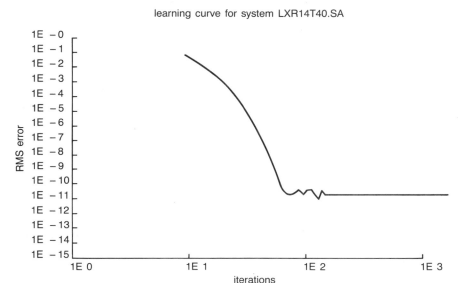

Fig 22   Training point convergence plot for SLLUP with fuzzy EXOR problem (one training point per class region).

15.   Comparison of multilayer perceptron and SLLUP

It has already been noted that the task of a supervised learning machine is to generate a mapping from an input vector, X, to an output vector, Y. The complete mapping function has to be learnt from a rather sparse set of training examples of the function.

The complete function can be obtained by interpolation between the training examples and this is achieved in the SLLUP by convolving the training example values with a kernel function. In other words, the discrete function values are passed through a low pass interpolation filter whose impulse response is the kernel function.

In the multilayer perceptron, the interpolation is achieved rather differently as illustrated in Figs 26. This shows a two layer perceptron containing two hidden units suitable for generating a vector to scaler mapping. The output, y, of the MLP can be considered to be the weighted sum of the outputs of the two hidden units which are in turn functions of the input, x.

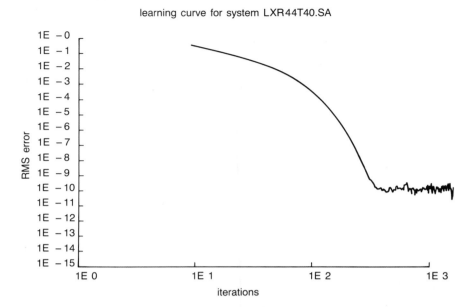

Fig 23   Training point convergence plot for SLLUP on fuzzy EXOR problem (four training points per class region).

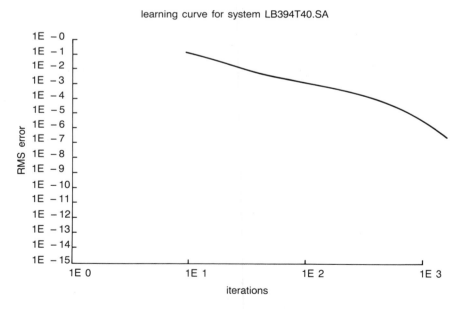

Fig 24   Training point convergence plot for SLLUP on three class bi-modal problem (nine training points per class region)

learning curve for system IB394T40.SA

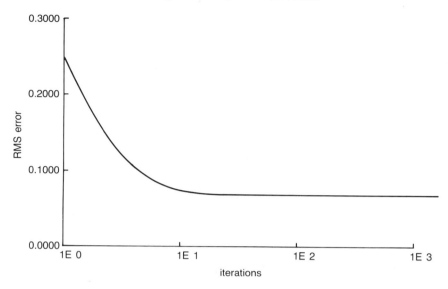

Fig 25   Global convergence plot for SLLUP on three class bi-modal problem (nine training points per class region).

i.e. $y(x) = \alpha_1 f_1(x) + \alpha_2 f_2(x)$ ......(16)

The functions $f_1(x)$ and $f_2(x)$ are determined by the form of the non-linearity in the hidden units and by the weights B_i connecting x to each unit. Normally these functions have a sigmoid shape which is conveniently described by:

$$f(q) = 1/(1 + \exp - q)$$ ......(17)

Of course, in the case of the MLP the hidden unit functions are learnt and are not orthonormal. They are not therefore basis vectors in the strict sense. However, the analogy shows that for a finite number of hidden units, and thus basis functions, the bandwidth of the synthesised function will be limited and the function itself correspondingly smooth. Thus although the MLP weights are only adjusted to make the synthesised function correct for the training example input values, the smoothness of the hidden unit function $f_1(x)$ ...... $f_N(x)$ ensures that an approximately correct output value is produced even when an input value lies between the training examples.

To test this view of the operation of an MLP, machines with two and four hidden units have been trained on a simple EXOR problem in which the class one output target is 0.8 and the class two target 0.2. The mapping function produced by these two machines after extensive training are shown in Fig 27 and 28. It is interesting to note that if only two hidden units are used, the synthesised function can only have one minimum value. The sigmoid function from one unit producing the rising edge and the second unit producing the falling edge to the synthesised function. To obtain the correct EXOR mapping, this minimum is arranged as a valley along the diagonal through the input space which lies between the two class 1 regions.

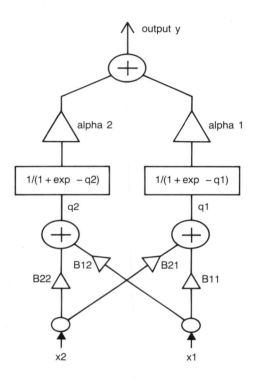

Fig 26   Two hidden unit MLP.

In the case of the four unit machine, the synthesised function can contain up to two independent minima or maxima as evidenced by the synthesised function shown in Fig 28.

16.   MLP learning times

Direct comparison of the MLP and sllup learning times is rather difficult because in the case of the MLP it depends on the number of hidden units which are used. The minimum number of hidden units depends in turn on the complexity of the mapping function to be generated. The SLLUP complexity does not depend directly on the function complexity.

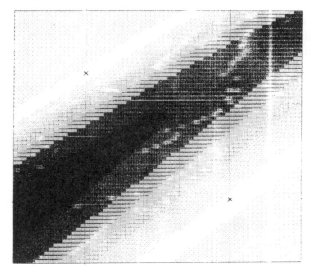

Fig 27   Mapping function developed by two unit MLP on EXOR target.

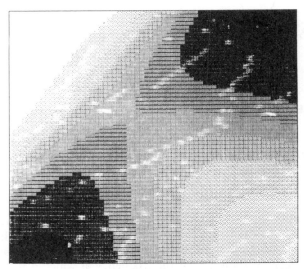

Fig 28   Mapping function developed by four unit MLP on EXOR target.

Bearing in mind this lack of direct equivalence between the MLP and SLLUP, we present the learning curves for two simple MLPs which contain just sufficient hidden units to deal with the fuzzy EXOR problem defined in Fig 17, i.e. a two unit and four unit machine.

The learning curves in Figs 20 and 30 shows the root mean square error between the actual output and target output after a particular amoung of training. The averaging is done over all the possible input values. In this example, one point is used from each class region and therefore the averaging is done over four possible inputs which are used to train the machine. For comparison purposes, the learning curve for a SLLUP working on the same problem is shown on the same figure.

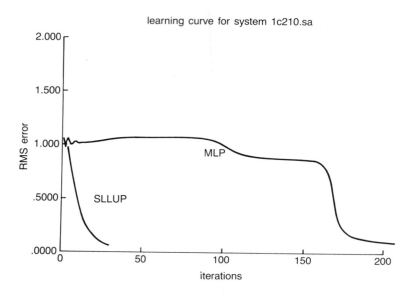

Fig 29   Learning curve for two unit MLP.

Conclusions

It has been argued that the purpose of any supervised learning network is to synthesise a continuous non-linear mapping function from a sparse set of training examples of the function. The continuous function is generated by *interpolation* between the discrete examples of the function.

An important implication of this argument is that the number of training examples must be sufficient such that the function is sampled at least at the Nyquist rate. Furthermore, generalisation or interpolation is only possible if the bandwidth of the mapping function is less than half of the frequency at which it is desired to sample the function at the output of the machine.

The MLP achieves the interpolation by synthesising the function by the addition of a set of *smooth* 'basis functions' created by the hidden units in conjunction with their sigmoidal non-linearity. The SLLUP convolves the discrete training function samples with a kernel function or impulse response of a low pass interpolation filter.

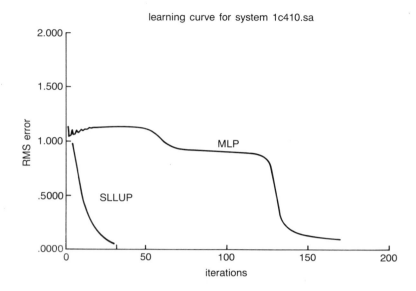

Fig 30   Learning curve for four unit MLP.

The SLLUP uses comparable amounts of memory to the MLP for all but the most trivial functions and in general will learn the required mapping function much faster than an MLP because it is a single layer machine in which error gradients used for its adaption can be calculated directly from the output error. Moreover, because it is a single layer machine, the error surface for the SLLUP is always quadratic and therefore always converges to a minimum error.

INDEX